THE BACKYARD PARABLES

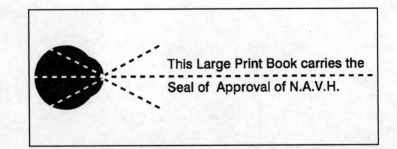

This Large Print Book carries the
Seal of Approval of N.A.V.H.

THE BACKYARD PARABLES

LESSONS ON GARDENING, AND LIFE

MARGARET ROACH

THORNDIKE PRESS
A part of Gale, Cengage Learning

GALE
CENGAGE Learning®

Detroit • New York • San Francisco • New Haven, Conn • Waterville, Maine • London

Thorndike Press, a part of Gale, Cengage Learning.

Library of Congress CIP DATA on file. Cataloguing in publication for this book is available from the Library of Congress

ISBN-13: 978-1-4104-5793-6 (hardcover)

ISBN-10: 1-4104-5793-1 (hardcover)

Published in 2013 by arrangement with Grand Cental Publishing, a division of Hachette Book Group, Inc.

Printed in the United States of America
1 2 3 4 5 6 7 17 16 15 14 13

For Marco Polo Stufano, who — I suspect against his better instincts — made room for me so I could grow.

WHAT WE NEED IS HERE

Geese appear high over us,
pass, and the sky closes. Abandon,
as in love or sleep, holds
them to their way, clear
in the ancient faith; what we need
is here. And we pray, not
for new earth or heaven, but to be
quiet in heart, and in eye,
clear. What we need is here.
— Wendell Berry

❖

For myself, I am grateful to nature, not so much
when I see her on the side that is open to the
world, as when I am permitted to enter her
shrine. Then one may seek to know of what
stuff the universe is made, who is its author

or guardian, what is the nature of God....Life would have been a useless gift, were I not admitted to the study of such themes.

— SENECA, 4 BC–AD 65, FROM
NATURAL QUESTIONS, BOOK 1

PREFACE

Once upon a time, a faithless twenty-five-year-old got down on her knees and fashioned her first garden. It was a sorry thing, but also a matter of great pride, this perennial checkerboard imprinted on a sloping bit of ground outside her family's kitchen door.

As if pricking through a preprinted canvas pattern of counted cross-stitch, she populated the tiny strip of inadequately cultivated soil with an equal number of two kinds of perennials. Half were low-growing, succulent rosettes called *Sempervivum,* or hens and chicks, houseleeks, or live-forever — since as she tucked these first roots in, she unwittingly entered a world where all the characters masquerade behind multiple nicknames, and where art and science collide so that there's no straight answer to anything (which miraculously somehow makes everything perfectly clear). The others were *Kniphofia* (a.k.a., red-hot pokers, torch lilies, or tritomas) a tall thing with vaguely obscene wand-like flowers striped in hot sunset shades.

She did not leave proper space between, nor note the light conditions either plant required. But for that moment, there was peace on earth, and trust in her heart.

In the practice of blind devotion to living things called gardening, that is where I got started: assuming a posture of supplication and gridding out an alternating arrangement of plants that should never be combined, but what did I know? Just one thing, really:

I knew that the postage-stamp-sized color photos on their plastic nursery labels had made lust rise up in me. Over all the other choices at the garden center where I had innocently wandered that morning, seeking a distraction from things at home, I wanted these beauties for myself.

This is how it begins: with the deadly sin of lust. Then you kneel a lot, and when you finally get up again, you're not meek or humble quite yet but filled with the germ of another transgression — that of pride, which is said to be the worst of all and often the root of the others. Like the knees of your trousers, you will never quite recover.

Thinking back, I wonder: What was I greedily praying for as I knelt that very first day? Was it for the thousands of hapless perennial seeds — the entire contents of each of many packets whose cunning cover photos had also won my heart during that same nursery shopping trip? I had planted them in too-close quarters, set them in a porch where they'd be guaranteed too little light, and overwatered for good measure.

As I poured instead of pinched them into place, like a kid happily suffocating cookies with sprinkles or a card for Mom with glitter, I was imagining riot-of-color, meadow-sized beds that never stopped blooming. I don't think I knew enough to know what trouble the seeds, and I, were in.

No, I had probably come to these first two naïve, concurrent experiments of mad science seeking something with at least a little hope attached. Inside the house, just beyond that kitchen doorway and the ad hoc propagation porch, these were not sunny days but ones where a loved one struggled with illness, and would not get well. I flailed in various ways as I tried to find the answer to *why,* and sought any shred of optimism — the powerful potion of possibility or, better yet, belief. I got a garden (such as the wretched patch was), which in itself can feed the soul and even the body, but I also got occupational therapy, then eventually faith in

11

the bargain, faith cultivated by a sequence of life lessons that all the digging and weeding and watering that followed brought to the surface.

Even now, thirty years in, new ones are turned up, and my collection of backyard parables — deceptively simple, instructive stories from a life spent digging ever deeper — grows. Preposterous as it seems, since we are not exactly quoting catechism but merely talking about lily-beetle larvae (revolting) or what deer won't eat (nothing) or how to keep a fifteen-foot *Viburnum* in a spot that can only accommodate six (you do the math, then cut it down), the parables illuminate and help me puzzle out every corner of my existence, providing a lens sharper and brighter than the default one I came with.

"I believe in parables," Barbara Kingsolver wrote in *Small Wonder*. "I navigate life using stories where I find them, and I hold tight to the ones that tell me new kinds of truth."

Me, too; me, too.

WHAT IS A PARABLE?

Like a thornbush brandished by the hand
of a drunkard is a parable in the mouth
of a fool.
— PROVERBS 26:9

Trust your gut if you wish to garden (or write books). Then, before anyone notices your rough edges or other shortcomings, do some serious homework.

I came to the start of my work on *The Backyard Parables* semi-ignorant of what a parable is, even though I was aware all along that the word — which I now know derives from the Greek *parabolē,* for "juxtaposition" or "comparison" — would be the main event of the book's title. I had in fact suggested the title myself, but when I delivered the proposal with *The Backyard Parables* typed confidently across the top, I thought, as I suspect others may, that all parables were in the New Testament, stories a man named

13

Jesus told to his disciples and other followers in attempts to articulate aspects of life and God. I vaguely recalled from my brief, none-too-rigorous religious instruction that they read like extended analogies or metaphors, meant to shed light on something other than the facts of their actual plot.

Indeed, depending on which expert's count you adhere to, there are between thirty-seven and sixty-five parables in the Gospels (in Matthew, Mark, and Luke, specifically). No religion corners the market, though, and the ones in the New Testament were not the first, nor the last. There are parables and parable-like sayings in virtually every cultural tradition and religion throughout history: in Hinduism, and in Buddhism (as well as from philosophers of the Confucian tradition, and from the ancient Greeks, such as Socrates and Aristotle). For all their often-acrimonious differences, the root traditions and most holy books of Islam (the Koran contains forty parables), Christianity, and Judaism agree on at least two things: that parables are an effective way of teaching, and that it is hard to find a more bountiful source of compelling script material than the examples set by the natural world and mankind's interactions with it.

There are budding (or barren) trees and

vines, some that bend in the wind and some that break; all manner of seeds sown on all manner of ground; farm fields filled with weeds or rich with hidden treasure; harvests reaped — and those lost, to flood and drought and all extremes of dramatic, heaven-sent conditions. Nature is no fool, nor does it suffer them; from its mouth come utterances that we should not disregard because it sets the best example of life's rhythm. It has busy times and down times, it surges *and* it rests. Nature also utters a constant invocation to look past the in-your-face stuff of life, to where the real action is. So do parables.

Parables are not fables — that is, there are no fantastical happenings, such as talking animals, to entertain. Who needs such invention when you have the distinct character of each season and its displays of the almighty elements — when you have the natural world, and the man-made contrivance within it that we call a garden, all ripe with "aha's."

There is one definition of parable that I like best, from contemporary New Testament scholar Klyne R. Snodgrass. Parables, he says, are "stories with intent," and that phrase became the title of his massive work on the subject, published in 2008.

They are provocative.

Like the garden is for me.

To my ear, and heart, the garden is a perennial dharma talk — a meditation, a reminder to reflect. It teaches us to live with intimacy and attention, and asks that we feel the pulse of more than just our own interior life force, instead seeing ourselves as part of a vast, complex organism and story. As Emerson wrote in *Nature,* "every natural process is a version of a moral sentence."

The garden and its backdrop of nature are good — the best? — places to learn something beyond how many clutches a robin can lay each spring (up to three) or how deep to plant a herbaceous peony if you want it to bloom, not just survive (a mere inch or so, and by the way, if you are south of Birmingham, Alabama, don't bother planting them at all, since as with lilacs, a real winter chill period is required — *let it go*). I'll cover some such tactical dirty secrets in these pages, in a series of practical sidebars, but I do so in the hopes that the facts of horticulture and of botanical science will serve as catalysts to deeper engagement. The tips are my bribe, but not the main ingredient — they're like the literal surface level of a parable, but by no means the whole story.

Not long ago, I was speaking to a garden

ply "not-two," or Advaita, as the concept is expressed in Hinduism? Yes, that's more it. *Not two.*

Does bowling or bridge or knitting invite this depth of communion, or explain so many bigger-than-us mysteries, or bring us into full awareness and contemplation of the cycles of life on earth? From the garden I have had to face my powerlessness, and the limits of exerting control. I have embraced losses as opportunity; put aside pride and asked for help; faced facts and started over. My upright stance and larger brain notwithstanding, I have come to see myself as a cog in the food chain — for truly, are we any more, or less? Realizing that has been the biggest payoff, the prizewinning pumpkin at the county fair.

If I am an evangelist for anything, it is for harvesting the *something more* in every season spent sowing, tilling, weeding, and hopefully reaping. Gardening is not outdoor decorating. Do tackle the philosophical equivalent of double-digging every time you step outside; *please do.* Frankly, this other level is the best part, and it's also where I derive my basic approach to gardening, a style I call "horticultural how-to and woo-woo." Even the worst weather can't trash the *something more* — in fact, adversity can club and as always mentioned my connection to the garden — our relationship, the garden's and mine, and how it has a powerful spiritual quality. Afterward, over china pots of tea and plates of homemade cookies in the historic church's basement, a woman with nearly fifty years of horticultural experience came up to me.

"I never thought about it before listening to how you spoke about your place today," she said, whispering almost conspiratorially, as if we were back upstairs, in the church nave, "but now I do think I'm intimate with my garden, too."

We Westerners call gardening a hobby, but how can "hobby" do descriptive justice to the way garden and gardener become one, interlocking pieces of the same puzzle that's bigger than the sum of its parts? I often wonder who's tending whom, really, but never have to wonder who's actually in charge. It's not me.

"It is, you see — though many people find the idea amusing — the garden that makes the gardener," said the late Alan Chadwick (1909–1980), founder of the French biodynamic school of horticulture, an early inspiration in my love of growing things (and of my loathing of chemicals). Are it, and I, some equation of cause and effect, or simfoster a bumper crop of it. I have said many times since I began writing about the subject twenty-five years ago that gardening is my spiritual practice, a moving meditation not unlike the motions of a well-practiced *vinyasa* in yoga. It's as if gardeners — provided we pay attention — have an invitation to receive the secret from the source. Like those disciples of diverse masters who were privy early to the lessons that made their way into all the holy books full of parables, dare I say gardeners are in a position to really start to see the light?

SAVED BY THE GARDEN

I can state with conviction — and did, in *And I Shall Have Some Peace There* — that my garden saved me. It would not be an overstatement to claim that it has all the answers, but most simply put, gardening lifts the spirits. Even the esteemed mathematician and philosopher Bertrand Russell was struck by that fact:

"I've made an odd discovery," he wrote. "Every time I talk to a savant I feel quite sure that happiness is no longer a possibility. Yet when I talk with my gardener, I'm convinced of the opposite."

I'd venture to say it's because his gardener — any gardener — feels part of something:

Perhaps for the first time, he finds true connection, clear purpose, and even the sweet, succulent hope of a potential homegrown harvest (the most local form of locavoreism).

So many beginner gardeners give up after a nonstop-color English herbaceous border dream or wildflower-meadow fantasy fails to materialize out of that first tricky seed packet, as it did with mine. Feeling gypped — as if it were a Duncan Hines mix but the cake just didn't rise — they are gone. I am grateful that I am not among them, despite my embarrassing start, with the grid of *Kniphofia* and *Sempervivum,* and that what I have never dropped since I found it is my long-handled shovel, a seeming divining rod for life's impalpable jackpots. If you keep at it for more than four seasons, until the patterns inevitably repeat themselves, that should give you that first big hint: *This has been going on like this since before you ever stepped into the circle, and will do so after you leave.* Perhaps you'll get lucky and glimpse the elemental cycle playing itself out outside — and recognize that it's not that different from the measurements of our own human lives. That's why I have always counted six seasons, not just those official four, in my anthropomorphic gardening calendar of sorts.

In my head, at least, the year goes like this:

It starts with the season of *Conception,* in January–February, when you order seeds, conceive of the garden on paper, and otherwise make plans.

Next is the season of *Birth,* in March–April, as the first shoots of snowdrops or hellebores push through, offering signs of life again and new beginning.

Youth comes next, in May–June, when everything grows so fast. It's the Jack and the Beanstalk, high-energy time as the days get longer and the kids outgrow the space you allotted them the way you once outgrew your sneakers and winter boots — along with every other article of clothing — before each new school year.

In July–August it's the season of *Adulthood,* when full potential is reached. In my temperate climate, most things are at the peak of growth, before this next tricky stage comes on:

Senescence (in biology, the process of deterioration that comes with age of a cell or larger organism) takes hold here in September–October, or at the current time in my own life. It's the start of the downhill slope, the winding down — a wise, rich, and also unsettling moment of letting go in our lives and backyards as we witness and hope-

21

fully start to embrace the inevitable.

The season of *Death and Afterlife* arrives in November–December, where — here in the North, at least — parts of the garden go into hiding. But life will rise again, dust to dust, from the compost heap, where you just buried the remains of the latest casualties. Whatever our diverse and sometimes discordant belief systems, all gardeners can agree that there is reincarnation in the compost pile, no?

It was this six-phase structure that organized the first garden book I wrote, *A Way to Garden,* the one I named my garden website for almost a decade later, in 2008, and I still find it very helpful (and comforting, frankly) to think that way. But lately, in the years since I moved from a city career and weekend country life to full-time rural reality, I have come to feel quite a lot smaller than ever in the face of things — more speck than spectacular. This time, therefore, I will let the other side of the equation — not my comparatively measly humanness, but nature and specifically the *elements* — inspire the section titles. Isn't gardening, and all of life, simply a matter of repeatedly confronting the elemental?

The Backyard Parables, then, has just four chapters, beginning as the calendar year does where I live in a time dominated by *Water* — albeit in its wintertime frozen state, which puts the garden out of reach and does its best to disrupt activities as simple as opening the back door across its frost-heaved threshold.

Earth is chapter 2, as an emerging spring welcomes me back into reassuring contact with the soil.

Summer is the time of *Fire,* of intense sunshine (*fiat lux*: "Let light be made!") and hot, often dry days, the hardest season to stare down.

The *Wind* — the actual element, air, at its most insistent, when it is almost visible and feels like a solid — comes next, blowing in the stiffest change of the year each autumn and, on its heels, another frozen time. And so it goes.

I'm informed by the seasons — however we name them — and by how each element behaves in turn to give each its distinct character. I'm also regularly brought to awareness by other gardeners, such as my late grandma Marion (the first gardener I knew); my delightfully extant, outspoken sister, Marion (who coined the phrase, "I've got an urgent gardening question" as a hook left on my answering machine to start us speaking again years ago after a terrible rift during our mother's decline to early-onset Alzheimer's, when we were in our early twenties); and my longtime inspiration Marco Polo Stufano ("I garden from a compulsion to make things beautiful," he says, but kindly tolerates my "woo-woo" talk). He and I met more than twenty years ago, shortly after each of us had lost someone close to us to illness. I like to think we made space for each other the way that gardeners do for new plants after a storm or a wicked season, when beloved things are felled — hurt and in mourning, yes, but also knowing that if those losses hadn't been suffered, we might never have had an opening for this new creature in our lives. Marco, the founding director of horticulture for Wave Hill in New York City, one of the nation's most-loved gardens, was my literal silver lining to such sadness, a silver-haired and bearded wise man who also has a particular inclination toward silver-leaved plants.

And then there is the case of my other dearest friend, Erica — not a gardener, exactly (and sadly lacking the *Mar-* prefix to her name that the aforementioned three share with me) but nonetheless a lover of flowers — to whom I gave paperwhites one year as part of her holiday gift. I had the best intentions, I swear that I did.

"Why don't I have flowers yet?" Erica's phone call started, a little ashamed and also somewhat panicky, but with just the touch of gift-horse-in-the-mouth undertones. "Why do I just have all this white spaghetti growing up out of the soil?"

Oh dear... and then some. I guess I forgot to tell her which end was up.

Maybe that's the biggest lesson of all: Which end is really up will show itself to you if you garden long enough. Would that we were all innately as smart as bulbs and seeds planted other-than-upright, who, thanks to gravitropism — a response to gravity causing stems to grow up and roots down — will in time right themselves, unless stuck in a tiny pot in Erica's apartment, where all bets are off. The more we engage with growing things, our consciousness shifts, too. We can learn to have a bright take on "bad" weather, or at least within reason (the boundaries of which the ailing planet seems to regularly go beyond these days). We learn the senselessness of grasping as if anything living can be permanent — even if it is just the right rare, slow-growing tree that you set in the perfect spot so many years ago, where it became the garden's focal point, the tree that simply didn't leaf out this year but stands as a defiant skeleton, because there is no budget quite yet to have it taken down. *That will show you for relying so heavily on me, Missy.* Our senses sharpen to the point where on a breezy fall day we can differentiate whether the tree above us is an oak or a maple just by listening — eyes closed — or detect a mourning dove taking flight anytime, or know that the rufous-sided towhee's *just over there* because the distinctive scratching in the leaf litter sounds different from a chipmunk's (really: no peeking).

There is no greater practice for cultivating sensuality than shutting your eyes and smelling long-needed rain hit soil and plants that couldn't wait much longer, or standing silently in a bed as noisy bumblebees cover their velvety selves in taxicab-colored pollen by darting hungrily in and out of every last flower in the joint. Oh, to be able to touch their cherubic forms without recrimination. Some longings — *many* longings — will never be fulfilled. If all our desires were sated, what would the fun or motivation be?

Through gardening, we learn that even some of those who are not "like us" turn out to be, when you overhear them at the post office telling the postmaster, who prides himself on his tomatoes, how their dahlias are doing — not talking about the politics you might so heatedly disagree on. And then, as if they heard your unspoken disbelief that you have anything in common and want to erase that doubt, they turn to ask if you could use some tubers this fall, once they're dug and cured, and at almost the same instant another person pulling mail from his box across the little lobby asks if you need help getting that damn rabbit he keeps seeing scurry under your fence lately. *Happy to pop it for you, Margaret; just say go.* Brethren, all.

Though the pursuit of horticulture is all about control — asking nature and particularly plants to submit to cultivation at our hands — it's also where everything is totally out of control. Things die when they feel like it (making big holes). Others self-sow where you didn't place them, outlining and then coloring in pictures prettier than the ones you intended, but for which you can take credit if you desire, maybe using words like "serendipity" or "happy accident" with false modesty (and perhaps a sense of relief that at least *something* looks really good).

It's there — in risking surrender to the possibility of what on a scorecard might read as a losing round some years, and there will be plenty — that the real growth we're all after begins.

WHY THIS, OF ALL THE YEARS?

While helping a prominent charity evaluate gardens that are applying for preservation advice or funds, Marco came back from one such site visit with his highest form of praise:

"It was wonderful — you know, right on that fuzzy edge where it's all about to fall apart and be lost forever."

I remember that edge with fondness. I glimpsed it here in a few corners of the place not long ago, and then it — and those parts of the garden — got away from me, as gardens have a particularly exasperating compulsion to do.

It is a bit in that good-news, bad-news, sweet-and-sour way that I was contracted to write a garden book at this particular moment in my life, and in the life of my garden. The assignment, one I'd hoped for because there is nothing I like to write about more, is rife with irony — or perhaps it's just that my garden has my number and is quite the prankster, acting out and acting badly because it knows I'll always be there, even if it takes me for granted, as I sometimes do it.

Like an old married couple, the garden and I have been together a very long time, and we are both showing our age — facts that make for a different sort of story than the one of the blind exuberance of our rising-sap phase twenty-five years ago, or even the one I wrote about in my first garden book, *A Way to Garden,* in 1998. As with any relationship, it was much easier before it got so big and involved. In this case, familiarity has bred not contempt, exactly, but chores, endless chores. I know we are going to have to make some serious adjustments if we are going to last the rest of the way through to the till-death-us-do-part phase — for every time you buy a plant and bring it home, that's the implied commitment, no? *Till death.*

We are intimates, but also antagonists at times, and truthfully, I have on many days lately come to doubt that I know how to do this any longer. Accepting an assignment to write about the relationship has only heightened the crisis of confidence that perhaps I am a fraud or at least a burned-out case who just doesn't have what it takes. Nothing like being surrounded by your subject matter 24/7/365, and for every weed pulled or swath of turf mowed to be undertaken with *how does this fit into the book?* on your mind.

Despite any such reservations, I am grateful that the overriding emotion is that of a consuming devotion. I know we could not live without each other, for better or for worse. A garden without a gardener is a jungle waiting to happen (another vintage

Margaret-ism), and a gardener without a plot is soon in tatters, too. But where did that person disappear to who toiled happily until she could not even climb the stairs at night, blithely wearing her yellow-jacket bites and *Berberis* and *Rosa* scratches as if they were merit badges? The one who was happy to sleep on the couch — a sofa covered in drop cloths, actually, since the house was gutted at the time, with endless DIY works-in-progress inside and out — and start all over again at dawn?

Oh, yes, of course; she's outside mowing. Mowing, with its instant, visible signs of progress, is the way I productively procrastinate these days about tackling the jobs that a middle-aged garden requires — not just the brutal decisions about what to do with misshapen shrubs now too closely planted after decades, or masses of bulbs that no longer bloom because they are likewise overcrowded or in too much shade, but also the actual work. How *do* you divide thousands of square feet of overzealous perennials, or all those many thousands of sulking bulbs? I sometimes think it would be easiest to advertise for people to come take it all away — you know, like kittens: "free to a good home" — and start from zero, but of course there is no shortcut through to our next stage of life, the garden's and mine, except to dig in and do it, to stay put even when it hurts. But wait, look — there's another chance to defer and delay: *The grass needs cutting again… phew!*

I came to this latest writing assignment and this latest year of gardening feeling grateful and panicky, and then the plot sickened: Would it surprise anyone to know that the heavens didn't hear my plea to help me craft a dynamic narrative by delivering a dramatic year, but one with only happy endings? That winter stayed too long, followed by the spring-into-summer of pounding rains and hail — which amounted to the best weather anywhere in a nation otherwise violently flooding or baking without relent? That the one week it stopped raining, a postcard arrived from the power company saying they'd be on this dirt road soon to do their every-ten-year "pruning," and that the results were not what I'd seen in any pruning manual, and worse, they dropped limbs from the giant native roadside trees so carelessly that things in the garden below got crushed, yielding needless extra casualties?

That the smartest team of woodchucks I have ever played chess with took up residence, along with three battalions of chipmunks, who carved tunnels with openings just big enough to lose a foot in (and I did, repeatedly)? That following a nighttime hunting injury, Jack the Demon Cat — a stray who was for nine previous years my protector, my living rodenticide on four legs, and an outdoor cat (ah, the days of no pet hair!) — would morph into an almost-total wuss, signaling to the chipmunks and yet another rodent relative, the rabbits, that all was fair game around here: no guard on duty; enter at will? *Have at it, guys.*

That the ample rain would require twice-weekly mowing of the grassy parts (a total of seven hours' work every seven days from late April well into November) and that my favorite mower would give out, the only one I've ever found that I could easily push around the endless curves of this place with all its amoebic, sloping beds and borders? That while humping the new, much heavier and less nimble machine, my left shoulder capsule — the tissue around the joint — would give out or at least get stuck, rendering it painfully frozen with only limited range of motion, for months and months? That the driveway would wash away — twice?

That a relative of the yellow-bellied sap-sucker who killed a precious lacebark pine not so many years ago, this year targeted the most prominent remaining tree in the garden? By systematically drilling into a magnolia that has stood across from my kitchen door since I arrived and planted it, he is well on his way to delivering to it (and to a little part of me) a very slow unwind. And then, deciding all that was just the pregame show, it really got going, nature did, so that by the time a sixth of the year still remained, we were fourteen inches (about 30 percent) ahead of "normal" precipitation for the year, with most of that delivered in pounding deluges.

As I often remind myself and anyone listening, there is the one thing I know with certainty about gardening after thirty years of study and practice:

Things will die.

But not everything does — which is what keeps those of us who are in the game addicted — and besides, I am getting ahead of the story. You cannot rush a garden, or a season, even in its retelling. All of that will unfold in due time in the year portrayed on the pages to come. Let's start at the beginning and see what the elements — those bossy bastards who hold almost all the cards — had in mind for us.

CHAPTER 1
WATER (WINTER)

*The likeness of this present life is
as water that
We send down out of heaven,
and the plants of the earth mingle with it
whereof men and cattle eat,
till, when the earth has taken on its glitter
and has decked itself fair,
and its inhabitants think they have power
over it,*

35

*Our command comes upon it
by night or day, and We make it stubble,
as though
yesterday it flourished not.
Even so We distinguish the signs for a
people
who reflect.*
— THE KORAN, SURAH 10:24,
"JONAH"

*Author's footnote: The Koran (AD 610–629) variously
uses "We," "He," and "Allah" to refer to God.*

I awaken to gunshots. Have I fallen asleep with the television on again? No; no electronically induced gloaming emanates from across the room. As that fact of darkness registers, so does awareness that it is no longer deer season — meaning that cannot be it, either. No one is shooting, not some *MI-5* character on the TV monitor, risking peril in defense of the realm; not some local hunter tromping through the woods in the predawn, hoping to fill the freezer or perhaps just bring home bragging rights with a six-pointer.

It is winter, a very cold night in winter, and the trees are talking back.

My aging skin is talking back, too, thirsty for the thick, steamy aftermath of an August

36

sun shower, or even of the fog that settles here on fall mornings as the earth releases warmth it stored all growing season and with it moisture into a receptive, alchemical sky that completes the equation, sending down the lowest kind of cloud. Why hasn't my species adapted better to life indoors in winter, the way many bromeliads shaped themselves to their high-in-the-sky, not-rooted-in-the-soil native treetop homes by forming their leaves in a cuplike arrangement to catch whatever droplets fall (and the occasional yummy insect, who turns the collected water to nourishing broth)? I absentmindedly scratch the dry patch on my forearm in the mist of semisleep, take a thankfully insect-free sip from the Mason jar located by groping in the general vicinity of the nightstand, and try to settle back.

Someone fires off a few more rounds.

Apparently none of us can get comfortable tonight — not the trees, and certainly not one fifty-something gardener sequestered like a piece of tinder inside a heated box she calls home in every season, not just in this brittlest one spent mostly therein confined. In here — or truthfully maybe anywhere, anytime at my age — I cannot take in enough water to plump up all dewy and fresh. I am no garden after a spring rain; I am not spring at all, any longer, except in my ever-juicy cache of recollections. Nothing lasts; just yesterday, I stood before the mirror in the dining room and pulled back my face momentarily as if a too-tight ponytail were doing the pulling, while contemplating mini-face-lifts, low humidity, and the inexorable ravaging of age. Outside, the native black locusts and maples are feeling not old or parched, exactly, but rather overstuffed — too big for their britches, or at least their bark — as sap and other liquids inside them expand beyond capacity.

Bang. Bang-bang-bang. Shoot 'em up, baby.
Nobody seems to be at ease right now, a consequence of the watery nature we living things have in common, the trees and me included. It hurts to be too dry or too cold when you are really just one of nature's many intricate vessels, as we all are, far more labyrinthine than the jelly jar beside me perhaps, but each a mere vessel just the same.

And so I adjust again in the darkness, shifting the duvet and my hoodie and nudging at the men's white cotton sweat socks, the ones I buy in the plastic three-packs, urging them upward one after the other with the toe of the opposite foot to *please cover any gap* where the cold might find me. Then I nestle in to listen to the arboreal artillery. Might as well enjoy the show; there's no fighting back.

As another long night evaporates a drop at a time, I find myself thinking in liquid form: like how frogs and their amphibian kin seem most comfortable in their skins in a rainstorm — the bigger the better — when they move about on the hunt with positive celebratory abandon. (*Slugs and insects beware!*) I recall longingly how in the wake of soaking rain recalcitrant weeds become compliant, agreeing to slip, roots and all, from the ground with just a gentle tug. It's as if they are happy to come away with me and give up their lusty ways — as if it were their pleasure, not mine. I think about days when the sweat socks stay in the drawer and bare feet press, four prints apiece, into dew-soaked grass when they step outside first thing, even before tea, to feed the fish and birds out back — the ritual like an ablution with which I baptize each new day — then make their way back home.

I contemplate the pull, and power, of water — the place where all life began, and the only naturally occurring substance found in all three states at earthly temperatures, solid to liquid to gas — until it is time to welcome another dark morning and put the kettle on to boil. As much as I can study up on water, memorizing that it weighs 8.33 pounds per gallon, for instance, or that beneath a depth of 656 feet almost no light penetrates the ocean, I do not thereby become one ounce more capable of convincing this primal element to do as I would like, tonight or anytime.

None of us can have his or her or its way, at least not now; we must simply try to lay low, each in our own manner, until it's over — not unlike what our analogs in the driest, hottest places must do in their most severe season, in the torpor of estivation. Frozen water, no water, too much water — obstacles all for we who try to live on in spite of something. (No wonder we coined the expression "in hot water" for troubled and uncomfortable times. *Ouch!*) Though they have been unseen since November, I know that aquatic frogs, whose mad splashing and syncopated belching delight me when conditions allow, now lie in a *semifreddo* hibernation on top of the muck at the bottom of my backyard water gardens. The weeds have mostly likewise made their retreat, but they have posted rhizomes and roots and seeds like sentries on stakeouts so they can recapture territory for each of the invader species the minute conditions are deemed favorable. That will be no time soon; we all have months to go, whatever our intentions. I shouldn't even think such thoughts, though, as they stir the start of a shiver no socks or sweatshirt can insulate against. How much longer; how many more times must we call for the gravel spreader to liberate us, or have the oil tank retopped?

We must wait, because the year ushers itself in at 42.11°N latitude and 73.51°W longitude — the center of my universe, and my center of gravity — not all fluid and co-operative and available, but typically quite inhospitably frozen, as if to say *just go away*. Many sometime-resident songbirds did just that, and other creatures burrowed under-ground or into a crevice somewhere before the current realities set in, in rock or trunk or maybe even in my penetrable old founda-tion and the holey basement it pretends to enclose. *Brrr, baby, brrr.*

On the most brutal days, sap, soil, and every surface is as solid and cold as ice, or even enclosed in or bursting at the seams with water's winter avatar, since it's not that things like silt or clay or sand or gravel or rocks freeze, exactly — it's all about the pores. The water that filled the pore spaces between those particles of soil, or between bits of stone large and small or any other void it could find, has been transformed to pore ice, taking up more room as a solid than it did in liquid state. *Ouch* again. Up comes the fencepost; there go the *Heuchera* I tucked in a little too late last fall in the bed along the front walkway. Such levitation acts are going on (unsanctioned by me) behind the curtain of snow, I know they are. Ice is the puppeteer; all of us are merely its marionettes, and for my part I am inclined to lose my footing with regularity when in its not-so-nonskid grip. My bone density scan indicates this is a bad place to be right now.

I live on seasonally frozen ground this time of year, like more than half the land in the Northern Hemisphere, an equation whose main causal factors are temperature and water. But other than in such violent heaving as always befalls my *Heuchera,* or when the wind gets really bossy, or when I dare to try to walk over to the sand-and-salt bucket to treat the driveway when I should be crawling, we are all — living and nonliving things here alike right now — joined in a suspended animation of sorts, or at least on notice not to push it; to take things really, really slow. Trees dare not bend too far; I, too, hear my joints popping in complaint when I climb the stairs each night (or even late afternoon, when I have had it with days that go dark at four and cannot endure an upright position of attention a moment past five).

We wait, all of us — though some more quietly and uncomplainingly than others.

This is my twenty-fifth winter in this place, though I suppose I am stretching it a bit to say this piece of land and I have endured twenty-five winters of each other's company. It's only since the closing days of 2007 that we have lived together nonstop. In that time, I have spent only a single night away, to lecture in Princeton, New Jersey, in 2011. We are constant companions now, yes — truthfully, neither of us has anywhere else to go or to be — but you know how that is: Some days are frankly better than others. And some are downright rocky, even when you have paid your dues in time and attentiveness, as we both have, each in our own way.

Perhaps the garden's and mine is a long marriage by virtue of the very fact that for most of those years we were long-distance lovers, unable to be together more than weekends and vacations. I had a job, and it fed both of us, keeping us in shovels and seeds, so off I went each Sunday night or Monday morning after another embrace or temporary fusion of a gardener and her garden, each an all-too-brief encounter. I had to support my spendthrift darling, who always had a real jones for plants that I was happy to indulge. As it goes with all such geographically challenged affairs, though, you reach a moment where either you break up or one of you must relocate, and the garden wouldn't move. That's why I live here today.

Twenty-five years. Looking out the window right now, I think how fitting it is that to commence our quarter-centennial, nature delivered to us a gleaming tundra — a nonstop silvery winter landscape, a gift wrapping, if not a gift exactly. Its windblown surface is wildly beautiful if also a bit overwhelming, not unlike the way I feel about the garden beneath the surface when the wrapper melts and (s)he gets naked and shows her truer, needier side.

Happy silver anniversary, baby. I'm sorry that I always try to push you around, and make you do things that don't come naturally. I'm sorry that I am a control freak and a critic, even worse, walking around with my stupid clipboard muttering about and noting your vulnerable parts that I deem to be in need of cosmetic surgery (*look who's talking*), but never making similarly bulleted, exclamation-pointed lists of your many assets. Was your life better when you had more privacy, and weekdays to yourself?

We try to make each other happy — we really do — but sometimes, well, (s)he can be a little relentless and demanding, or at least that's my side of the story. I assume I would be accused of being distracted and even neglectful; of spending too much time staring out at the situation or writing my ridiculous to-do lists rather than taking action — of *letting her let herself go*. Relationships, particularly long ones, take patience and passion both, two words springing from one root — the Latin *pati-*, "to suffer," whose past participle is *pass-*, meaning "to feel," or "suffer," or "endure," or "submit." (Makes you want to ask your doctor to start calling you a client, doesn't it? At least the root of that word only means "to listen, follow, obey," which beats suffering.)

"Patience is passion tamed," wrote the late-nineteenth- and early-twentieth-century progressive Congregationalist clergyman Lyman Abbott, who also confessed a fondness for flowers but not for dirt, preferring to buy rather than grow his blooms. Smart man; it saves a lot of heartache, laundry soap, strokes of a stiff brush — and time.

Winter, in particular, takes a taming of one's passion and extended patience. Things are locked up tight, and there is no set day marked for the reopening, though for me summer, with its sometimes-blazing heat and potential shortage of rain resources, is the most hard-hearted time of all.

Deep freeze or no, the garden never closes. Yes, I am upstairs burrowing — though not as productively as the local female black bear, who actually often delivers her young while in hibernation in January or February. My other fair-weather cohabitants are underground or underwater or gone south, but even in an old-fashioned winter such as this one's proving to be, the garden never closes.

Each fall, gardening friends can be heard swapping tales of garden cleanup and whatever the year's aberrant weather brought, while also sounding their annual lament: "The season's almost over," they say, the level of their voiced despair growing louder as each week passes. "Another year gone." Maybe I am just stubborn — not a bad quality to have when you work a steep hillside in USDA Hardiness Zone 5B — but such talk rankles me. I see no evidence that the garden is ever really out of season. Not even today, at 19 degrees Fahrenheit with thirteen inches of snow on the ground. It doesn't close up shop or shut its doors on me or to visual enjoyment. It never stops teaching, either, making its at-once spectacular, scientific, and sensual appeals for awareness. The local garden centers may need to stand idle a portion of each year, between the last Christmas tree strapped to a car roof for the trip home (*fa la la la la, la la la la!*) and the first flat of violas or pansies put out for sale just over three months later, but not the landscape itself.

And so, stubbornly and defiantly all these years, at first accidentally and lately more intentionally as my knowledge has grown, I suppose I have made a garden for 365 days. Good thing I did, since I now live in it year-round, having left my career, paycheck, and the relentless city for a place where not much else is on the social calendar but staring out at it or writing about it or being outside in it, depending on the time of day and year.

Hear my confession: To make a year-round garden was not my plan, or at least not a conscious one I could have explained when I began digging holes on an overgrown, bramble-infested bit of Columbia County, New York, land, a steep tract two-plus hours and a world away from Manhattan, where full wheelbarrows fight against maintaining an upright position and carefully applied mulch relocates great distances downhill at the slightest provocation in the form of a downpour. The spot had little more to recommend it horticulturally beyond a half-dozen very old apples, two big conifers, and a mismatched trio of ancient lilacs — two pale lavender *Syringa vulgaris,* sort of your basic old-time garden variety, and one a slightly less typical silvery-blue variant. My 365-day garden style was actually a happy side effect — but in this case my curiosity about birds was the catalyst.

Because birds' needs vary at different times of year, I read up and intentionally filled the garden with plants to satisfy them — and in the process unintentionally surrounded myself with plants that do more than flower momentarily and then just stand there, the way a lilac does, or (*shudder*) a forsythia. I call that ubiquitous yellow upchuck "vomit of spring," and prefer to look at it from a distance, like the two very large unpruned old *Forsythia x intermedia* far beyond my fence line that probably once marked a long-gone farmhouse's drive. The genus *Viburnum,* for instance, became one of my original collectibles, as I sought among its many species a self-serve automat of summer fruit, fall fruit, and even some winter fruit to sustain avian visitors who were raising families, traveling onward, or staying here into the tough times and somehow keeping warm. Fruit comes from pollinated flowers, so (in pursuit of fruit) I got the blooms to enjoy in spring — and in some cases good fall foliage, too (though that had nothing to do with the reproductive process the way the flowers did). It was from plants like these that I learned that the garden was willing to show off without a day off — and also attract the maximum number of birds if only I helped it a little with some strategic decisions (more specifics on how to make a bird-friendly garden are in the sidebar on page 304).

Winter's first major flock of cedar waxwings took on fall's remaining supply of crabapples yesterday, for instance, and I got an even better view when they came to drink at the frog pond this morning, treating the floating deicer as a pontoon from which to launch maneuvers. Like his accidental mother, Jack is a birdwatcher. He is, for good reason — to protect songbirds — not allowed outdoors during daylight hours unsupervised. But he's content these days to watch the feline "Discovery Channel" I have long called Cat Network TV through the windows and glass doors pretty much all day, or at least between naps and meals. These crisply painted birds with their crested heads and masked faces home in on off-season fruit in the garden, such as the hollies' and the crabapples' and the eastern red cedar's (*Juniperus virginiana*), from which the waxwings get part of their name. I have a giant such tree in my front yard, and I can watch them from my bed each morning, which, because the site is so precipitous, is on a level with the top third of the juniper — not something I planted myself, or planned. Knowing what I know now about the pleasure of birdwatching in bed, however, I would highly recommend figuring this angle of observation into a garden design. Bed as treehouse? Dreamy.

That from-inside-out anecdote is an example of the other important thing I know about garden design, another insight I got inadvertently as well, simply because I never sit down in the garden long enough to really view it from outdoors. *Out there,* I am typically doing something — weeding, dragging hoses, mowing (or simply panicking, which takes a lot of time, but is good exercise if you pace or stagger about and wring your hands while in the throes). It's from indoors that most of my garden viewing takes place — including long hours just watching in the colder-weather months such as today — a fact that motivated me to make the "off-season" scenery more inviting with massed winterberry hollies, colorful twig willows and dogwoods, or remarkable conifers, for instance, on various axes from my favorite seats. Looking out the window is where any home landscape design process must begin (see the Garden Design 101 sidebar, page 52).

Making any garden, but especially one with more than one-trick-pony performance in spring or summer, requires a combination of tactics, not all of them horticultural. There must be water that remains unfrozen, whatever the weather — even a little water, a trough or a birdbath or a small-scale in-ground pool with the right-sized floating heater to keep it open, not iced over. No other element works harder than water to sustain the garden's community; we are all made of it. And yes, you must also select good plants with a range of features and peak moments, and site them well — easiest to accomplish by first going inside and looking out the window, imagining what the desired view is before digging any holes. But that's all the intellectual part — make a water feature, choose multiseason plants — that's part of the "how-to."

I am no garden designer over here, but this much I know: Look out the window if you want to make a garden. That's step 1; that's where the siting of a successful home landscape should begin. After all, as a gardener, aren't you usually *working,* not *viewing,* when you're outdoors? With that in mind, here's my pretty basic Garden Design 101 for Real Gardeners:

Ask yourself this: Where do you see your garden from most often, and at what time of year? Where does the magical light of various times of day, or year, happen to catch your eye? For me, it's a few places. The best seat in the house is the dining-room table, where I often plunk my laptop and heaps of messiness when writing, and where I just generally like to be. (So does Jack, who adores the west view in winter in particular.) It's technically the center of the house, and I can see a long way due west from my old Chinese wooden chair, and also pretty far south, with a short easterly snapshot as well...so those directions, starting at the point of my favorite chair and emanating outward, are the primary axes of my garden. From my bedroom window, and also from my bathroom, where I chose a clear shower curtain because the view's so good, I see the bird's-eye view of a similar westward scene. The garden stretches out to the west *from where I see it,* and gets backlit in the afternoons to boot. Nice.

Along that axis are some spring things, including viburnums and lilacs, to draw the eye in each of those moments, but mostly I use foliage, which is typically longer-lasting than a single plant's bloom period. Gold foliage does a great job of screaming. Heading west, the eye stops for a second at a gold cutleaf sumac, *Rhus typhina* 'Bailtiger', for example (better known by its patented name Tiger Eyes), and then, way in the distance, a grouping of carefully placed gold-leaf *Spiraea thunbergii* 'Ogon', and the ghost bramble, *Rubus cockburnianus* (which has white stems in winter once its yellow leaves drop) just shy of those will signal to me April through November or even December, in the case of the spiraea, after the closer-in things have had their moment. I place a big, potted red-leaf Japanese maple on the one corner of the terrace to the west, echoing the little red shed door in the same direction. The terrace itself, sited perpendicularly to the house as if it were an old foundation of a wing or garage that no longer exists, does a good job of commanding attention as well, a platform for staging potted gardens.

On a flatter site that lends itself more to linearity, the botanical barkers could be something as loud as an *allee* — or you could use a nonliving element to announce a destination, such as a bench, a statue, or a structure.

I mostly stick to plants here, and being greedy, I want good company when it's not "gardening season," too. Even after the leaves have fallen, a mass of maybe twenty winterberry hollies (*Ilex verticillata*) shouts from all the way west near the fence line, forming a wall of red — my long-distance view from October to January or so, which looks like so many holiday ornaments strung up out there in the shrubbery. When working on long axes, remember to amp up the impact with multiples of each element.

Due south from the best seat in the house is the bigger of the two homemade frog ponds, watched over by the Indonesian buddha, who stares right back at me through closed eyes, and straight uphill from him an increasingly massive copper beech I planted more than twenty years ago. I don't have to move to see them. When I work in the kitchen, I am treated to the scene of a nearby magnolia that's underplanted with many little treasures to entertain me whether it's March (the first minor bulbs) or November; the aging magnolia's massive gray trunk itself is beautiful 365 days.

And then there's one particular living-room window that catches my eye most of all when I come down the stairs, as if to say hello each morning. To heighten its importance, perhaps fifteen feet beyond it lives a true four-season shrub: the red-twig dogwood *Cornus sericea* 'Sunshine', whose gold leaves scream in fair weather and whose red stems pick up the job in foul.

Did I know this when I started here twenty-five or so years ago — to look out the window and plan the garden accordingly? No, not at all; it still startles me that I managed to do this well, which I know is mostly because I didn't overthink it. In famously twenty-twenty hindsight, I realize this was what was at work unconsciously: I was building a garden that I could enjoy, because it could be seen from where I really live when I'm not out there in the moment of doing it. I instinctively placed beds and created axes in spots I related to, being not just the gardener here but also the resident of the house's interior. I have never regretted these somewhat accidental gut decisions.

Whether your best seat in the house is a deck or a den or a favorite reading chair for winter afternoons, or even the place where you stand a few minutes each day and brush your teeth, plant yourself some well-placed pictures to greet you, and you will be well on the way to a garden that works. One more thing: Sometimes people do visit, of course, and I guess I almost forgot my tip on that score, when it's not all about me. Gussy up the front walkway — the first thing people who don't live in the house will see (and, as a side benefit, the route you probably use yourself more days than not). Once inside, invite them to sit in your chair and enjoy the view.

I am fairly certain that to make a 365-day garden you must also learn all over again how to *see* — to see beyond the big blue *Hydrangea* and other obvious show-offs, right down to the shapes of buds and textural complexity of bark, and the way the play of light and shadow, sounds and smells, and even movement contribute to the living pictures. When I go lecture to garden groups, a process that builds to a crescendo of incessant (insane?) hand-waving as I speak, I always notice that I touch my chest reflexively when I talk about this last bit, as if to say, "You must learn to see with your heart; the eyes won't do in the hardest months." You must look viscerally, not somatically; it will take you in the direction of the light. This critical cultivation of the other senses forges a deeper communion between garden and gardener, and recognition of the one life cycle "it" and we are both part of. And that is where the "woo-woo" portion of my gardening equation comes into play: when that connection is made.

A dose of "woo-woo" definitely helps, particularly when you are looking out on the dead quiet of an old-fashioned snowy winter as I am now — quite a different scene from the one in May, or even October. Most days I can be patient, but at this moment I am the little girl I was on all those annual winter trips to Florida, hocking my weary parents from the backseat of the green Ford station wagon: *Are we there yet?*

I do tend to take a bird's-eye view, even from my preferred vantage point on solid ground. During a break in a big storm one night, I made the ritual rounds: shovel, sweep, salt, sand the walkways — and then somehow found my way to a few special conifers in the garden, high-stepping in my tallest boots. With gentle upward strokes, I moved to lighten the snow load on those who bear their burdens badly, but whom I could not bear to lose.

Whoosh! Out from the invisible interior of one tree's limbs burst a spray of dark-eyed juncos (*Junco hyemalis*), like four and twenty blackbirds baked in a pie. *Oops,* but also:

58

Aha! What a startling reminder for uncertain times that would seek to blow us off course or ruffle our feathers: best to just hunker down and wait it out. If creatures weighing in at just over three-quarters of an ounce can find shelter in a storm, so can I.

This is how it is between me and the birds: a constant dialogue, even when they are not singing. Like my grade-school teachers bringing a wiggly class to order, or the Zen master sounding the alert anytime, birds always seem to be calling, *Attention! Attention!* I openly admit to paying them heed, since to do otherwise would be to forgo some of nature's most instructive and inspiring object lessons. The birds are guides, totems, and trusted friends. I count on them, so it is a small price to grow all those hollies to provide lipid-rich wintertime fruit, or fill the feeder and keep the frog pools unfrozen all winter, where the birds don't just drink but also bathe — feathery shades of the Coney Island Polar Bear Club.

Not wishing to disturb anyone either botanical or avian, I use a household broom on some shrubby conifers, always working with an upward action — no rough stuff, either — because the coated branches are heavy enough without me pulling them downward that way, and can be brittle if the weather's really cold. I used to use an apple-picker with a red basketlike contraption on one end, but I seem to have misplaced it many years ago — if you can misplace something ten feet long that does not fold or otherwise voluntarily shrink from view. But a broom can only extend my reach so far, and this is not ladder weather. For the upper reaches, I have repurposed a twelve-foot length of ¾-inch quarter-round molding from the lumberyard, a piece left over from some long-ago home renovation that serves its unintended task well; adaptive reuse. It's strong but flexible, the best combination of qualities in so many situations both botanical and otherwise — *bend but don't break, baby* — and I weave the flexible piece of wood up through the branches and then kind of jiggle it as if it were a lasso minus the noose at one end. My action causes a reverberation up top that shakes loose the snow without seeming to harm anything. It's all in the wrist.

The reincarnated molding-that-wasn't serves for tackling beginning icicles on the eaves that would in time form dams on the roof, too, if I let them get ahead of me — or if the winter is just too incredibly mean, like this one wants to show me it can be. *Bully.* But I go at it anyhow, eyes ever roofward toward a harsh and frozen heaven. Think pole-vaulter without the liftoff; me and my long strong-but-flexible stick. I've got all the moves, but I never quite get off the ground.

I do slightly crazy things, but I have my reasons — or so I tell myself on the attempted rebound from each questionable episode as I dust or dry off and apply the appropriate balm or bandage. I blame the garden, and the water gardens I dug twenty-odd years ago in the backyard are particular culprits in my many mini-demises. Lead me not into temptation? *Nonsense.* A girl can really take a walk on the wild side in any season when there is a large water-filled hole, plumbing parts, and electricity involved, all ringed with irregularly shaped, winter-wobbly, summer-slippery paving stones that drop off abruptly at the man-made shore-line. If I were an Olympic diver, the move I made last night would have a degree of difficulty of 3.6, though I hoped to skip the somersaults and never even hit the water, with or without a clean entry.

For this attempt to rescue my frog pond's inhabitants from death by suffocation under ice (apparently the floating electric deicer meant to do so failed), it was almost dark, air temperature 7 degrees Fahrenheit, winds eighteen miles per hour. The approach: Snow shovel at the ready, I maneuver through thigh-high drifts maybe halfway to where I approximate the snow-covered copingstones begin at the pool's edge, just under thirty feet from the kitchen door. I cannot be sure since this all-white moonscape renders even my familiar backyard devoid of landmarks or perspective; I could be anywhere. In that last stretch of the journey, though — maybe for the final ten feet — I stop tromping through the deep white camouflage and dig a trench wide enough for my body and then some.

Before I lower myself into what I all the while try to avoid imagining may be my grave, I gently slide my shovel back behind me in the trench. Not gently enough: Like a luge on a well-prepared track the tool travels scarily fast to the end of the icy surface, jumping up and out onto the deep snow where my excavation project ends. *Note to self: Move slowly. Or else.* Then I lie facedown in the glacial hollow, now filled not with fresh snow that had some traction — the stuff I'd tossed aside — but with the residue of last week's and last month's precipitation, compressed, collapsed layers of the freeze-thaw, freeze-thaw slippery variety. This is the first prostration; I surrender to the holy water. I am hoping my head and shoulders are positioned near the pool's edge now, but I cannot tell what starts or ends where, pool-wise, because ice covers its surface. That's how I knew something was wrong and embarked on this mission: I had by chance looked out the upstairs window just before dusk, and the pool's surface was all one color — white — meaning no yin-yang dark-light blend of unfrozen-frozen, such as it remains when the floating deicer is functional. In good times, open water reads as nearly black; ice as white. All black would be all right, but not all white.

Next I stretch my left arm almost beyond its reach hoping to find the outlet I know is positioned on the low wall behind the pool. Always best to power things off before attempting a repair, even if they seem to have oh-so-inconveniently done that themselves already. If I am guessing right, it should be about *here,* I calculate, and I dig in the snow with a gloved, outstretched hand, not a tool, to locate the gray metal trapdoor to the ground fault circuit interrupter box. Jamming a shovel in the vague direction of a buried electrical device seems imprudent. *Bingo.* I have found, and pulled, the floating heater's plug.

Oh, but *shit.* Where is some small electrical device — a night-light or anything I should have carried to test whether there is power getting to the duplex at all, whether it's the plug or the appliance that's kaput? Forgotten. No turning back now; assuming it's live, I need to disable the box, too. (*Buy one of those pen-sized voltage testers, Margaret, won't you?*) Off with a glove, and then, a Braille-like moment of running a fast-freezing finger over the face of the now-empty duplex. I'm feeling for six holes and — if I can find them — two nearly flat buttons each half as wide as my pinky fingernail but elusively set almost flush with the rest of the works. Oh where are the buttons and which one is off? Groping, groping. *Ah!*

Electricus interruptus.

Finally. Onward; there is other work to do. From the pockets of my warmest jacket, which is nowhere near warm enough for lying in an icy ditch — *um, do breasts get frostbite?* — I grab a flashlight in one hand, and in the other, a hammer.

And now, finally, the big move itself, the one I came out here for: to crack the ice somehow before it's too late. I am lucky; it's not too thick yet. Banging on ice isn't very friendly to those who slumber beneath, but neither is suffocation from a lack of gas exchange. Had it been thicker — oh, right now I can't even think about that possibility, not until I thaw myself a bit, but failure would have involved a metal mixing bowl set on top of the ice dosed up with endless refills of boiling water to gradually melt a hole. It would have required lots of trips back and forth over a glazed surface with a steaming kettle in one hand to this impossible spot on this impossible night.

I have broken through, but I am not done. Can I get the heater to work after all? I have a backup I can try — or is it in fact the plug? Seems so. My hands can't take this kind of work for long in these conditions, so I must soon surrender. Repairs to be continued.

Low-tech Plan B, requiring many fewer trips than the mixing-bowl scenario: I repeated the hammering periodically throughout the night, setting the alarm at three-hour intervals, to protect my beloved amphibians. Who needs beauty sleep, when potential princes are at risk? Damn the complexion, and what's another cracked and bloody cuticle among many? A gardener — especially one with a frog pond in wintertime and friends who sleep therein — must be versatile, well equipped, and ever at the window, watching for beauty, yes, but for trouble, too.

In my very fluid imagination, one thematic current of youth long past goes like this:

No school today! Mrs. Schelling cannot torture me about my awkward penmanship, a casualty of skipping third grade when apparently the art of smoothing blocky capitals into connected shapes was taught, or the fact that I — *yes, again, ma'am* — seem to have left my wooden recorder home. *Freedom.* It is Saturday morning, and I pedal my hefty pink-and-white-and-silver Schwinn down to the pet store, streamers catching the wind of my locomotion. Two long walls of stacked glass aquariums on heavy welded-iron stands hold countless tropical fish — hundreds of gleaming neon tetras, their metallic bodies striped blue and red; silver tiger barbs, whose black markings ran top to bottom instead; vivid orange platys; kissing gouramis the color of the palest pinky-peach inside of a shell, but pearlescent. Everyone shimmers, catching rays of simulated sunlight from fluorescent hoods that delineate the artificial tropospheres of their approximated tropics.

At first I imagined it was Mona who pedaled along with me on her bike, but of course my adult-brain reality check says it could not have been, for we would have had to cross busy Northern Boulevard unsupervised to get to Mr. Van Asch's store that sat on the city line, straddling Queens and Nassau counties. That was beyond the limits of our privileges, I realize now, and of sanity or safety. Perhaps I biked there with Vivien, whose father kept giant tanks of salt- and freshwater fish in their basement, where in another alcove the female elders of her Hungarian family stocked brine-filled jars of pickles and other canned goods on heavy shelves, each awaiting its turn at the table. *Glug, glug, glug.*

Vivien lived on the same side of the boule- vard as the pet store, but even so, I did not — so how did this all work? — but no mat- ter, because in the fusion of accurate images sometimes recombined inaccurately that forms my story of growing up, I rode my bike there, and often. Creative license.

However I found my way, I can state with- out much hesitation that *Elodea* and sword plants were my first attempts at growing botanical things of any kind. I buried their rubber-banded, cut-off ends in gravel long before I sliced into any soil, and I confess that I included their plastic counterparts — yes, artificial plants, and not even good, believable ones in those days — in the sub- mersed designs. My horticultural roots are not in the landscape but as an aquascaper; the first magazine after *Highlights for Chil- dren* that I subscribed to: *Tropical Fish*

Hobbyist. It would be another decade or so before I traded up, literally, to above-the-surface-focused publications such as *Horticulture* or the Royal Horticultural Society's *The Garden.* Maybe I should have stuck to aquariums and the similarly contrived, contained terrariums that have come and gone as a passion a few times in this life to date, too. Everything looks so much more manageable in a garden where a tweezer is the biggest tool, and no one can creep (or swim) out of bounds, beyond the glass walls.

I can also say with certainty that those dozens of Saturdays and thousands of other hours spent staring into watery worlds — and the happy gurgling and splashing provided by a charcoal-and-glass-wool filter that I'd dutifully change each week without being told — was the training camp for my older years as friend of frogs. It also explains the four pet-store comets (goldfish-like, they can live in water as cold as 35° and do here out back in winter). Feeding fish is something I have almost always done each day, like drinking tea or washing my hair. Water soothes, transports, cleanses.

It is a sad time of year when the bedroom window must shut to cold, cutting me off from the sound of the water gardens. At first it's just now and then, a chilly evening or two, and eventually for good, when seriously cold nights one after another force me to close down the pump mechanisms sometime in November, so that the just-a-bigger-diameter version of the tubing I brought home in my bike basket doesn't freeze. Bubble, bubble, toil and (sometimes) trouble — but also pure delight.

Water made me do it. It was probably an upbringing beside a silt-choked bay that made me an organic gardener when I finally put shovel to soil instead of hook, line, and sinker into the drink, or an algae scraper into a twenty-gallon tank. Life beside the bay also formed me as someone who doesn't eat fish or other seafood, despite growing up in a household where kippered herring were not uncommon breakfast fare — and in case anyone had thoughts of sleeping in, think again: There is no alarm signal quite like the smell of those nasty little filets simmering in milk on top of the range. Paella was a dinner-party specialty of my father's, or if the weather permitted a clambake, the family even actually drank the gritty broth from the double-boiler-like granitewear contraption he had steamed the bivalves in. Each such day I — the milkman's daughter

I have been heartened in recent years to see some catalogs giving more real estate to organic seed. But why care? What difference does it make if the tiny seeds I start with were organically grown, as long as when I plant them, I follow environmentally sound cultural practices? I worry about contributing to pollution that "flows upstream" — and also want a seed that's well adapted to my garden, where I adhere to organic methods. I don't think commercially produced seed always addresses those concerns.

Unlike many vegetable crops we grow to eat — which are typically picked young and tender, and therefore grown for a shorter time — the same plant cultivated for a seed harvest must be grown to a much older age, requiring much more water, fertilizer, and chemical controls against pests and diseases. Seed crops require these "high inputs"; they are coddled, and regulations on chemical usage when raising them are also looser than on growing the same vegetable for the food market. Besides the pollution and waste of water resources this results in, it fails to do something else really important: It yields seed strains that "expect" this kind of pampering — not ones that are well adapted to organic conditions in our home gardens, where we (hopefully!) don't rush in with a chemical at every turn of events, or prop things up on synthetics as a quick-fix substitute for diligent soil care.

There is not sufficient organically produced seed of every variety that gardeners, or farmers, might like to grow to say, "Buy only certified organic seed always" — and besides, many seed growers who are not technically certified are farming responsibly without a dependence on chemicals. Demand for ethically produced seed can foster supply, so I for one am sending more dollars in the OG seed direction when it's available — happily paying a premium price for those packets — and being sure to buy the rest from vendors who meet other standards, even if they or their products are not "certified organic."

If there's no organic seed, that's OK with me — but I am inflexible about this one thing: I shop for seeds for my edibles only from companies that take the Safe Seed

Pledge, committing to not knowingly using or selling any genetically modified, or GM, seed, properly called transgenic hybrids. More than one hundred companies have signed since the pledge was initiated in 1999 by Vermont-based High Mowing Organic Seeds, a mail-order vendor specializing in certified organic product.

I read the fine print in the catalogs, too (and often turn for guidance to the Organic Seed Alliance website, out of Port Townsend, Washington, when I need to learn more about an issue regarding seed). Any reputable vendor, not just those few who sell mostly or only certified organic seed, should freely express its point of view on transgenic hybrid seed, treated seed (that to which fungicide has been applied — I say no to that, too), and generally how their seed is grown or sourced. I am suspicious in these times if a catalog or website says nothing on these matters.

The 2011 catalog of Maine-based Fedco Seeds, for instance, said that 28 percent of its seed assortment (accounting for 36 percent of its seed dollar volume) was certified organic, and Fedco also explained how it sources the rest. Many growers cannot make the certified-organic claim — whether because they have not yet met government guidelines, the cost of certification is too high, or they ideologically disagree with some aspect of the standards or bureaucracy — but nevertheless follow sustainable practices and ethical land stewardship. A seed company should be proud to tell you the care it has taken to find high-quality products for its customers, I figure, products that match my ethics and way of gardening.

— prayed that someone might throw me a culinary life preserver.

Long before I learned about the implied meanings of so-called "signal words" on household and gardening products — revealing whether a substance is merely worthy of "caution" or rather rates a prominent "warning," or even "danger," and possibly even "poison," too — I had my own evaluating system, basically guided by my nose. I still remember my first experiences with the chemical aisle of the garden center, and how you could find it without looking at the overhead signs or asking. But what came first in olfactory memory was a whiff of what was dumping into the bay.

Giant pipes carrying storm runoff and with it presumably some effluent from hundreds of local septic systems jutted through the water side of the seawall ringing our town, pouring into Little Neck Bay where New York City meets Long Island on its north shore. Eventually, in the late 1960s, big rigs undertook a dredging project, and we finally all started to use the word "pollution" with regularity, as if it had just been discovered — or perpetrated for the very first time. Such sights taught me an early, lasting lesson about humankind's formidable waste stream, and especially its impact on those creatures (literally) downstream from it, who can't run, or fly, or swim away — mollusks, for example, such as the American hard-shelled clam that was once an edible prize of local waters. Equipped with one primitive "foot" more suited for burying themselves than traveling, it is hard to go anywhere, even if their habitat got clogged with deposits that didn't make a suitable bed any longer, and loaded with toxins they couldn't filter out with their set of long siphons the way they might a too-big chunk of something more benign.

The hard-shelled clam, also known as a littleneck or cherrystone depending on its size, was once shipped from Little Neck Bay to restaurants in New York and even Europe, but it didn't take long for pollution to shut the industry down just before the turn of the twentieth century. (Further digression from this admitted digression: I love the quahog's Latin name, *Mercenaria mercenaria*. Isn't the language of taxonomy wonderful for christening things? I suspect it derives from a related root word that's earlier than the one meaning "hireling," as we imply when we say "mercenaries" — perhaps from *merces,* for "reward or wages." Could it have been chosen because the shells were the stuff of Indian wampum? I wonder. Put it on my life list of things to find out someday, the list I'll need several reincarnations and then some to ever get sorted out.) Whatever else you call the clam, you can call it a victim, and along with the resident fish, they were the first environmental victims I knew about, before I owned a garden book or a nature guide — or understood that we would become our own environmental victims, too, killing ourselves slowly with supposed progress. (A related rant, about transgenic hybrids or GMOs, and why I don't do business with companies who don't guard against knowingly selling them, is in the sidebar on page 70.)

Apparently my mother remained attached to a happy ignorance before the dredging crews arrived, and as she had during her childhood in the same town, we fished off the local dock for winter flounder, often catching horseshoe crabs or eels in the process, or the occasional bluefish from the little beaches along the shoreline. Besides a revulsion at the suggestion that I bait my own hook with a madly protesting worm, I couldn't get past the image of the enormous pipes spilling all that mystery liquid into the bay. Trying to catch dinner by dropping a line into a noxiously seasoned bouillabaisse? Disgusting.

Even after the dredging was done, rendering the bay deeper and presumably cleaner for a moment, I had questions. Where did they put the stuff they removed? If a clam declared it uninhabitable, what do you do with it? You couldn't put all that tainted slurry just anywhere — or could you? These were the years of land grab by landfill, with significant local salt marshes lost before the wakeup call, so I'd bet that someone lives and maybe even gardens on the discards now. There were other horrors, such as when a developer filled a former marshland in town to create a new community, including a model home. The family that bought it were all either killed or badly injured when the house exploded one night because a gas line cracked as the house settled into anything-but-solid ground. The resounding lesson: You can't fool mother nature (though the marketing ploys on bags and boxes and bottles of gardening products seem to insist otherwise, even today).

I admit that certain such bloom-, butterfly-, and bird-covered labels tempted me into a couple of rescue missions in that vilest-smelling garden-center aisle at the start, when my beginner crops of some plant or other were limp or pekid or otherwise imperiled. Like a young mother, I went into save-them-at-any-cost mode. After all, James Underwood Crockett, the original host of *The Victory Garden* television program and author of my first and most formative garden book, *Crockett's Victory Garden,* had said it was OK. With certain crops he preferred treated seeds — the ones to which fungicide has been applied — and used various individual chemical fungicides and pesticides, plus a so-called "all-purpose" spray containing carbaryl (often known as Sevin), Malathion, Diazinon, and dicofol. His peas, potatoes, and limas went into the fungicide captan before planting; the flower garden was sprayed early and often to keep it looking its best.

To be fair to this fondly remembered figure in our twentieth-century gardening history, Crockett did hint at the changing times, though he wasn't ready to disarm himself — and frankly, I understand why. We are a culture that expects packaged remedies: from the drugstore, the cosmetic counter, the local nursery — even the supermarket, if you can consider a frozen entrée, ramen "bowl," or HotPocket a remedy for supper. In the early years, facing serious, mature poison ivy, I used glyphosate (the chemical in Roundup) to knock it back, buying into the claims of safety — assertions that this relatively new kind of herbicide was nothing compared with what had come before, with short residual effects environmentally, no harm caused to humans or animals, and therefore "safe." I doubt I have to explain that all such statements have been outed as less than accurate in the ensuing years, and the entire issue of the rise in Roundup-ready transgenic agricultural crops and their impact on the environment and its creatures has also been raised to terrifying effects. Tedious as it may seem, I now solarize (smother weedy areas with plastic sheeting and bake the unwanted vegetation and seeds to death) rather than spray, and regularly dig out poison ivy seedlings and established vines by (disposable surgical-glove-clad) hand.

With insect pests, I am pretty much live and let live — using fabric barriers to give certain vulnerable crops such as crucifers or cucurbits a chance; hand-squishing a few particular demons such as Asian lily beetles and tomato hornworms and various potato beetles and, better yet, the eggs of all of the above; and cutting off and destroying twigs of viburnums in late fall onto which egg cases of *Viburnum* leaf beetle have been laid. I might disturb a nest of tent caterpillars if it were in the crabapples near the house, or step on the occasional slug, but I don't even have any horticultural soaps or oils or pyrethrins or *Bacillus thuringiensis* in the cupboard here, or other least-toxic remedies such as those that organic gardeners can technically avail themselves of. I just don't bother, frankly. I figure the pests that are eating my plants are fattening up to be somebody's dinner, so I try to keep at a minimum my intrusions into an intricate food system that I do not pretend to grasp. The biologist E. O. Wilson, who understands very well and calls the earth's small creatures "the little things who run the world," warns that without insects, fungi, bacteria, nematodes, and the like, the rest of life would very simply disappear. When panicking at the discovery of a chomped-on leaf or the start of powdery-mildew season, or looking at the vigor of my lawn weeds, I try to think about that — assuming it isn't something drastic, such as the Asian longhorn beetle, that the USDA wants to know about expanded sightings of at once.

I confess to missing the voilà-ness of one product: sustained-release fertilizer beads (such as the brand Osmocote) that are so convenient for use in pots, but based on conscience, I have forsaken them, too. It is encouraging to see some organic brands trying to tackle that slow-release niche for container gardeners lately, and as I write this, I am in Year 2 of trying the ones I've found available locally so far. We shall see. Diluted blue liquids provide no miracles, in my opinion, when you figure in the chemical dependence and environmental impact they represent. In my rural surroundings, diluted all-natural organic liquid feeds such as fish and seaweed emulsions (both suited to container plants, though not long-acting or as convenient as timed-release) attract animal pests, especially skunks and raccoons, who dig up everything in the container, which apparently smells like a big bowl of fish dinner to them. This is irritating, of course, but they usually quit after a few rounds, once the replanted plants start to stay planted long enough to finally grow in. Thinking back on all this now, I feel certain that the various beasts would have likewise liked my family's cooking in the formative years of life by the bay.

Marion (grandmother, not sister) was allergic to shellfish, oranges, and some other food whose identity continues to elude me. Eggs, perhaps? It has been so very long. I will never forget, though, how she loved a man named Harold, who shipped off on September 10 to France to join the American Expeditionary Forces in 1917. His economical handwriting is as familiar to me as hers of all the flourishes, because I have been the holder of his love letters since her death in my teens. Its spare style belied the spirit of his messages to young Marion, whom he planned to marry when he returned.

He spoke openly of his fear, and of "what I think of my chances," and expansively of his great fondness for the girl he called Snooks. Sometimes there were little extras tucked into the envelopes, now faded to an almost-military gray tan and lined with blue tissue even thinner than old-style airmail letters.

Once, an ornate poker chip from a needed leave in Monaco; another time, two tiny wildflowers on a single stem.

"I'm sending a flower I picked in a church-yard a few days ago," Harold wrote to young Marion back home in Wisconsin, where they had been together at college until he enlisted. "The church and the graves were all torn to pieces by shell fire. This flower was growing from the moss on the debris of the church roof, in February. Spring in France seems to come early. We've had no snow since the middle of January."

One day, long after that French spring, Marion made a big garden around the house she and my grandfather Harold built early in their marriage. For most of her life thereafter she gardened, and then tirelessly dried the best bits in an old wooden press, the layers of cardboard and blotter paper held closed ever so tightly around the precious formerly living things by a heavy dowel mechanism threaded with substantial rope. When they were just right, she transferred the preserved gleanings to empty nylon-stocking boxes lined with tissue, and in her filing system of the stacked, shallow cardboard containers there were ones for ferns, ones for other foliage, ones for small flowers, one for her stash of larger blooms such as iris or the occasional rose. Eventually pictures were recombined from the delicate inventory, arrangements that looked like flattened bouquets on fabric under glass, as if to make their moment in the garden last forever.

I like to think she was honoring the tradition of that dried nosegay from Harold's letters, and trying to keep their moment alive, too — his and hers — though the first of Marion's two Harolds had never made it home. *Ver perpetuum;* forever spring. With this as my example, it would be hard not to have a special affection for dried things, though my taste runs to the three- and not one-dimensional, to gourds and bean pods and heads of the biggest alliums and fertile fronds of *Matteuccia struthiopteris,* the ostrich fern. All, and more such kin, live on indoors with me.

Grandpa Harold died when I was four, and in the rest of the years that I knew his widow there were few stories offered up to backfill around the loss, to make him real to me beyond the fact that he worked for the phone company, or how he kept smoking after the first heart attack. The Harold I came to know was the original one, the letter writer, and he was brought to life again and again, as Grandma Marion never tired of the retellings, of dusting off and displaying

83

the precious but faded bits, ephemera made eternal.

Ephemera. The garden is all about it, loaded with things that do not last or at least don't stay fresh for long, and so is the big two-drawer chest in my living room, which used to be in Grandma Marion's. A recent exhumation, the loot from a binge of cleaning-out-of-boredom: a faded spiral-bound school notebook circa 1961, containing selections of my early prose. Printed in stiff, blocky letters in pencil:

"We saw the man go up in Space today."

Though not even haiku-length, my sentence filled one entire page. This effort earned me a star (which seems just right for a penmanship exercise about space travel), and marked the day the first American, Alan Shepard (who in 1971 would walk on the moon) went up in space, which is nearly fifty years ago, as I write this. The day before, the notebook reveals my mind had been on matters more befitting a gardener in the making than someone out in the wild blue yonder. Four lines of painstaking letters, meant to be identical except that my hand was none too steady yet:

"Days are longer. Days are longer. Days are longer. Days are longer." Yes, please; bring it on.

■ ■ ■ ■

Each week I get at least one blog comment or e-mail from a stranger — sometimes many more — about my beloved Japanese umbrella pine, one of two plants that traveled with my belongings in the moving van when I first bought my house as a weekend fixer-upper project twenty-five years ago. Thanks to the magic of search engines, gardeners elsewhere read about my big old plant and wonder if I can help them with theirs. When I hear the troubles people are having after transplanting one, from needle loss to branch decline to downright death, I shudder: How in the world was I spared, and what if I had not been?

Blind faith apparently has it hands-down over expertise in some aspects of horticulture.

I knew nothing at all when I heaved the then-very-rare, chest-high young *Sciadopitys verticillata* out of the ground in the borough of Queens in New York City and plopped it unceremoniously into a bushel basket for the trip several hours north. I picked a spot where there was nothing but one giant rhododendron standing alone in the yard behind the house, connected to nothing — and also reminding me unfavorably of all the raucous-colored *Rhododen-dron,* the kind commonly called azaleas, of the gardens of my youth. I almost offed the rhodie, almost rubbed the giant blob of a broadleaf evergreen out of the picture with my big, sharp eraser of a saw, but instead made the umbrella pine its companion, and hoped they would get along. There was no back porch then; there was no nothing but unmown grass and wild raspberries tangled throughout it, and my youthful enthusiasm. There wasn't even a flat space like there is now, but rather simply the hillside running right into the rear of the house. The result: The house was a wreck; the back foundation, in fact, had collapsed, and a sheet of heavy, milky-looking "clear" plastic sheeting was all that formed the barrier between outside and in, below ground level, perhaps fifteen feet from where this most beautiful of conifers, the umbrella pine, now stands about twenty feet tall.

After a session of that quarter-round-molding snow-removing gyration trick, I always say thank you to the Japanese umbrella pine for holding up to twenty-five winters of uneasy snow loads and countless ice storms; for not suffering winter burn in the spot I chose with no particular knowledge of the plant's needs or the garden's future direction; for settling in without so much as losing an extra needle. For looking handsome every single day of all those years, even when I was not looking so good myself. Sometimes, just sometimes, we have enduring, enormous successes in this funniest of pursuits, in spite of the insane odds. I mean, what is the over-under on a thirtyish-year-old woman from Queens dragging a rare Japanese conifer in a moving truck to a spot a couple of hardiness zones colder in rural New York State — sandwiched for the ride by a crew of gorillas between the couch and floor lamps and a king-sized box spring — and the two of them living happily ever after for a quarter century and counting?

I never did anything, really, except to give it a decent home with the basics, and then delight in it. Maybe that's the best approach. The Confucian philosopher Mencius (c. 371–289 BC), told this parable about cultivating not *Sciadopitys,* but chi (or qi), the life force:

One must work at it, but do not assume success. One should not forget the heart, but neither should one "help" it grow. Do not be like the man from Song. Among the people of the state of Song there was a farmer who, concerned lest his sprouts not grow, pulled on them. Obliviously, he returned home and said to his family, "Today I am worn out. I helped the sprouts to grow." His son rushed out and looked at them. The sprouts were withered. Those in the world who do not "help" the sprouts to grow are few. Those who abandon them, thinking it will not help, are those who do not weed their sprouts. Those who "help" them grow are those who pull on the sprouts. Not only does this not actually help, but it even harms them.

My intention was for success, but I didn't know what to expect — I had never seen a mature umbrella pine, any more than I could foretell what my own maturity would look like. In this one case, unlike some of the subjects I tortured, including myself more times than not early on, I didn't push — or pull.

You'd think bigger would not be better when you're talking about a dwarf conifer — a plant you presumably chose for its implied smaller habit — but to the contrary, I'm loving my overgrown "dwarf" white pines (*Pinus strobus* 'Nana') more each year. After twenty-plus years in the ground, starting from mounded creatures maybe three feet across and two high, today they are close to fourteen by eight — like giant bonsai someone hasn't clipped lately. (That would be me.)

First, the disclaimer. I said the plant is specifically *Pinus strobus* 'Nana', and that's how the pleasantly mismatched pair came to me, but here's the wrinkle: 'Nana' is kind of a grab-bag variety name for many relatively compact- or mounded-growing eastern white pines, a long-needled species native to eastern North America, from Canada to Georgia and out to Ohio and Illinois, that in its tree form can reach fifty or even eighty feet or taller. Today, you can shop for named dwarf varieties that are more compact, with distinctive and somewhat more predictable shapes, or so the catalog listings say. But what I didn't know when I got my generic "dwarf" pines was this: "Dwarf" doesn't mean "small forever" — they aren't collectible miniatures on a curio shelf — but rather it connotes slow-growing, and not reaching the stature of the straight species (in this case plain old white pine, or *Pinus strobus*). The sense of "slow" catches up with you after twenty-some years, and not just in white pines. I'm not as young as I used to be either, you know.

Things will die in the garden, yes, but

things will also grow. It has taken me so long to ready myself properly for either eventuality, to have some degree of equanimity about whichever outcome the forces prove to serve up. At least you can plan for the latter, I suppose, by leaving ample room.

I could have pinched the tips of the pines' new growth, or candles, back by half each spring to keep the shrubs somewhat more contained, but frankly I like that they are unplanned testaments to the time line of my days here, having grown up along with me and the rest of the garden's original plants. (Oh, and I am horribly lazy about such fussy tasks.) I did not literally nip things in the bud, but no matter, as there is not a day in the year I am not happy to look out at the two, set about twenty-five feet apart behind the house. One was meant to be the right flank of a small frog pond I'd dug early on — not the one I almost perished into the other night, but the first of the two inground pools. With the Japanese umbrella pine on the left side and a dwarf white on the right, the relative newcomers straddle the vast, unloved rhododendron I'd inherited. Now the three have largely overrun the pool, stretching their lowest limbs toward the center of their huddle, overlapping like the hands of teammates about to face the next play together. The comets who have lived in the watery hollow for years, grown crazy fat from daily offerings tossed onto the surface after I clap to call them to me, don't seem to mind. Neither do I. Trained fish, untrained pines.

Despite being old enough and then some, and living in conditions that match their needs, the dwarf pines don't set cones; I frankly don't know why with certainty. I have read that some dwarf conifers have what's called a long juvenile phase — can I resist saying I have dated some specimens with this condition? — and therefore don't make cones, which would be a sign of achieving sexual maturity. Maybe that's it — arrested development — but I want to know for sure. This semi-knowing irritates me, the one they called "Encyclopedia Britannica" as a child, the one who always wanted answers and still does — even when there is no answer to be had, exactly.

Like other conifers, the dwarf pair will purposely shed their least-efficient foliage each fall, when the oldest, innermost needles — having grown shaded, so they no longer photosynthesize effectively — turn brown and are let go. I don't panic, though I confess it took many years to suppress that urge. It's disconcerting when suddenly something we refer to as "evergreen" isn't and they all start turning brown from the inside out. As long as what's dead is on the inner portion of the branches or twigs, not at the tips, and it's relatively late in the growing season, I simply give the tree a nod for knowing when to let go and lighten the load. If it's unsightly, I rub the dead bits off with a gentle pass of my hand, the way I run my palm across the painted ochre floors inside the house between proper vacuumings to counteract the one less-than-ideal effect of life with Jack the Demon Cat, the unplanned pet who adopted me the morning of 9/11, when, in a hurry, I pulled into my then-weekend driveway from Manhattan. At this time of year, Jack's coat is thick and at its most stable — and I can hear him just behind me on one of his many new cushioned thrones performing the crunchy routine that I call "chew-foot," a loud and violent-looking self-manicure — but I have absolutely no idea what's going on with the conifers' inner needles, or the outer ones, for that matter. The relentless, enduring snow has seen to my not seeing that.

Oh, happy day. Frigid, but happy. Window-view gratitude list at midwinter, rough count (temperature 19 degrees Fahrenheit, snow cover in excess of twelve inches): 1: the aforementioned prize Japanese umbrella pine. 2, 3: a pair of dwarf white pines, ibid. 4: the golden Hinoki cypress (*Chamaecyparis obtusa* 'Crippsii'). 5, 6: two graceful weeping Alaska cedars (*Chamaecyparis nootkatensis* 'Pendula'). 7, 8: two Korean firs (*Abies koreana*); 9: a Concolor fir (*Abies concolor*), with near-turquoise foliage. 10–15: a group of low-growing *Microbiota decussata,* holding the steepest bank above the frog pond, now displaying its bronze winter needles. 16–21: the gnarled silhouettes of six remaining standard apple trees from the first half of the twentieth century. 22: my tea viburnum (*Viburnum setigerum*), pendulous coral fruits. 23–31: a mass of yellow-fruited *Viburnum dilatatum* 'Michael Dodge'. 32–34: Kousa dogwoods (*Cornus kousa*), with their camouflage-pattern bark. 35: a Japanese stewartia (*Stewartia pseudocamellia*) — good bark, too. 36, 37: two big *Miscanthus* stands, now faded to wheat color. 38–41: yellow- and red-twig dogwoods groupings (*Cornus sericea* varieties). 42: the Loebner magnolia called 'Ballerina', with its gray trunk and flower buds tucked away in silvery, pubescent wrappers (damn that yellow-bellied sapsucker, damn him). 43–53: eleven crabapples on the hillside, naked except for varying crops of not-yet-eaten yellow or reddish

fruit. 54–56: many dozens of winterberry
hollies in fruit (*Ilex verticillata*), in each of
three big groupings. 57: that once-loathed
rhododendron, now not a solitary eyesore
but part of an evergreen trio. 58: an espaliered Asian pear against the south face of the
house, a giant candelabra. 59: the sensuous,
female shapes of this snow-covered hillside.
60: a vignette of mature white birches in the
native forest beyond the fence line. 61–63:
birds, birds, birds, here, there, and everywhere. 64: daylight reflected off the snow,
almost two more minutes of it than yesterday.

To be continued.

When she was about eight, not so many
years after she began piano lessons, my
niece looked at me very seriously one day, a
look that politely insisted upon attention.

"Yes, Grace?" I said.

"Aunty," she replied, "music is like mathematics." I could count each syllable in that
last word of her earnest pronouncement,
1-2-3-4.

Oh, I see.

Actually, though I spared the uncannily
numbers-savvy child this thought at the
time, gardening is like mathematics, too
— and not just in the way nature engineers

table; make the bed, change the bed. Simple. *I can do that.*

Perhaps I imagined it, because to imagine anything else would have been so daunting as to prevent me from ever starting. I needed to think — *to believe* — I'd achieve a moment when the garden was like that table or that bed: At some point in time it would be *all set,* the equivalent of a perfect 10 or 100, or whatever reliable measure of time my niece heard in her piano practice. I was sure if I just kept at it in spring, I'd get there — to *all set* — and that I could sit back at least till fall and enjoy the scenery.

Yes, gardening is mathematical, but more in the manner of one of those legendary unsolved problems that foundations and other institutions offer a lot of prestige or even a million dollars to solve — a botanical strain of the Goldbach conjecture, maybe (on the surface so obvious-seeming, though no one has been able to solve it since it was first posed in 1742), or a Riemann hypothesis. Like generations of math geniuses, we gardeners just keep trying.

My gardening math goes like this: In the columns of the balance sheet that I can pretend to have authority over — not the ones owned by woodchucks, hailstorms, or some blight or other whose origin I'll never discover, among the many other players — there are addition months and subtraction ones, with some months featuring both activities. Prime addition time slots here are April and May and maybe early June, depending on the rising heat, then again in September and October (with small entries in the plus column all growing season long in the vegetable garden, where I might resow a short row of salad greens or carrots or beets or cilantro or even bush beans every two weeks, among many choices, to have a constant fresh supply). Outside the vegetable garden, which, as I say, has its own subset of gardening math (those calculations are on page 181), my subtraction starts in a big way in June with deadheads, thinning, and the first cutbacks, and continues through hard freeze. Most of the year that means I garden by reduction — then, in the coldest winter months, neither add nor subtract, remaining at a neutral balance unless my silent partners in this thing are hungry for bark, roots, or entire treasures I had hoped to see emerge intact again one day.

The garden is a willing, receptive partner. That's the position I must hold to now, all current evidence to the contrary. *This I believe.* Thoughts that the garden, and in fact

I realize that restraint is not my strong suit, but when faced with little other midwinter company but a snoring cat, a pile of seed catalogs, and a data line linking me to hundreds more, strictest impulse control must become my code of conduct.

Resisting buying everything requires an annual review of the mathematics specific to vegetable gardening, forcing myself to crunch the numbers and get at this answer: How many of my desired A, B, and C plants can fit into my suitable X square feet of vegetable-growing space (and for what cost in seeds, supplies, and labor)?

It's that simple, and that impossible.

I work gradually toward a solution each year, navigating a series of smaller questions, starting with: *What do I have left over that's viable from last year?* This may require a germination test to answer accurately, or if there are too few remaining seeds per packet to allow for that, a serious moment of reckoning around factors including the "packed for" date stamped on it, the conditions I stored it in, and what is (was) slumbering inside, as each crop has a different shelf life even in ideal circumstances. It would help if there were some reliable sell-by date for each variety, some ultimate authority, but even presuming we all adhered to optimum and identical storage conditions in our nonidentical, nonoptimum homes, every expert has a slightly different take on the matter, making memorization of any absolute rules impossible. Looking through my on-hand supply of leftover vegetable seeds the other morning, I wondered what it really amounted to: Was I all stocked up, or sorely in need? At face value, no way to tell.

Most seed will last a couple to several years — but there are disclaimers to even that general a statement. Treated and pelleted seed have a different shelf life from seed in its natural state. (I prefer my carrot and onion seed pelleted; so much easier to sow.) The condition of the original crop the seed was harvested from will also, of course, affect its perishability, perhaps more than anything.

So where is there consensus? Onion seed lasts just a year, every expert seems to say, with parsley and parsnips also very short-lived in storage. Cucumbers and muskmelons last about five years; watermelons slightly less. Corn about two, maybe three, and likewise for peas and beans. But every reference I consult reveals disagreement around things like lettuce (some say two, some six years) and spinach (one to five — and yes, it does all sound like possible prison sentences, doesn't it?). I suppose the safest strategy is to order a backup supply of anything you might really feel caught short without. If it turns out you don't need the backup seed, you can always use it next year. Well, unless it's onion.

Of course the question I want to duck answering is this next one, and it's easy to do that on a sunny winter day at high noon, without a leaf on a tree and while there's a giant reflector of snow spread over the ground bouncing back lots of light off its white surface. But here it is: *In the growing season, how much room in a sunny spot where the soil drains well do I really have? Tell the truth, Margaret.* Refusing to prune

SEED-SHOPPING RULES:
YOU CAN'T HAVE IT ALL

nearby shrubs that have grown substantially means that half of one bed of the vegetable garden and a third of another are now too shady for other than parsley and maybe some summer salad greens; deduct those square feet (or get out the handsaw and loppers). The answer isn't the same as it was twenty-five years ago, when I arrived here, nor even the same as last growing season. Things grow, and sometimes at the expense of other things that you might like to grow in their advancing shadows.

Most vegetables crave sunshine, as do a majority of annual cutting flowers, if zinnias and such are lumped into the vegetable-seed order, as mine are. The growing of food competes unfavorably here space-wise with my love for ornamentals; there's never enough ideal space. Another wrinkle: We are talking about space with not just sun but also easy access to water, as food crops generally rely on regular, deep soaking for maximum yield.

I try next to reckon what really rates a parcel of that precious square footage, based on these two factors: (a) *What do I eat most of/can't live without,* and (b) from that list of big loves, *what is available locally for a reasonable price in season?* This second bit of thinking may help those of us who define "can't live without" as "the entire botanical world."

The essentials list includes items I put up for year-round use, as I do all my tomato sauce and soup base, and various herb pestos and other frozen herb concoctions (such as my parsley "log," see page 253). If I consume a lot of something, and have the proper spot to store it, whether fresh or canned or frozen, it may be worth growing. Examples: As a vegetarian, I eat a lot of white potatoes, sweet potatoes, and winter squash — heavyweight items that, when purchased by the pound in the organic-produce section, really add up. A mere three dollars of 'Delicata' or 'Blue Hubbard' seed (or better yet, a packet of each that will last two or more years) yields a lot of squash if grown well (meaning protected from cucumber beetles, with vigilance and a lightweight insect-barrier fabric such as Agribon+ AG-15 or the equivalent, which is removed once flowering begins to welcome pollinators). The last year, organic 'Butternut' ranged from $1.79 to $2.49 a pound at my food co-op, and an average fruit in the bin weighed nearly three pounds.

I also grow a lot of chard and kale, and the year's basil and Italian flat-leaf parsley, because I eat a lot of each one and simply will not pay a couple of dollars per bunch for the herbs, even in winter, or double that for the greens. (I raise my onions and garlic, too, and some seasons succeed in harvesting half my year's sweet potatoes, but none of those comes from seed.)

What won't I be growing, if I follow this thinking? This is why I went to all those meditation retreats: to try to let some things go. Years ago, I stopped making space for eggplant, for instance, because I only ate them once or twice a month, and could more efficiently buy that eggplant or two when I had a taste for it than grow a crop. I use celery, sure, but maybe a bunch every month at most, and it's always available at any market, so why give it a place in my sun?

SEED-SHOPPING RULES: YOU CAN'T HAVE IT ALL

Certain specialty items are either too pricey or unavailable for purchase locally, meaning I must make room. If I wanted to make salsa — perhaps I'll master this someday and can a year's worth, neither impossibly hot nor insipidly watery as my trials so far have been — I'd want to grow the tomatillos. Grow what's scarce, or precious: For the price of a single pound of organic baby mesclun, I can buy seed for a couple of years of abundant salads, April to November or thereabouts.

Once I have my wish list, the final challenge: *Which are really worth starting from seed myself?* The obvious group is anything that does better direct-seeded than started in cells and transplanted, or that I want to make repeat sowings of — buying transplants wouldn't satisfy that last bit, since seedlings tend to be sold in a big push in high spring but not all season long. Things I'd direct sow, once or multiple times a season, include beans, peas, squash and pumpkins, cucumbers, root crops such as carrots and beets, spinach, salad greens, greens for braising (kale, chard, collards, leafy beets, Asian varieties such as pak choi or mustard), plus dill, cilantro, melons, and corn (though I don't grow the last two). I start basil indoors a few times each year, then transplant it.

With things that do fine from transplants, such as tomatoes or peppers, or that I only want one generation of per season, I think this way: How many plants of each will I need? I have taken to buying one 'Sweet 100' and a 'Sun Gold' cherry plant at the garden center, or begging them from a friend who has extra, rather than ordering a packet of seeds for each or purchasing a six-pack per variety. Who needs more than a cherry tomato plant or two? With paste tomatoes, of which I grow about a dozen plants, my thinking is the opposite: no wasted seed or effort there by starting from scratch.

Questioning myself over and again, I page through the catalogs and sites, trying to choose carefully, and reluctantly leaving behind some beauties. I try to force myself to look through every one twice, and write up all my orders before placing a single one, always trying to stave off impulse-buyer's regret. I will confess, though, that after following all my curmudgeonly guide-lines, I add a couple of indulgences back onto my order that don't meet the require-ments at all, since nobody's looking.

---

the entire out of doors, is some ice queen whose only word is "no" might be backed up irrefutably by the view from my chair at the dining table, but must be banished as quickly as they arise. It is time to order seeds, an act of absolute and utter faith, and even defiance.

The first to-do of the new garden season starts with their purchase. I know the rou-tine: After making my selections (my "rules" for how to decide what to order are in the box on page 99), I send the order forms and money away. I receive in return mostly near-weightless paper packets, envelopes that offer no special protection to the tiny living organisms inside — no vacuum seal, no cli-mate control, no nothing that you wouldn't provide for your phone bill or insurance-premium remittance when they are likewise en route via the United States Postal Service.

The lives in those seed packets traveling within the larger generic mailer are often so small that handling with human-sized fingers negates any prior claim to manual dexterity. They are also perilously close to death — one wrong move and I could off the whole batch, or at least drastically lower their vigor. Properly stored garden seeds may contain something like 8 or 10 percent water — just the right amount to remain viable and at-the-ready, but without much margin for error. Consistent conditions are what dormant seeds want. Too dry, and they could become hard and resist germination. Too moist — well, if that event coincides with the presence of enough oxygen and favorable temperatures, they start to think it's time to germinate, but quickly perish if the emerging seedlings' other needs aren't met. Storage is most successful when seeds are kept dry and cool (below 40 degrees Fahrenheit) — meaning in a tightly sealed jar or plastic bag stashed in the refrigerator, for instance, or in my unheated mudroom closet. That's where some harvested garden vegetables, each also a living thing and some filled with seeds of their own, likewise make it through the long stretch of shortest days without sprouting before I've had my way with every last delectable one of them.

A typical gardener (who herself contains something like 60 percent water by weight, by comparison) might order six or ten or twenty or more seed packets in any given winter. Each holds a dozen to many hundreds of embryos with the potential to become plants that might contain as much as 95 percent water (think lettuce) when up and growing. Then after rescuing them at the post office, she might toss the whole lot in the backseat of the car and forget them (pray for cold, dry weather, please, and that she parks in the shade). Or maybe the little ones are lucky enough to get as far as the kitchen table with the rest of the mail — hopefully not on top of a radiator or near the woodstove; even the heated house itself is anything but inviting to a seed — and then into a drawer, perhaps. So much for consistency — and do embryos really belong shacked up anywhere near a ball of saved rubber bands; two spare AA batteries and one extra for the smoke alarm; the makeshift sewing kit; a few each of thumb tacks, bull clips, and safety pins; a half-used box of colored chalk; keys I cannot remember the purpose of but am afraid to toss; a finial broken off a chair, and various other such "junk"?

Next stop: Sometime later in the winter or

in spring they will be asked to perform when united with the soil or the next in the chain of purchases — sterile seed-starting medium and maybe some new cell packs and trays, or more-efficient T-5 fluorescent tubes in a reflective hood to replace the generic version in the shop-hood-turned-grow-light. But even knowing what I do, even knowing the odds, I cannot say honestly that I have actually ever gone straight home from the post office, unpacked the mailers, immediately put the packets in proper jars or other sealed containers, and then into some form of cold storage. Not once.

Doing the risk-assessment math — thinking about all the stops along the way — makes mail-order seeds sound even crazier than mail-order chicks. At least the chicks speak up for themselves, reminding the postmaster to call and say, "Come and get them" — nudging the recipient to open the box immediately once home, and transfer them to a proper spot fast. But voiceless mail-order germplasm, with not even the benefit of a "contains live cargo" message boldly stamped on the package to command attention? Preposterous — and positively fantastic. Thanks to the basically survivalist nature of seeds, another gardening season is now officially under way. Not a seed or slip has been planted, but I have already been tested, and provided with many thousands of tiny opportunities to demonstrate my gaping shortcomings as steward of this spot.

I am not a horticulturist — having had very little formal training — and beyond that, there is this far more important fact: I am not a "horticulturalist," either. That chalk-on-blackboard nonword (just ask *Webster's Unabridged* or *The American Heritage College Dictionary* if you doubt me) is what so many people in the business of using plants professionally and managing gardens call themselves. Even the *New York Times* sometimes describes garden-industry professionals it profiles that way, but it's as if the owner of your local eatery called himself a "restauranteur" when there is no "n" in the middle of the word for that food-service career path — or as if a newspaper food critic did. I admit that I confuse geriatricians and gerontologists (both are actually specialties, though, and actual words), but I don't work anywhere close to the field of either one, so hopefully that's forgivable.

No, I am not a horticulturist. I am (to use the phrase of the late Francis H. Cabot, the garden artist and plantsman who founded the Garden Conservancy), more of a "garden enthusiast." Actually in my own case I'd refine that further to "plant enthusiast," because I just love plants; I don't even grow them better than other people or have substantial confidence in making gardens with them, but I keep trying. Enthusiasm — and a comfort with the fact that all life's activities are merely trial and error — is what propels me forward. I am a "better to have loved and lost" type when it comes to plants (and various other experiments with living creatures). What I am blessed with: a good eye for good ones, and a heaping portion of patience.

I am on the Freezer Diet. In gentler days the regimen will be replaced by the Asparagus Diet, the Snap Pea Diet, the Green Bean Diet, the Kale and Collards Diet. For decades I have tried to eat in season, and this is freezer season, a time when the garden manages to provide anyhow, despite prevailing conditions. Make do with what you've got, no? I began eating locally and seasonally in my twenties, inspired by the teachings of macrobiotics, which I practiced for perhaps a half-dozen years. But Michio Kushi wouldn't call eating from the freezer "in season," exactly, and would especially disapprove of my store of tomato sauce, cooked up from one of those naughty, oh-so-yin nightshades, or solanaceous crops, that were basically taboo in the yin-yang macrobiotic system.

The Freezer Diet isn't bad, really — it's not like vintage TV dinners (though I do confess a past addiction to that little hollow that held the apple crisp, and how the mashed potatoes overflowed the boundary of their molded foil well to marry, all bubbly and hot, with meatloaf gravy). The Freezer Diet might actually be called the Give-Winter-the-Finger Diet, and I am delighting nightly in doing just that, especially pleased that I mixed it up last August through October while stocking the shelves. I am no different from the red squirrel who had ambitious caches of green conifer cones, but wasn't satisfied yet. He'd add some fungi or perhaps an apple (first setting each foodstuff high in a tree branch to cure, his slow-tech dehydrator). Following his energetic lead, I, too, have varied and colorful choices, each a distinct taste of brighter days.

Red sauce, applesauce all pink from the bright skins, frozen herbs, soup base with tomato, vegetable stock, two finished soups (sweet potato with kale and chard at the moment, and I think I saw some lentil), some kind of stir-fry or a curry made from whatever there was too much of to keep up with when it was fresh — when supply outpaced demand, the inverse of this moment of the year. If the crystal palace of wide-mouthed Weck and straight-sided, shoulderless Mason jars stacked inside my two 6.5-cubic-foot repositories is any indication, I had a bumper crop of green beans and a yellow crookneck squash, in particular, the latter a warty kind that sprouts every year in nearly the same spot, defying me to say no to its increasingly enthusiastic land grab, even though I don't know its name or where it came from. Could it be 'Early Summer Yellow Crookneck', a real old-timer probably grown by Native Americans, or more likely that heirloom variety accidentally crossed with a winged gourd I once tried here? It seems to really like me; something to be said for enthusiasm, no? The green and the gold pieces found their way for just a minute or so into a pot with a nearly ready, bubbling-hot mix of onion, garlic, and tomato, and then into a long winter's nap. The undercooking of the last-minute additions (my beans and squash) — like merely blanching them, but in an impromptu red sauce — is the key to the vegetable bits arising not so mushy at reheating time. The freezer as scrapbook; each jar a memento with shreds of a lost season's story inside.

■ ■ ■ ■

Come to Mama, 'Red Swan' beans, with your promised sweet-tasting, flat five-inch pink pods. We'd be good together, 'Cortland F-1' onion; your predecessor 'Copra' and I lasted a blissfully long time each year — usually right through until the following summer — and I hear you are an improvement, if such a thing is possible. You are my kind of chard, 'Argentata', with your thick white midrib — no flashy cousin of yours, such as 'Rainbow' or 'Rhubarb', can make me look away from all your *zaftig* goodness. And 3 Root Grex beet — wild child of three heirlooms with your neon range of possibilities, all in a single packet — who dreamed you up? Lucky me, if you agree to give my place a try. Maybe lucky you, too? I have just the spots for every last one of you. Interested?

And so it goes as I spend a fair amount of tea breaks and bedtimes paging through the profiles and photos in the seed catalogs. They are my resources, and entertainment, and also my textbooks: I learn one night, in the Fedco Seeds catalog, that it was Dr. Alan Kapuler, the microbiologist founder of Peace Seeds, a longtime bastion of organics, genetic diversity, and a believer in breeding

It surprises people to hear my take on heirlooms and hybrids, which is often referred to these days as heirlooms versus hybrids, as if it's an either-or decision, some kind of party politics you must choose between or else. Sorry, but I grow both — again, assuming they are offered by one of the seed vendors I trust according to the standards mentioned on page 70 — and wouldn't think of taking sides. I am not afraid of seeds whose mating process — whose transfer of pollen — has been influenced or at least set aside from the rest of the population by a human breeder, amateur or professional. It's genetic engineering (when the reproductive process is skipped entirely and genes are spliced into a plant in a lab) that frightens me, but not the kind of work that Gregor Mendel did in the nineteenth century with his famous peas, nor for that matter what farmers and gardeners have been doing with their crops (and livestock) through the millennia: selecting for the best traits, and breeding the next generations from those most desirable plants or animals.

The generally accepted definition of "heirloom" is an open-pollinated variety that's more than fifty years old, but just because a variety is open-pollinated (synonymous with "nonhybrid") and of a certain age (another definition of "heirloom" sets the cutoff date at pre-1940, rather than only fifty-plus years ago) doesn't guarantee it will suit my garden conditions. Taking an heirlooms-only stance according to these interpretations means I'd be missing out on some recent developments — both among hybrids and newer O.P. varieties. So, for one famous example, there would be no sugar-snap type peas as we know them now, which are sometimes called a modern heirloom, since they're open-pollinated but not old, for instance (of 1970s vintage, specifically). There would be none of my favorite cherry tomato, either ('Sun Gold' is a hybrid), and no tomatoes with disease resistance bred into them such as prolific 'Juliet', which has lately become my favorite for making sauce.

Unthinkable on all three fronts.

As I have been for twenty years or thereabouts, I continue to be inspired to avoid either-or thinking by such modern pioneers as founder Rob Johnston Jr. of Johnny's Selected Seeds in Maine, and John Navazio, Ph.D., an esteemed plant breeder, educator, and senior scientist for the Organic Seed Alliance, a nonprofit advocacy and educational organization in Washington State. As they both smartly and repeatedly remind us from their slightly different perspectives, the gardeners and farmers who developed the heirlooms in the first place wouldn't have stopped tinkering, and would have always been open to an enhanced version of a crop, and another, and another. In fact, many outstanding O.P. varieties are made by starting from the genetic material in hybrids (an example: the 'Clear Dawn' onion was developed from the hybrid 'Copra', known for its exceptional keeping qualities). This tinkering is not a new-fangled idea, but sort of an heirloom form of thinking in itself. Even Mark Twain agreed: "Training is everything. The peach was once a bitter almond; cauliflower is nothing but cabbage with a college education."

Picking a point in time as the cutoff for all my seeds? No thanks. Bring on the next generation — which will also yield the next generation of plants worthy of keeper, hand-me-down status.

---

for the public domain, who developed that rainbow of a beet I'm craving, 3 Root Grex. He's a man of science who gets the parable thing, who has described the garden as "a metaphor for having a place to develop an ethical way to understand life and to make a life that is ethical." And then the Fedco listing got me thinking: What's a *grex,* anyhow? Turns out it's not a variety at all — so no single quotes around the name — but from the Latin word for "flock," connoting a group of all the offspring of a particular hybrid cross. My beet-to-be is birdlike, and travels in a flock. Oh, joy.

These catalog adventures are the closest I come in this life I have chosen to browsing the latest crop of possibilities on Match.com. I am partial to both heirlooms and certain hybrids (see an explanation of why on page

116), and in both categories there are always some new faces, and others I've met many times before, including some real scoundrels I'm still trying to erase any trace of.

It's a day of muffled sounds and lots of shoveling. A day tucked in feeling thankful the wind hasn't taken out the power, even though it keeps devilishly re-covering walkways as fast as I can clean them, invoking its formidable power of drift. I know that means it's a dry snow, the kind that cannot settle but keeps repositioning itself with each gust, as if it finds each surface it tries too cold for comfort and moves along.

It's a day indoors with Jacko the Wacko, and it began at four thirty a.m. Someone, you see — someone who wasn't a sleepover-type house cat in the first nine years, not until this winter, not until a bloody middle-of-the-night run-in with some wilder creature tamed him slightly a few months ago — has learned to open the door to the upstairs. Where I sleep. Or worse, he has learned to *try* to open it, involving as that does a lot of clawing at the distressed old wood to which only bits of crazed paint cling here and there, fewer with each of Jack's predawn eruptions.

In Round 1 of this new day together, he comes out fighting. When I reach the top landing and hit the light switch, all I can see is evidence of mad desperation bursting forth from the crack between the bottom of the worn door and the first weathered step — two upstretched paws, claws bared, the feline "arms" they are attached to pumping like a boxer at a speed bag. No cat; just frantic front legs. No *good morning, how'd you sleep?*, but simply *I want out.*

I descend, taking the initial steps toward obliging the first of dozens of requests that will punctuate the hours ahead. I crack the outside door.

But no, on second thought, maybe not. It's snowing; can you clear me a path perhaps first?

I bundle up; I get my shovel. A path plenty big for even my very big cat is hollowed out as I am buffeted in an eggbeater environment of hectic wind and snow. At least the stuff is virtually weightless, not like the last rude dump.

He inspects my work.

No, I think I'll just wait a little while longer. I can hold it.

OK.

But I think I'll scream pretty much nonstop while I wait.

Perfect. Maybe you'd like to claw the staircase door again awhile, or some other piece of woodwork, while you howl?

Oh, no; I don't want to be any trouble, no. But thanks for asking.

And then, finally, at first light, out he goes — barreling headfirst into a snowbank, completely forgoing the paths I'd shoveled, and quickly digs himself a little snow cave of a restroom exactly one cat's-length off the back porch. He pivots, and carefully backs into it.

Charming. I turn away, allowing him his privacy, and go fill the kettle.

Then: What's that scratching noise? Is a mouse still awake and going at it inside the wall? *Not again.* No, that's my semiretired wildcat, the longtime gamekeeper of the place, who, though recovered from a bloody midnight massacre last fall, may or may not deign to hunt again when spring arrives. He's at the window now, pawing the glass so that it squeals under his damp pads, clawing the frame madly, wanting back in — more of the pumping motion, *go, go, go.* Do his forelegs have any other move but this one, and kneading of pizza dough on the upholstered furniture? Lately he jumps up and makes that motion on me, reaching up farther after every few rounds until he can deposit a smudge of nose juice on my neck or lick my bangs, grooming me as he does himself.

Who is this animal; where is my former wild man? Beyond him, in the gathering light, I can see the top two courses of the fieldstone wall above the frog pond, and the big Indonesian buddha's bust looking back at us from his perch on top. What must he think of this conversion I have undergone to such loyal service to my cat and master?

And then before I can even turn to get my mug, the whole scene I thought I saw is erased in another giant spin of the beater, an exhalation: *Poof!* Pranksters all, this cat, this statue, this wind — especially this hanger-on of an old-fashioned winter.

I was smaller then, but I was no child when I began cutting the first beds into my Tilt-A-Whirl tract of glacial till, which this morning looks less like land and more like the glacier that deposited it. Everything was smaller because I was relatively new to this gardening business, and tentative as those fresh to something vast and mysterious and oozing with life and death are apt to be. I imagine I would have behaved as gingerly at the start had I tried my hand at war correspondence, Lamaze class, or the volunteer ambulance corps — all of which share traits with gardening, though you're wearing different gear.

123

And so I went small, frighteningly so. I cut stingy beds — cots, not kings. They seemed so big to my untrained eye that I feared I would never be able to turn them without a gas-powered tiller, and that even if I did, I would not be able to afford enough plants to fill them — and if and when I got past that hurdle, that waiting for the plants to spread would take the rest of my lifetime.

To remind myself of just how small I thought then, I have left a drift of daffodils in place that used to demarcate a stretch of one such original plot (if one can call so penurious a grouping of *Narcissus* a "drift"). Most of the flowers are doubles — meaning that technically they are classified as Division 4 among the thirteen possible descriptive divisions a *Narcissus* can find itself placed in by the adoring subset of mankind that likes putting things in proper order. It was by acquiring a box full of labeled, perforated brown-paper bags of various kinds all those years ago and then noticing the similarities and distinctions that I began to learn that there even were divisions, and which ones I favored (besides the doubles, it is the dangling, bell-like flowers of Triandrus types, such as 'Thalia', in Division 5, and the small-cupped types like the Poeticus ones, or 'Geranium', of Division 3). The bulbs I refer to in the badly drawn bed are nothing special or rare, but familiar, fragrant old faces such as 'Cheerfulness' and 'Erlicheer' and 'White Lion' that I simply tucked in to fill the depth of my very first border, front to back.

Which was probably about two feet.

What was I thinking?

At least in their moment sometime in April, which feels right this minute like it will come no time soon or perhaps not ever again, they sit like a tight little selvage along the back boundary of a garden now multiple times wider than their pitiful formation, filling barely one-fourth the depth of the plot as it currently exists. Only I know why this measly strip of daffodils is there, all out of proportion and otherwise looking like a mistake. For what it lacks in aesthetic effect, the ill-fitting footprint of my earliest adventures is quite effective as an ongoing reminder that (as they say) you have to start somewhere. I don't know why I wasn't paralyzed by such early goof-ups in gardening the way I was in school, music and art lessons, sports, and so much more, where feelings of intimidation allowed me to quit instead of push onward, failing myself. Perhaps the plants themselves were easier to be with than fellow teenagers, their silence and generally cooperative natures a great relief from the taunting and the competition.

The bed also reminds me that in the garden, it is sometimes better to overdo it, rather than plant little rows of miniature soldiers here and there about the place, each struggling to defend their own too-small encampments. This is especially true with most bulbs. For now, all evidence of my miscalculations and recalculations are concealed from view by snow cover, but even on this day I know very well how I began.

Please release me, let me go. That's what I am singing to the winter that just won't quit after the latest ice storm overnight Sunday into yesterday. Every bud, needle, twig, trunk, vine remains totally encased, a world of glass. Even I, the 365-Day Gardener, have run out of patience.

Rhododendron leaves are curled in reverse fashion from the way my tongue can, stating their objection to prolonged serious cold. How long can they go on like that, I wonder? (How long can I stay curled up here indoors?) There are signs of winter burn on the gold Hinoki cypress (*Chamaecyparis obtusa* 'Crippsii'); a branch the wind played rough with is hanging by a strip of bark from the biggest of the Kousa dogwoods.

So what, the weather says in a voice much louder than any plant's; *what do you plan to do about it?*

Just as I think I can bear no more, it lets go — literally. It was a noisy end: Ice that had gripped like mad to everything finally shattered — as if some frequency of sound had been reached and it all just blew apart, millions of giant glass beads or chandelier crystals suddenly exploding into the air, glinting a moment in the sunlight that had been their undoing before they crashed. I sight land, after months at sea. The latest dose (an April fool's storm) had almost done us all in, but with the outdoor meltdown, the inner meltdown starts to improve.

A giant flock of common redpolls (*Acanthis flammea*), birds I never see here but that are not rare, technically, landed on the newly revealed patio outside my window, looking for nibbles in the cracks and crevices just hours after the latest halfhearted snow disappeared into the earth. A male goldfinch, already in his vivid mating plumage, flashes extra-bright against the last patches of snow. Once the slushy cold stuff gave up its hold on the stones by the frog pond, out climbed three friends, looking no worse for the winter wear. By the gate, the pussy willow catkins are all a silvery fuzz, and I swear the winter aconite (*Eranthis hyemalis*) perforated the leaf litter and jumped up an inch to open its goldfinch-colored flowers within a half hour of being exposed to light, determined to win the race for first bloom of the new year — just this once, maybe, beating the *Galanthus* and *Helleborus niger,* a race it never captures, but that it also never stops trying to own. There is hope, and the proof is in all of it.

And then it simply starts to pour.

CHAPTER 2
EARTH (SPRING)

He spake also this parable; A certain man had a fig tree planted in his vineyard; and he came and sought fruit thereon, and found none. Then said he unto the dresser of his vineyard, Behold, these three years I come seeking fruit on this fig tree, and find none: cut it down; why cumbereth it

the ground? And he answering said unto
him, Lord, let it alone this year
also, till I shall dig about it, and dung it:
And if it bear fruit, well:
and if not, then *after that thou shalt cut it*
down.
— LUKE 13:6–9

It's like taking out a splinter you have learned to live with: painful at the moment of actual extraction, but then also a great relief — and one that is wildly disproportionate to the dimensions of the expressed matter now being examined en plein air between the tweezer's tiny points.

Yes, yes, I know; the new season is meant to be all fresh and tender and newborn, and here I am talking about violence, because it is also a time for some serious upheavals, for extirpations — or even for murder, perhaps. The garden's maimed and its outright carcasses reveal themselves as fast and as loudly as the early bloomers, though in a ruder voice. In earliest spring — especially after so many previous early springs when I played Mizaru, the monkey who covers his eyes and sees no evil — it is time to say good-bye to a long list of woody plants.

The risk of not facing up to this task — of pretending we can just go on forever, all of us pack-ratted together here without enough space or the means to care for ourselves properly — strikes me as risking a fate somewhere between Miss Havisham's and Little Edie Beale's (though in my hope chest, I have neither a wedding dress nor skirts that I can wear upside down, Grey Gardens–style, and there was only the one cat on the premises at last roll call).

Writing down what needs to go completely (because it is either too cramped or damaged beyond corrective pruning's limitations), or what will get cut back hard in the hopes of regeneration (to a foot, or more or less, depending on the plant's innate habit and current structure), I keep finding myself thinking about rowing, or at least about the language of the sport more than harboring any desire to *pull, pull, pull*. I worked as a copy editor in a newspaper sports department many years ago, near the start of my career. Although I managed to learn very little about sports in general, continuing to loathe the playing or the watching of most every one — or is it all of them, truly? — there are certain words from the vocabulary of athletics that just stuck.

From boxing, I love "bolo," a sweeping sort of uppercut that can be used as a distraction — some might say showboating — or as the main event of aggression by those few who master it. Sugar Ray Leonard did. Imagine the arm motion powering a Filipino machete-like agricultural knife, called a *bolo,* in the sugarcane fields, a seemingly effortless harvest swing of a rhythm fiercely brought to bear upon an unsuspecting cane — or chin. (I was amused when I later came to know *bolo,* from the Sanskrit, as the word for "chant" or "proclaim," a common part of devotional phrases sung in yoga — *Rama bolo!* — and delivering an entirely different sort of punch.)

I love the prissy word "dressage" (right down to the beasts' plaited manes) and the sound of the beat-the-clock autocross variant called "gymkhana" (deceptively involving no prepubescent girls in leotards at all, nor any pommel horses — and the latter should be in the lexicon of equestrian sports, come to think of it). But best, I like how they do it in rowing, where repechage heats give the fastest losers of the elimination rounds another chance to compete for a spot in the final. I long for a do-over — what human being does not, on some front or other? — and this is my year for it, at least horticulturally.

My repechage — the one I have won the right to participate in by simply staying around so long in the same spot — starts with the Copake Chainsaw Massacre. The snarling machine is manned by Herb, the first neighbor I ever knew here, who has watched over me from the start of my time on our common dirt road. He will be eighty this summer, I realize as he fires up the familiar-sounding beast that has seen me through the aftermath of many an ice storm and worse. Oh, can it be that he was my age, or thereabouts, when we met? Thirteen shrubs are marked to go (some for good; others until they rise again from their own stubble), along with three trees. Several shrubs were felled last fall, before courage filled me for the longer hit list — which I know still isn't even close to all that needs to be banished from my overpopulated domain.

I normally time such brutality for late winter or earliest spring, when regrowing energy is in long supply, unless I'm feeling greedy and want to see one more bloom from those who flower in April or May, therefore staying their executions. Their reward for the curtain call? Off with their heads as soon as their final performances begin to peter.

Gone for good: several purple-leaved *Berberis thunbergii,* or barberry, including the beautiful arching, upright one called 'Royal Cloak', that had outgrown their spaces (and are now regarded as environmental weeds, anyhow), along with two dwarf Arctic willows (*Salix purpurea* 'Nana'), sentenced for my same crime of too-close spacing when they were small all those years ago, as were some just-too-big-now *Hydrangea paniculata*. Why did I try to stuff so many shrubs into each bed? Anyone looking would ask, and no wonder. Ten or fifteen or in some cases more years back, they were miles apart, mere rooted cuttings purchased by mail, their golfball-sized root balls arriving tidily cinched into a sandwich bag with a rubber band. Once unbagged and planted, they read unpleasantly as specks on a sea of mulch. *Gross.* It took enormous discipline even to space them as far apart as I did — which wasn't far enough by probably one-fourth their mature girth.

Condemned after being damaged beyond repair: some old winterberry hollies (what varmint tunneled under them until they lost their roothold?); a big, beloved specimen of a lilac with a purple-and-white variegated flower (*Syringa vulgaris* 'Sensation') that a yellow-bellied sapsucker had taken a fatal shine to. A couple of *Viburnum* were falling fast to *Botryosphaeria,* a fungal pathogen causing wilt, dieback, and even death — a plague whose marks I have long known, but only lately by its proper name; before that, my plant friends just referred to it as "the grunge." Their misery is now over, but I am miserable imagining being without them. What dearly departed recent losses am I forgetting?

The *Heptacodium miconioides,* or seven-son flower, a small tree with extravagantly peeling pale-colored bark, got off with a bit of pruning, but as I look back at it in the aftermath, I know I was too lenient there. It will be extracted in the next round, as will two big old Norway spruces (*Picea abies*), from a gang of six I planted as the start of a screen when I first came here, but before I knew that they outlive their usefulness when their lower limbs get brittle and sketetal, and that they also grow far too big for most any home-garden scale. I have said so many good-byes this month already, I couldn't go on, telling myself the birds will enjoy one more nesting season and protection from the wildest weather days tucked into their needled boughs.

Often this moment is harder for the survivors — those staying behind, like I am — than for those who have been sacrificed. Put away your chainsaw, Herb; let's drag this brush over to the mounting pyre-to-be, and say a silent prayer for such old friends.

That's it — that's enough grim reaping, at least for now.

It seems foolhardy, even positively contra-indicated, to be chopping down shrubs in what is the shrub season of my gardening life. For that is where it heads, eventually, for gardeners who last: away from the flashy, more momentary seduction of herbaceous plants — the annuals and perennials that want us to fuss over them with tasks like deadheading and, in the latter case, division — and back to the shrub aisles of the garden center.

"One day, if you're at all smart, you figure out it's just too much trouble," Marco said the other day, when I was droning on about how many herbaceous things here were already screaming for attention. You learn that it's better to go back to woody plants, he went on to say, perhaps taking with you what you've learned about really good perennials so you can spread them over the ground below. This from a man who spent his life and career growing everything and making one of America's most celebrated public gardens. *Why didn't he tell me sooner?* I guess there is no shortcut to this point of awareness, except straight through the perennial beds (the way he had to go himself).

I made various big shrubberies early on,

in the days when the moment alluded to in the phrase "when it grows in a bit" loomed hopefully ahead of me, rather than seeming, as now, the sum of my undoing. Old things fall apart; the younger things between them flourish, perhaps too well, and then they are all in one another's woody faces, snarling branches everywhere, jousting, nobody agreeing to stop advancing — let alone to retreat. You have to make some hard decisions, or leave them to further disfigure one another with their encroachments. And then, if you are still aboveground when the ones you spared become the next generation of old things, and start to fall apart themselves, it's time to steel yourself and do it all again: to play God or at least the Lord High Executioner, and point at those who stay or go.

If I could tell a beginning gardener anything, it would be to read up on the mature width of every woody plant before placing it, and to add 15 or even 25 percent to the published estimates, since most of my older things are already much bigger than they were *supposed* to ever get. The spike winter hazel (*Corylopsis spicata*) I planted almost upon arrival is now twenty-something feet wide, and one of spring's earliest woody bloomers, though it wasn't promised to even be hardy here at the time I adopted it, and has consumed half the width of the front path, poking at me as I try to get by. Few weeks go by when someone on the garden blog or in my e-mail doesn't write to ask how far away from the corner of their house (garage, walkway, *fill in the blank...*) to plant the young, innocent-looking Japanese umbrella pine or weeping Alaska cedar they just adopted — knowing these two very good conifers have lived with me here for many years. "Figure they will be at least fifteen and more likely twenty feet across at the base someday," I say, "so place the trunk half that distance plus some breathing room from the eventual impediment." *"Really?"* is the inevitable reply (often in a different, bolder font, the increasingly indignant e-mail colored now in red or hot pink; *temper, temper*). "But that will look so awful." Tell me about it — but we must endure our awful period either now or later, so which shall it be? Not every woody thing is so happy to be kept on as tight a leash as a yew or privet will tolerate.

I would (and do) therefore say — especially to myself — to really think about that when laying out the bed and digging the holes. Looking now at my own predicaments, I am keenly aware that it was my choice whether it would be five or fifteen years, or never, before a number of things would have to go. Some culling, some editing and rethinking and moving the pieces around (and out) will always be part of the process — but a twenty-five-year-old specimen conifer is not an easy thing to have to cull. Instant landscapes of large-scale woody plants plucked out with tree spades and carried in on flatbeds are for the very rich, and more a matter of check-writing than the practice of horticulture. The rest of us pay for a mature garden with our time. Give the youngsters some breathing room, within the limits of having to suffer through decades of a too-empty garden, if such a happy medium can be struck. (This is why we need all those needy perennials — to fill the space while we wait for the woodies to catch up.)

I need more shrubs, and drifts and oceans of special but really good, serviceable groundcovers beneath them. I need fewer complicated herbaceous beds that take days of work apiece at either end of the season, and tinkering such as pinching, staking, and the like along the rest of the growing-season calendar.

I need more shrubs. But first, I have had to cut down many that I already have. We reach our full promise, only to face decline.

■ ■ ■ ■

Down periscope: Time to look deeper still. Is it bigger than a breadbox (or just barely wide enough to trip you up)? Who dug that hole?

I am seized by this preoccupation from the first moment in each year when the soil encourages me to come stand on it again. Though it is an annual reunion, that of foot and earth, my invitation might arrive in March, and other years it's almost May. It can take that long before the thaw is thorough enough — till all that pore ice relents and melts, and once-trapped moisture-turned-solid begins to drain away. That's what must happen before I can go forth with impunity, whether to take down old friends who have outstayed their welcome or to harvest the debris that winter has left as its calling card, its voiceless version of *remember me?* (Why is it that the two lists — what needs removing, and what the winter chooses to carry off — never quite match up?)

I move gingerly in the earliest outings, not sure of my footing as for months now I have been more attuned to vigilance in antiskid maneuvers, or gauging whether I was still light enough to walk on the crust of aging snow, in a landscape made of baked Alaska,

I gardened with the deer for nearly a decade, and then I said, "No more." I'd sprayed, sachet-ed, blood-mealed, and Milorganited myself into a meltdown; I just couldn't wrap or erect pens or hang aluminum pie-plate mobiles or otherwise defend individual plants any longer. After all, the deer would just eat whatever wasn't "protected," indiscriminate feeders who were happy to move on to the next course as the previous one runs out. So I finally fenced.

Fencing is the only real deer-proofing method there is (assuming your fence is the right construction for your location and animal population, and is well maintained). No other tactic offers complete control, keeping deer out of the garden.

Even what have sometimes been labeled "deer-proof" plants prove deer-resistant at best, and besides, the garden-design limitations such lists impose provide insufferable restriction for someone like me, who can't resist a hot plant. I'm as much of an omnivore as were the deer; we just couldn't cohabit peacefully.

The garden's backbone — its woody plants — were being disfigured. Forget the occasional hosta stripped of its leaves; ugly, yes, but it sent up new growth relatively fast. The deer damage to woody plants I'd invested money and then time in (waiting for them to go from twenty-dollar youngsters to a real part of the landscape) was mounting fast. Some viburnums, in particular, had taken multiple hits and were beyond corrective-pruning rehab, as were many hollies — two of my favorite genera of shrubs. The cost exceeded the actual plant-specific losses, too: All those half-effective potions and gadgets, and the time it took to use them, were an investment.

And finally, one day, I looked out the window and realized this: I garden largely to enjoy viewing the landscape I have created, not to view a bunch of vulnerable specimens each encased in its own private cage, like a military encampment of impromptu tents and tepees pitched here and there in a time of battle. It was a sad sight. Enough.

First in my exploration, I turned to scientists and agricultural experts (*not* garden-product marketers), always my preferred first step. To choose a style of fence that will work for your garden locale, you need information about the local deer species, their habits, and their capabilities (read: how high can they jump, and how low will they go). Managing deer in a suburban environment can vary greatly from doing so in a rural one; hilly terrain and flat land each has its challenges. And so on. Great resources for location-specific insights: your cooperative extension; a nearby botanical garden or conservation or agricultural organization that compiles information that is product-agnostic.

I quickly learned that fence could be of several classes and complexities:

- Electrified or not (the former generally being cheaper because less material is involved; wire's cheaper than other fencing)
- Slanted or vertical
- Made of materials ranging from board, to wire strands, to high-strength polypropylene mesh (best when reinforced with high-tensile wire), to woven wire
- Temporary (seasonal) or permanent, both versions of which are available

in most of the aforementioned kinds
- Requiring professional installation or at least expertise and equipment, such as a posthole digger (a nearby, fenced-in tree farm helped me find a capable contractor); or in other cases more DIY.

I also learned a couple of more things, some the hard way:

- That cost per foot can vary from very little to very large
- That no matter how tall your fence is, what you do at ground level to exclude the deer is just as important. Deer are happy to do the limbo anytime and to wriggle on in, particularly fawns.

It wasn't until years after I began gardening, on a trip to the Northern California hillside of salvia expert Betsy Clebsch, that I learned how two rows of low fencing situated parallel to each other will also work: specifically, two four-foot-tall fences spaced five feet apart. The gap between is too wide for jumping (and deer hate entering an enclosed space, anyhow, which "reads" as if they might get trapped), but the gap's big enough for your wheelbarrow and mower — or you can plant it, a garden ringing the garden. This is a great solution for small gardens or areas near the house where a tall fence would be unsightly, creating a space like the old-fashioned dooryard garden, but with two rows of fence. One caveat: If you have heavy deer pressure, plan to put low fences up quickly, all at once. Don't let the animals get accustomed to a piece here or there, and adapt; change their pattern of movement once only, for good.

My property is bordered on three sides by state parkland and forest, so I was able to make good use of the natural tree line as part camouflage and part support for my fence. That really influenced my choice of a high mesh barrier. On the front boundary, along the road, where I did not wish to have the caged-in look of a very high fence, I adapted Betsy's system, using a modified double fence. I used extra-tall posts (eight-footers that when buried stuck six feet out of the ground) between each piece of standard four-foot-high picket fencing, and strung the poly mesh reinforced with high-tensile wire (not electrified) to reinforce the top. Outside that layer, a three-strand trip wire on low posts forms the "other" fence.

My own fence journey has had two major phases: First, after that initial research, I used heavyweight polypropylene black mesh meant for deer fencing. I got very good, but not complete, control from this seven-and-a-half-foot material for about six years, until one too many animals had run into it or tree limbs had fallen on it. Some of the limited life span was my fault, because I had failed to reinforce the mesh with several strands of high-tensile wire running horizontally through the top, bottom, and middle, kind of woven in. Today, in one spot where I still use this system, I have it properly reinforced (and also flapped and pinned down at ground level with earth staples to prevent invasions from below, as I always did). Once the poly had done its service, I recycled panels of it for pea trellis and other duty, but switched to woven wire, a very heavy eight-foot-tall metal material. Sliding farm gates on rollers span my driveway; ugly, yes, but not as ugly as what the deer would do. Nobody's been in since — well, except when I left a gate open.

without falling through into the softer crumb of cakey white below. Feet upon semifrozen or wet soil — even feet elevated as mine have been for months now above the coils of strapped-on Yaktrax — do concrete make, and concrete will not support a harvest.

This year I am especially tentative. Nothing feels right at the moment, with incomprehensible news of meteorological and nuclear havoc from Japan, but enough of another late snow melted so that I finally just grabbed a rake yesterday and went outside to work while grappling with all the thoughts. When I confessed that online, a reader quickly reminded me of the Shaker wisdom, "Hands to work, hearts to God," and I was grateful for such guidance.

From a check of the deer fence to the first cutbacks, I simply got started: walking the perimeter, looking for breaches in the eight-foot-tall metal mesh barrier between me and *them;* gently raking debris off a few small areas that were dry enough, starting right near the house. (My 101 on deer fencing begins on page 141.) Selfishly, and because of the inclination to get overwhelmed and even paralyzed by the bigness of the cleanup phase, I always start in close like this, with areas I'll get to see regularly — a sort of reward and further inspiration in one. Each expedition outside will be a little more ambitious, and farther-ranging, creating widening circles of clean, but for now it's evergreen herbaceous things whose last-year foliage is tattered that I'm concentrating on: hellebores, European ginger, epimediums. Next up will be ornamental grasses, and heucheras, and in a small gesture of optimism, I think I'll plant the peas and spinach. This is how it always begins: modest, uncertain, especially now, with all the too-bigness — my messy yard's, the messy world's — tugging at me as I explore. Sometimes making sense of things just comes down to doing something, anything, outdoors.

Today, though, I needn't take too many steps — all the while silently reciting "Sticks and Stones" like a schoolchild, for that is what I see left in the fading season's wake tossed down from on high and up from down below, respectively — before I come across

148

more trouble in the form of some hole, and then another. Some are more a maze of narrow surface tunnels, others larger-mouthed; there are mere divots and then there is one so big, I fear, as to portend a network of caverns beyond.

The season's first horticultural whodunit: *Who dug it?* (*Who ate it?* will come soon enough, as will *What killed it?* and even — worst of all, in cases of total disappearance — *Where's my plant?*)

Who dug it? Was it snout of skunk? Claw of squirrel? (This already sounds like the start of a recipe for some fearsome witch's brew, or an episode of one of those British crime shows I devoured in the long, dark days, but with a twist: The Nature Channel meets *BBC Mysteries*.) Chipmunk? Woodchuck? Mole? Vole? Who can be credited with (blamed for?) the sizable excavation at the base of the oldest apple tree, the one closest to the house, the tree that from mid-March or so into early May, when it leafs out, consorts with masses of extra-early herbaceous things I tucked in beside it, not because I thought the tree was lonely but to satisfy my own pleasure. I needed the company. The apple had stood alone for perhaps three-quarters of a century, and didn't even seem sad or self-conscious at the loss of most of its branches sometime along that course. Today, and as long as I have known this solitary old-timer, it is just a craggy trunk, jagged and topless as if a giant beast with a very uneven bite had simply ripped its head off. It is also mostly hollow — the pileated woodpeckers have seen to that — boasting an artful spray of far-reaching limbs but with no central leader or any middle part to its canopy really at all. I love this beater of a tree, no longer a beauty, but someone you like to stare at, anyhow.

Maybe a decade ago, using tiny seedlings at first, I plugged its root zone with hellebores and trilliums and violets and snowdrops and such for no other reason but this selfish one: because, after surviving each winter, I wanted a beacon during mud season. (My under-planting how-to on the next page.) I hungered for at least one spot I could see from inside to buoy me if I were still marooned, perhaps no longer adrift in snow and ice but (the latest insult!) in sodden, sloppy soil, a sea of muck. I wanted — *required* — one visible bed that defied the last vengeance of winter and the tardiness and sloth of early spring, one real-ized dream in the mess beyond. Today, and each year around now, I gratefully spy those ephemerals with my winter-weary eye. The sight of all these holes, however? Far less in-

Confession: I came very slowly and painfully to the lesson of underplanting, dragged by some much more talented gardener friends. The lessons have involved some yelling, and even some tears (mine, not theirs), but now instead of sheets of a dull "groundcover" or two under trees and shrubs, I know it is possible to have complex gardens, with many months of interest even in a single space. I've learned to think mosaic (not monotone). Ten steps are required to get there, which follow after this one disclaimer: These mosaics are more work to maintain than sheets of a solid groundcover or two or three combined, so implement them in spots where someone will appreciate the extra work, and interest, like right by the front walkway or outside a key window — and keep the sheets approach for the outer reaches, which rate a lower level of commitment. The steps:

1. No ring-around-the-rosey, thanks anyway. Rather than circling the drip line of trees or shrubs (or a group of trees and

shrubs) with groundcovers and bulbs and such, you have to get all the way in there, even right near the trunk, to make it look un-man-made — as if it just happened.

2. No polka dots (except at first): Like I said, It's all about learning to "think mosaic," which doesn't mean onesies dotted here and there, but sweeps and drifts and deliberate repetition of said sweeps and drifts. At first, though, no matter how many plants you buy or what you feed them, the new underplanting will look like hell (well, like polka dots, and a lot of mulch). Which leads to the next lesson:

3. Patience is required. (If you did not know that already, I suspect you have not started a single seed, let alone planted a young tree.) This gardening nonsense is all about patience — frankly I think it's a patience-building practice more than anything else. Your bed will look better next year, and almost great three years after planting. After the fourth year or so you can start harvesting divisions of the most co-

and colors, coming mostly from foliage (as the leaves will be there all season or even all year, and the flowers just come briefly). Think of the color range of heucheras alone you could employ, or hostas — foliage is hardly boring. Which relates to this lesson:

9. Texture is also a great ally. Work it. I cannot imagine "mosaics" succeeding without some linear things (grasses, or sedges), contrasted against some ferny things (such as, well, ferns, or the dwarf goatsbeard, *Aruncus aethusifolius*) and against some large-textured things (such as bigger hostas like 'Sagae', or perhaps mayapple, *Astilboides tabularis,* a *Rodgersia* or *Diphylleia cymosa*). Subtler textural possibilities: You might play off matte versus shiny, for example.

10. Once you've selected a palette, repeat, repeat, repeat. Not just in the first area you underplant, but (if it works) in another area in need of some extra interest, where it may be all mulch right now or a sea of a single groundcover. Soon your first

experiment will afford you some divisions, and on to making the next beautiful mosaic you will go.

vigorating. If I could see my underworld in cross-section, I bet it would look like an ant farm, but for very large ants who are short two of the typical six legs of the genuine, original tiny models.

Though "down the rabbit hole" is a favorite expression in my somewhat Alice-in-Wonderland life view, I know that our most widespread North American species, the eastern cottontail, is not to blame. He is no real-estate developer, but only an occasional subtenant, usually renting — squatting in? — the House that Chuck Built. European rabbits dig, yes, but not our cottontail. Except to fine-tune a woodchuck's belowground handiwork and take refuge in extreme times, or (in the case of a female) to carve a scrape — a shallow depression in the dirt lined with fur and grasses as a nest in which to bear young — the cottontail doesn't do the heavy lifting of excavation projects. It's perfectly happy tucked away in a pocket someone else

156

made, an insignificant bowl-sized hollow beneath an old log or brush pile, perhaps. No, it wasn't *Sylvilagus floridanus*. So again: Who dug it?

Before I go making wrongheaded accusations and, worse, assumptions — for you will never outwit or even come face-to-face with an opponent you do not first correctly identify, and outwit I must — I calmly review the distinct forms of handiwork of my possible foes. *Steady, Margaret; you know this.* Yes, I remember: Skunks and raccoons (by night) and gray squirrels (by day) are divot-makers, though the first two will also appropriate someone else's hole. The networks of surface runways strewn with bits of what used to be my lawn? The meadow vole (*Microtus pennsylvanicus*), a mouse-like creature but with a tail maybe 40 percent the length of its body, made those eyesores, taking advantage of the cozy airspace between soil and snow — the subnivian layer, the same microclimate that gets my tiniest bulbs up and growing extra-fast. I must quickly rake out the messes, topdress with compost or soil, and reseed before weed seeds — coming alive in the light of their sudden exposure — capitalize on the bright opportunity and claim the spot for theirs. Red squirrels elude their predators in winter by scurrying around beneath the snow, too, to eat from their caches, but don't seem to shred the underlying vegetation in the process. I am definitely betting on the vole as the culprit in this mess.

The number of fresh-looking inch-and-a-half or two-inch holes is almost frightening, and they eerily have no loose soil piled nearby. The signs seem to say this promises to be the Year of the Chipmunk, a tidy excavator who needs no wheelbarrow; his cheek pouches can accommodate load after load of soil as he efficiently disguises the scene of his activity by carting away the evidence. Where the lawn feels like carpet that has come unglued and buckled, I suspect not rodents but those most formidable of insectivores called moles — and yes, there is some excavated earth piled up in a conical fashion, the proverbial molehill, to confirm my diagnosis, but with no actual tunnel entrance in evidence. Each of us has his or her distinctive trademark, and the cleverest also possess tactics to elude discovery.

The worst of findings is the one beneath the apple, though, nearly twelve inches across with loads of soil around the entrance — the distinctive, impressive work of none other than a woodchuck (*Marmota monax,* elsewhere called a groundhog). My first walkabout of the new garden year — *five, six, pick up sticks,* a new nursery rhyme, same chore — revealed just the one burrow entrance, and it's not apparently active at the moment, I see, since the soil looks like it was upturned before the winter and has gone to mud beneath the melting snow. I know better than to feel secure, however. Other seasons have taught me that he will come to call, all in good time — or perhaps he is down there but simply set his snooze alarm and will be up and at it any moment now.

Today, the soil says welcome and the big, pollen-rich nectaries of the first defiant flowers — the *Helleborus niger* and *orientalis* hybrids, the winter aconite and snowdrops — serve up visual encouragement to me and life support to a few just-awake, hungry honey bees. I'm not sure who needs it more. I dare not grow too excited, too attached, however. Spring is freedom, and also slavery; I am liberated from my own burrow, but only to face a growing list of concerns, repairs, to-dos. In time, some force or other — some mammalian Roto-Rooter, some meteorological aberration, some lapse in care on my part — could take it all away again, putting us back to a blank slate, or worse. Word of the new day: "precarious."

■ ■ ■ ■

Appearances can be deceiving, though when it comes to gravity, I am not rattled by the illusion it creates but rather happy for the (false?) sense of security and groundedness. The earth is not any more beneath our feet than the sky is above our heads, but I am comfortable to simply go about my days as if both were certainties. I have a dizzyingly hard time with reality in this case — the thought that I (along with every tree and other living or nonliving thing) am actually sideways, sticking off the planet at some angle like a clove poked in an orange pomander, makes me vaguely long for Dramamine. The facts of science I am happier to see just as they are: those of soil science — what makes the combination of particles called sand, silt, and clay (think: small, smaller, smallest) that I am standing on different from the mix under another gardener's boots across the hill behind me, the county, the state, the globe.

I suppose in its genesis it was the provocateur of ice at work, specifically the glaciers, and where and when they moved — and what they left behind. The soil at these coordinates of our forty-five-million-century-old planet's surface is a glacial till, deposited sites but situated only a few hundred feet higher in altitude, just up the road, working the ever-more-measly supply of soil gets a lot trickier, with bedrock that's more insistent, closer to the surface, and composed of a foot to nearly twice that thickness of folded shale. I was attracted to this hillside perch of a place, but never knew that it might prove hard to get a hold on — a naïveté that represents the most breathtaking near miss of so many propagated by pure ignorance early in my gardening life. Only one thing would have been worse — a toxic site — and I had blessedly and miraculously been outbid on one of those, a seventy-nine-acre farm in nearby commercial apple-orchard country. My salvation came just weeks before when, horribly disappointed that it had slipped through my fingers, I found this tiny spot instead, as the consolation prize. It was a heartbreak at the time, until I realized what living in a constant state of spraying from all sides would have been like (not to mention that I could never have afforded the taxes, upkeep, heating bills, any of it).

I was a true flatlander — not just "not from here" — the intended meaning applied by locals who referred to weekenders such as myself that way — but actually from the flat and low lands of New York City and as ice made its series of advances and retreats across what is now Columbia County, New York, between three hundred thousand and ten thousand years ago. With each southern advance, pieces of bedrock and soil were picked up; with each retreat, the jumbled-together gleanings got set down in their new home, the place that for this mere blink is mine.

It scares me now to think that I didn't do so much as stick a single spade into the ground here to see what it was made of before I put down earnest money and signed on to own the place. As with all new-home inspections, a cast of costly strangers with presumed expertise — were they actually ringers recommended by the Realtor to guarantee a good outcome? — came to evaluate. They wrote up reports on the structure and the systems, mapped the boundaries (my tract of 2.36 acres is almost an isosceles triangle, but with one of the bottom corners missing), and even tested the water — but a soil sample was never on any of the checklists that led up to closing day.

I planned to garden here.

How close I came, though, to picking a site that would yield only to pickaxes or dynamite, that no mere shovel would ever convince to cooperate. On similarly inclined

Long Island, quite a different sort of place geologically speaking. When I finally did dig in, I got lucky, meeting a mostly deep, dark-brown silt loam that seems to go on forever, that drains well, and that is palatable to a range of plants. There are stones, the kind that fit in your hand and are easy to just toss over your shoulder toward some out-of-the-way place, such as the woods, but there are no giant outcrops to contend with. A garden nearby has one lovingly referred to as "Moby Dick" as its central feature, but as dramatic and defining as outcrops can be visually, it's easier without. My biggest obstacle is not from bedrock but from the surface attitude — more inclined plane than level playing field — which encourages things to float or spill downhill against my strongest wishes otherwise.

And here it comes again: Teeming rain, more than the too-full ground still choking on an overdose of melted snow could swallow, seemed to engulf everything from just before bedtime until well into the morning hours. Rain on bloated soil means my short-lived invitation to go about the cleanup chores will be temporarily rescinded, but there is a bright spot, I know, out at poolside. Wet, forty-ish degree conditions were perfect for a Big Night, when amphibians

163

move from their wintering spots to vernal pools and other suitable breeding grounds — including my backyard, blessedly, where I'm certain the population figures just increased dramatically. I should charge admission, like a caravan park; another potential revenue stream for my sketchy household budget. This morning the only chore will be to carefully follow the stepping-stones and extend a welcome to the newcomers, some of whom I hope will be familiar faces, such as perhaps the pair of distinctively freckled bullfrogs I met last year. What will the soggy census reveal?

I admire, even envy, such spontaneity and decisiveness — *tonight we move!* — living as I do (as we all do?) trapped between my task lists: garden chores, household chores, shopping, writing and other work, bookkeeping, the usual range of appointments. The datebook tries to accommodate them all — but which calendar should I use to schedule my seed-sowing or other garden chores? The one on the wall or desk — yes, I am that backward, preferring paper to pixels for tracking time commitments — or the one provided by nature? I was reminded of this choice a week or so ago when a fellow garden blogger, who lives a couple of hours away, in a colder direction, remarked with surprise that I had already planted my peas, which I'd mentioned "out loud" on some virtual meeting place. "Are the peepers out there already?" she asked, because she plants peas when the often-heard-not-seen chorus frogs called *Pseudacris crucifer* peep, observing a practice based on phenological observations — the "what happens when" of nature-watching.

By marking down observations about nature year to year — what blooms when, what the weather is doing at the time, what birds or other animals and insects appear or depart on certain dates — and comparing them, then you are at least informally practicing phenology. Phenology is the study of recurring life-cycle stages among plants and animals, and also of their timing and relationships with weather and climate, a sort of nature's calendar. It serves higher purposes than providing conventional wisdoms for gardeners, and in this time of climate change, phenological records are proving especially valuable.

This way of thinking doesn't rely on dates on a Gregorian calendar — so things I have long used as mnemonic devices, such as "sow tomatoes indoors at tax time" or "plant peas on Saint Patrick's Day," are too vague to reflect how each year is actually progressing. It's not holidays or other human impositions onto time that matter in phenology, but factors including day length, temperature, and rainfall that affect what happens when, from year to year, and can serve as cues. The tricky thing is that everyone experiences, and interprets, the cues a little differently. Thankfully, science types are less emotional or subjective than most of the gardeners I know. Research at Ohio State University has demonstrated that plants bloom and insects emerge in virtually the same *order* each year — regardless of the severity of the winter, or whether spring came "early" or "late" from our human point of view. The flowering sequence is the same, even if it doesn't match up with our datebook-type man-made systems; this also means that insect activity can be predicted by observing plants, then plotting when to deal with the most damaging ones before infestations get ahead of you — if you're a farmer, for instance, or a gardener who has a less laissez-faire attitude toward most insect pests than I.

The first bloom on the eastern redbud (*Cercis canadensis*) will nearly coincide with the gypsy-moth-egg hatch. Adult white pine weevil emergence and the first flower on the star magnolia (*Magnolia stellata*) nearly match up in the areas Ohio State studied, too. Year to year, the phenological *sequence* is the same for a particular place — and is temperature dependent. Things both plant- and animal-wise will unfold when, and only when, enough accumulated heat — measured in growing degree days — has oc- curred, whether that's technically in March one year and April the next, for instance.

I suppose my gardening rhythms are guided mostly by instinct and how the weather and soil conditions seem to me; I garden the way I cook — by feel, rather than by formula, and often to simply sate a hunger. I shop for violas on the first day that the garden centers open locally — April 1 — because I cannot wait to shove several flats onto the backseat and see how many blocks away from the nursery I get before the few thumbnail-sized flowers that are open fill me up with what winter tried to mask, the scent of volition infused with forward motion. I cannot plant them outside safely yet, but I must have them. *Now.*

Sometimes, it is the voice of another pan- icky gardener that jolts me into action, like Marco's e-mail did the other day from his two-weeks-ahead location: "New plants all over my garden waiting to be given homes and others badly in need of curtailing their imperialistic tendencies." Yes, we will soon reach that point here, too. And if I had kept strict records, I'd wager I could add my phenological observations to the mounting evidence of a shifting climate, based simply on the date each year when I can no longer go without mowing. Not so long ago, it was sometime in the first week of May; now it's in the next-to-last or final week of April — and on the other end, it's stretching well into November.

Maybe I should hunt for eastern tent caterpillars (*Malacosoma americanum*) at crabapple bud break, since the two are closely tied where I live, with an eye to removing the most inconveniently placed bags before they disperse and do their damage to my favorite trees. Maybe I should plant potatoes when the *Amelanchier,* or shadbush, blooms; sow sweet corn with the apple blossoms, and prune roses at *Forsythia* flowering time. The cow's sort of out of the barn on the matter of the peas, however, at least this year. I sowed them, even though I hadn't heard the peepers yet.

It must be my age, the way echoes of what has been insinuate themselves into here and now. Looking around the yard lately, I see as many plants that are not any longer pres-

168

ent as I do ones currently in residence, at least in my mind's eye, recalling some of the departed with wistfulness and others with grateful relief. (The same thing happens with every reflection in the mirror, though there the wistful side definitely tips the scale.)

Never stop wanting more plants. That ethos of insatiability I was taught to garden by is not about greed, but rather speaks up in favor of maintaining perpetual curiosity. It was instilled twenty-plus years ago, handed down by Marco as it had been given to him by a gardener he admired named Harold, who, even when past ninety, still lusted for every new thing he could get a cutting of. But in this strain of lust, I have slowed considerably, my wants grown far more measured and selective. In the first days I was insatiable, hungry for everything, and grew so many plants, all of them new faces then to me, seeking not just something to look out at or proclaim about with the busting pride of a kid whose training wheels just came off, but also wanting knowledge. Each plant teaches some lesson or other; besides just filling its hole in the landscape, it starts to make the pieces of the wider puzzle fit.

The native spicebush (*Lindera benzoin*) introduced me to the interdependence of plants and animals, besides blooming bravely as few other shrubs dare do when winter has barely left. How did the big, dark spicebush swallowtail butterfly, *Papilio troilus,* find the small shrubs I added to this piece of property, where none were present before? I suppose you could say that about a tomato hornworm (*Manduca quinquemaculata*), too — which seems as if it must come hidden, perhaps freeze-dried, inside every packet of tomato seed. When I started growing the Dutchman's pipe (*Aristolochia macrophylla,* which I then knew as *A. durior*), along came *Battus philenor,* the pipevine swallowtail, whose throng of ravenous larvae traveled herdlike over the massive heart-shaped leaves that shaded the porch, chewing, chewing, as they seem to like nothing better to eat (though sassafras will do if need be, it turns out).

The gold-leaf cultivar of common bleeding heart that I know as *Dicentra spectabilis* 'Gold Heart' (though its new genus was verified as *Lamprocapnos* in 2006 by taxonomists) acted out the power of anthocyanins as I crawled around on hands and knees in the season's first days and noticed that not everything that pushes up and out of the earth is green. Its costar was a longtime resident of the same bed — the species or nonhybrid peony Molly the Witch

(*Paeonia mlokosewitschii*). Anthocyanins are the provocative red-and-purple foliar pigments familiar to autumn, revealed when the green of chlorophyll fades with the waning of photosynthesis and the taking hold of senescence, but they are also an important feature of spring. The coevolutionary thinking, apparently, is this: Are you planning to arise early in the garden year, when hungry herbivores are also waking? Paint yourself nongreen for safety — and since you will also want to compete favorably for the few awake pollinators available when you bloom shortly afterward, a purple-pink getup will probably read "flower" more than "leaf" and can't hurt in that respect, either. *Get your party dress on, girl.*

I watched as columbines of various sizes and shades — each chosen for its distinctiveness — sowed themselves around until I had none but some stubby overstuffed and very weird-looking mutts. Their blooms were neither gracefully shaped nor spurred nor brightly colored — a lesson in the dangers of free love, I guess, or maybe just a crash course in cross-pollination that makes a case for a little human intervention (parental supervision?) when raising sex-prone species.

I smile now to think how I once so treasured lamb's ears (*Stachys lanata*), when it

171

was my first silver thing. A tiny symbolic patch remains beneath an espaliered pear out back, sharing the narrow space with gold-leaf oregano, but it hardly recalls the role this plant once played here. It was so obviously hairy, almost animal-like, that I could not resist, and a silver binge followed — with adoptees like horehound (*Marrubium rotundifolium*) and *Ballota pseudodictamnus*. Meeting the gang of them set me about trying to discover what purpose the hairs served in their hot, dry native habitats (think: tennis whites on a hot court). While feeling the three beauties up, over and again, I also noticed their similarly strange square stems, which had nothing to do with their silvery-ness; never jump to conclusions with plants. It marked the trio as cousins in the mint family, as was nonsilver, nonfelted *Monarda didyma* 'Cambridge Scarlet', which delighted the hummingbirds by overrunning everything in its bed but another wildlife favorite, anise hyssop (*Agastache foeniculum*), a prodigious reseeder that thereby held its own (and speaking of various mint relatives that once lived here, another member of the Lamiaceae). Building blocks of a first garden, yes, but also of a beginning garden education. My age of discovery, and the best of times.

They came to me by various routes: Some now-lost plants were the result of succumbing to a marketing campaign, or at least a very good blurb in one of the mail-order catalogs that were the source of almost everything back then, though most of the original places I shopped at are, like my plants, long gone. As was the fashion at this moment or that, I had my coneflower years (black-eyed gold ones and purple, too); a lot of *Sedum spectabile,* and a stand of *Perovskia atriplicifolia*, the Russian sage, at the lower edge of the vegetable garden for a time. Early on, shopping at botanical-garden plant sales became a competitive sport, and I enthusiastically took on many things, including an assortment of *Deutzia* that a famous institution was de-accessioning, only to realize why firsthand, after the letdown of a few years of momentary white spring bloom and nothing much more to commend them. At the sale it had all seemed so exciting — a collection of shrubs, and with a provenance! — but exciting they were not. *Gone.*

Other plants arrived because I'd tried a cousin or two and wondered what else the genus had to offer. A success with my first *Euphorbia,* the undersea-looking, succulent, blue-leaved species *myrsinites,* which still sows itself between the patio pavers at will after outlasting everything else that ever grew there, put me in the mood for more. I promptly ordered every Zone 5 or almost-5 relative: *polychroma* and then the *zaftig* version *pilosa* 'Major', *griffithii, palustris,* and eventually the recent *amygdaloides* hybrids, too. If you had one *Physocarpus* shrub (I brought the yellow-leaf 'Dart's Gold' home from California in the early 1990s as a rooted cutting), why not try all the rest as they became available? The more the merrier here at the zoo. Those last two — the spurges and the ninebarks, as the *Euphorbia* and *Physocarpus* are called, remain in residence, so they or I must have done something right.

In counterpoint, there was a definite inclination toward subtle little oddballs: a vining fumitory (a bleeding-heart relative) called *Adlumia fungosa* that scampered around the front garden up and over other things, all lacey and romantic, for years, but whom I haven't seen in ages. A sweet haze of love-in-a-mist (*Nigella damascena*), with its balloon-like striped seedpods, reliably overtook the patio at some point each summer, and bamboo tripods held its soundalike love-in-a-puff (*Cardiospermum halicacabum*), whose bigger green balloons enclosed seeds on which a tiny heart was painted. I don't know that I actually like the color blue much, but besides the *Nigella* there was a profusion of globe thistle (*Echinops ritro*) and some fiercely sharp-toothed *Eryngium,* or sea holly, anyhow. All long gone, and who knows why we lost touch (or frankly, why we got connected in the first place)?

But see how much like the talk at a high-school reunion this all sounds — remember *him?* He was great (or loud, or pushy) — and what about *her?* Oh, she was so pretty. *Auld lang syne.* I have never been one for reunions, but when they come into my visual memory, suddenly a couple of the best old faces, such as *Phlomis russeliana* — a crazy-looking mint cousin with yellow flowers that always looked to me like spaceships — are feeling as if they are maybe too long gone as well. Whatever became of the rose called 'Veilchenblau', an old-fashioned-looking rambler, a hybrid multiflora with mauve-purple flowers, that shared a bed with alliums, perennial geraniums, and even a giant stand of pokeweed I allowed — encouraged — to take hold? What even happened to that bed, its entire outline now erased?

Never stop wanting more plants. I promise not to, until I myself am back in the soil, though admittedly they won't all be the latest, greatest strangers like at the start. Instead the party will be balanced by some repeat visitors, come back by special invitation to see me through my increasingly sentimental age.

I have had enough of some plants, thank you, but apparently they have not had enough of me.

I thought I had killed the comfrey, with its giant leaves and blue flowers that bees love, but a creature far too ambitious to behave well with its neighbors in a garden setting. Then, this spring, it surfaced again, after four years underground and presumed dead — dead by murder, specifically, as we'd dug and dug until we thought it was a losing battle and that *Symphytum officinale* was the victor. Next, though, it finally disappeared — as if to take another tack in the turf war altogether and try playing dead. Plants do this, you know — and in the case of comfrey, apparently the roots can go down ten feet, exceeding even the most frenzied homicidal instincts at its eradication. (I read that ten-foot claim in some English gardening book, and they know everything, right?) My best (worst?) example of possum-players: the gaudily beautiful and treacherous temptress called *Houttuynia cordata,* the chameleon plant (well named, you deceptive, stinking beast).

I bought *Houttuynia* maybe fifteen years ago, for the showiness of its (then) variegated red, green, and yellow foliage and its touted use as a groundcover in moist shade (or plunged right in a pot in water, apparently, as a leafy island of accent in a pond or trough). Certain that I had acquired a treasure, I was frantic when it didn't return from underground after its first winter with me. Dead, I reported in my newspaper garden column at the time. Gone.

It was another year before the chameleon turned on me again, and resurfaced. Its resurrection was cause for celebration. Not dead, not gone.

Anyone who has ever tangled with an invasive (plant/person) knows how the story goes: It behaved for a moment or two, charming me thoroughly as if it were my latest gem — *lucky me* — and then proceeded to get thuggish (and lose its variegation, reverting to the stronger-willed green version, a popular edible, apparently, in Southeast Asia and China, though I'd rather go hungry). *Oh, no,* I said, *not on your life,* as it overran pulmonarias and *Hylomecon,* goldenseal and trilliums at a gallop. *Oh, no you don't.* Out came the border fork and poaching spade, and after the seeming bulk was uprooted and sent to the trash, out came the sheets of

177

heavy black plastic, too, weighted down with stones all summer long, as I tried to smother the remainder to death.

By springtime: not gone, and a year later (by then two years beneath the sheeting), still not gone. Four years of this treatment did nothing but encourage it to travel farther and farther sideways underground, as if it were being aided and abetted by me in its Manifest Destiny, not acknowledging any enforcement of its borders. If I believed in applying herbicides, I could not use one to stop it in this situation, anyway: The *Houttuynia* is growing under a big magnolia with fleshy surface roots, which would have taken up the chemical, too. I even feared the plastic tactic, worrying about roasting them. Blessedly, yellow-flowered 'Butterflies' never blinked.

Again and again, as with the comfrey, the routine was followed: forking and teasing out everything in its path (not just the *Houttuynia*); bagging and trashing or at least washing all of it for fear of spreading snippets of the chameleon's roots, tangled among the others', and in total desperation, turning the area under the infested magnolia to lawn. Mowing for a few years will probably kill whatever resprouts, right? *Or not.* I remind myself that this actually was a good idea: I have killed poison ivy and substantial bramble patches in the field-like areas here with the submit-or-else mower blade, but with the chameleon plant several years later, the answer is *not* — meaning that the two most powerful nontoxic, or mechanical, methods of killing an unwanted plant, solarizing and mowing, have failed.

I have come to accept defeat with some other unfortunate acquisitions; I know there is no possibility of getting rid of the tropical-looking perennial *Petastites japonicus* var. *giganteus* from Asia, for instance. Instead of even trying to, we have made a sort of semi–peace pact. I ceded it a place where a ten-foot-across circular stand of its chest-high leaves, each nearly the diameter of an umbrella, actually look as if someone planned the spot around its incorrigible lustiness. "Is that *Gunnera*?" people ask, thinking they have seen that statuesque, nonhardy rain-forest type in my northern garden, where it would be a real rarity and require heroics to overwinter. Yes, in my dreams; *aren't I special?*

There is no peace with the *Houttuynia,* though it is tiny by comparison. In fact, as if to taunt me and show who's boss, the little chameleon emits a nasty scent with each pass of the mower — some sickening mix of jet fuel and tangerines, perhaps — as if belching and farting in my direction to show its contempt at the pitiful efforts that are all I can muster. Why won't this plant die? Because it's even more stubborn than I am, apparently. I have met my match in the impertinent creature sent to remind me that mankind has no true dominion in the ultimate scheme of things. *None.*

In that most counterintuitive of garden moments, starting around the end of the first week or so of June in Zone 5B, it's time to make things that were just very pretty look like hell (and then to plant more of the same vegetables you may not even have harvested your first crop of — that's covered in the succession-vegetable-garden sidebar on the next page). With some perennials, I stay busy making bad situations worse in the days just after the peak of spring bloom, which is exactly what has to be done to bring any garden from that moment to a visually pleasing high summer and fall. It's not unlike any other cleaning project: Things have to get pulled apart and look a lot messier before they get better. Really.

Why would any sane person hack big herbaceous portions of her front yard down to near stubble and mulch? Because many early

It's not just the beds of faded spring perennials and gone-by flowering shrubs that need a tune-up around here in June. The vegetable garden is screaming for attention, as cool-season darlings — the spinach and broccoli rabe and various other once-succulent things — stretch up in protest, saying "No more!" A continuing harvest depends on some simple succession-sowing tactics, and more garden math. My equation starts on paper, like this:

1. Make a list of what you want more of (or a first crop of, if it's a warm-season thing or if you simply didn't plant an earlier crop).

2. Make a list of things that have gone by or will soon go by, to assess real estate that can be utilized.

My lists:

Trying to Make Room Here for:
- Beans (pole and bush)
- Salad greens — repeat sowings
- Arugula — repeat sowings

- Cilantro
- Basil
- Chard
- Summer and winter squash (I reserved a row for these, where cutting tulips, now faded, grow)
- Maybe one bush cucumber plant
- Various kales and collards and Brussels sprouts
- Tomatoes, if they aren't in the ground already (and peppers and eggplants if you grow them; I don't)
- More carrots, beets, turnips

Space Coming Available Here From:
- Peas (two long trellises full)
- Spinach
- Arugula
- Endive
- Asian greens
- Garlic (not until later in summer, but I'm keeping it in mind for a fall prospect...maybe the late peas?)

3. Compare the lists, and start making matchups. Examples:

Pea trellises might be a good place for pole beans (or other vining crops such as squash or cukes)...but then I might want to plant fall peas. Which do I want more?

Sometimes I place my young tomatoes just alongside the peas, knowing I'll rip the peas out a few weeks after the tomatoes go in, but before they need all the space. Those years, I yank the pea trellises and insert tomato cages.

4. Look for marginal spaces that can be cheated by a few inches — or a foot. A lot of produce can be packed into beds that contain well-loved soil that is rich in compost. For instance, between your tomatoes and the path, hanging over the edge even, why not put parsley, the next generation of beets and carrots, cilantro, salad greens, or even a row of bush beans? I do.

5. As you start calculating, also study a "succession sowing" chart for your area, perhaps from the nearest cooperative extension's website or an organic-farming association, or even a seed-company website. Identify how long you can wait to sow what and still get a harvest by frost time.

My favorite one appropriate to my general region is from the Maine Organic Farmers and Gardeners Association.

6. Remember the basic "best practices" of vegetable-garden care to maximize yields:

- Plant short rows every other week for a sustained but manageable supply of salads, greens, bush beans, cilantro.
- Keep picking. Continual harvesting delays a plant's instinct to "bolt" or set seed.
- Weed to reduce competition for moisture, light, and nutrients (asparagus, onions, and garlic, in particular, really suffer with competition).
- Remember which way the sun travels in summer, and don't accidentally put someone who'll be small on the shady side of someone who'll be tall (unless it's intentional, such as to shade summer salad).
- Use varieties appropriate to each segment of the season — so a heat-

tolerant lettuce as summer approaches or a storage carrot or beet for a late planting.

- Water deeply on a regular basis, drenching the entire root zone. With a sprinkler, this takes many hours per section of the garden. Soaker hoses or drip emitters are more direct if properly placed in beds.

7. Waste not! Many "gone-by" greens (so long as they're not positively woody) are tasty cooked. Mustard, for instance, and many other elements in a "spicy mesclun" salad mix that have been allowed to stand a week too long to be salad material any longer could be served up beautifully with a minute in the sauté pan. Bits of kale or chard could figure into homemade vegetable stock (recipe on page 377). Don't just toss the arugula that's started to bolt; wilt it in garlic and olive oil that contains a chopped tomato or a little tomato sauce and a few red pepper flakes, then toss it all into pasta, along with some grated cheese for good measure. Or make a frittata or a

savory "pie" with the last of the spinach and other green leafy things. Sauté onion and garlic in olive oil, wilt the greens right in the same pan when the onion's tender, crumble in feta (or any cheese), and add some whisked eggs. Cover and cook on low heat till firm. Or combine sautéed ingredients with the cheese and eggs in a bowl, pour into an oiled baking dish, and bake in a 350°F oven. Dishes like those simple ones make vegetable-garden tune-up time like its own special harvest season, with a delicious reward for the work, and the promise of more to come. Onward.

performers — including some perennial geraniums, such as *macrorrhizum* and *phaeum,* which I rely on heavily in some beds to knit things together — will look a mess not long after bloom if I don't spare them the descent into that state with a stern haircut.

The butchery around here extends beyond the huge swaths of beheaded bigroot geranium (*Geranium macrorrhizum*), though, and its cousin, the mourning widow (*Geranium*

I take a tough hand to many perennials here as spring fades to summer, in the name of a garden that will hold up well into the fall. The pulmonarias, or lungworts, are shorn to near the ground after their early flowering, and quickly sprout a new set of fresh leaves (instead of tattered, about-to-mildew old ones). They would have grown a new set right up and over the old, but I prefer to just shear them, rather than fussily deadheading each long, messy flower stem. My favorite *Pulmonaria* that should be grown more is not pink- or blue- but red-flowered with plain green leaves, called *Pulmonaria rubra* or 'Redstart' — highly recommended for a little splash of red in earliest spring (even March here, if the snow is gone). Various low-growing early perennials, such as *Iberis* and *Aurinia* and some of the groundcover *Phlox,* will get untidy after bloom and can be cut back by half or so.

Perennial salvias, such as the popular 'May Night' and the *nemorosa* varieties 'Snow Hill' and 'Caradonna', can do with a good, hard cutback when they're done blooming. A new rosette of foliage will be emerging down below, and a lower-impact second flush of bloom will eventually be mustered. Catmints (*Nepeta*) look a mess when they pass their bloom, as do artemisias and even rhubard, so hack them back I do (again, same treatment as in earliest spring), forcing another flush of foliage and, with the catmint, perhaps more flowers. I cut lady's mantle (*Alchemilla*) back hard, too, leaves and all, when the bloom starts to go by. Again, most of all what I am seeking to do is avoid having to stare at floppy, fallen, or crispy plants long past their prime. I'd rather have a tidy, smaller mound of fresh green and a bit of a hole than a gone-by mess that also may be an invitation to slugs as it decays and collapses, signaling that a feast lies just ahead.

Eight-inch office scissors, the kind with extra-sturdy plastic handles and stainless blades that are substantial in size but lightweight and don't rust, are my preferred tool for this (and for fine-tuning edges where grass meets flower beds). With big masses of a single perennial used as groundcover,

I could use manual hedge shears to do multiple plants with one whack of the blade, and some gardeners like using grass shears or simply their pruners.

I have many more places, though, planted not in a sweep of something but in mixed mosaics of multiple perennials, especially beneath woody things (how I make such mosaics, or underplanting basics, is on page 151). It's quite a bit more fussy tweaking some of those, but the most successful spots, such as one of Japanese painted fern, *Primula kisoana,* European ginger, *Hosta* 'June', and golden Japanese forest grass (*Hakonechloa macra* 'All Gold') by the kitchen door, simply ask for a spring or fall cleanup, nothing more.

Among other kinds of tweaking, there is the kinky-sounding matter of preemptive pinching. Some later-flowering perennials such as chrysanthemums, autumn sedums, tall asters, and even *Aconitum, Helenium,* or the tall *Eupatorium* — again, it's a bit of an experiment — can be pinched by up to half so they won't get all droopy or splayed open closer to bloom time. If I for-

189

get to do this and it gets to be mid-July, I will have missed my chance, which is why I try to remember to do some pinching just after the rounds of the spring haircuts to the earlier bloomers are through — to make it all part of one pass through the place.

When I am going around shearing, there is always the temptation to have at the spent flower-bulb foliage, too. I must exercise absolute and total restraint, even though I so want to make a clean sweep of things, but no. I'll live with headless tulips and alliums and daffodils and the rest of them — or at least with their leaves — until each bulb has used the foliage to feed itself through photosynthesis, which can take well until we're into summer. Around July Fourth, I mow the big drifts of *Narcissus,* for instance, but let each kind of bulb tell me when it's done ripening.

phaeum is called that for her bowing head — the darkest-of-purple flowers — as if she's grieving). Some euphorbias or spurges, particularly the basic early-spring yellow species called *polychroma,* will start to flop

190

open and get mildew-y in my climate if they don't get a brutal cutback, so I repeat the hard trimming I did not so long ago at all, during the initial spring cleanup before new growth began. The newer red-foliage *polychroma* cultivar, 'Bonfire', seems to stand up better to summer here, so the first year I didn't chop it down, wondering all the while if I'd regret the decision. There was no way to know; it's all an experiment (and this is especially true since no two seasons are alike weather-wise, so it's more than just the plant's inclination you're weighing — it's also how it will act in the weather just ahead that you can't predict). My theory is to go ahead and feel your way through: Observe what is going on, and if it's not looking good, try cutting it back. The thing probably can't look worse than it's about to on its own, and it probably won't die, so I try to be brave. (More details on cutbacks, page 187.)

It was many years before I had the stomach for all of this — still clinging to the *all set* fantasy of a garden as a still snapshot, pretending the picture wouldn't get all blurry and out of focus. A friend aptly calls the left-too-long look "the shaggies," and in case there's any doubt remaining, the shaggies are much more charming and better-looking on a dog.

■ ■ ■ ■

I used to clean up pretty good. Now I don't really clean up at all, at least not on days when my workday will be spent outdoors. I simply wear one version of the pants. The pants number four pair, all khaki-colored. At first when peering into the Korean chest-on-chest in the upstairs hall where they lie layered, a trouser lasagna, in the top of the two compartments, the quartet's players all look the same. But in each one I am a slightly different individual; these are costumes of a sort, each with its own birthmarks and attitude.

Which shape shall I shift into today; whom shall I dress up as — which unknown farmer or mechanic or carpenter whose trousers I adopted in the basement bargain shop of the local Methodist church decades ago, becoming accidental heir to his pants? There were indestructible, all-cotton, hand-me-down work clothes and other treasures to be had then, and the ladies auxiliary might be serving homemade English muffins and coffee upstairs if you hit the timing right.

Has any of these men seen me in his trousers at the post office or gas station over the years, I wonder? (More embarrassing: Has his wife?) It would be easy to tell if they knew their work clothes the way that I do now as adoptive mother, intimate as I have become with each contour and surface flaw over these decades of wearing their pants, or how this pair or that one, from among four interpretations of the same basic fabric, comes out of the dryer with a slightly different hand. Each pair has its own DNA beyond its mere khakiness, and also its own scars earned by living hard. There are the small round burns in the right leg of one — the shortest and stoutest pair, perhaps anonymously bequeathed by a man half again as wide as I am but not even as tall — where I imagine that bits of glowing tobacco ash or sparks from a welding torch must have landed. I'd bet my money that it was a cheap cigar — or no, maybe a Pall Mall that also left behind a grain of tobacco on the glisten of his inner lip with every draw. Mr. Short and Stout's work trousers are the closest thing I have to short pants, a sort of wide-legged clamdigger when displayed on this five-foot-six-inch body, and they show off a risqué flash of skin above my sweat socks to not-so-good effect.

The longest pair — Mr. Big and Tall's — needs fastening first, then rolling up and over at the waist, though I suppose a belt would do to hold them in their place. I do not seem to have one, or maybe it is lost, like the can of black shoe polish and the copy of my last will and testament and the newer can of black shoe polish I bought to replace the misplaced one and all the other things I put in *just the right spot,* wherever the hell that is. The hem of Mr. Big and Tall's is frayed on the left leg, but no matter; if not for such a flaw, they would not have been bundled up for donation, and come to live with me. A third pair almost fits — Mr. Close Enough's — and I imagine its owner was a high-school boy or other young man who once filled them about the same way I do. None of the first three bears a label, but the last one does. The tag says Dickie's — not as in Richard Somebody's pants; this is no sewn-in name tag from a school uniform or camp gear, but the mark of the longtime manufacturer of work clothes.

The pants have seen it all, and though I cannot in honesty say I broke them in or otherwise got them off to a good start in life, I can take credit for ruining the knees of every pair. I am the naughty older sister, luring them into trouble, if not the attentive parent of the lot.

Long ago and far away, my mother chose the clothes. I can see us now just as much "in living color" as the day the photo was shot. Marion, not even two years younger but already on her way to being the taller of the two of us, with her red pigtails; me with a T-shirt gridded in big blocks across its front, like a period linoleum floor pattern of purple, green, orange, gold. Why in the world did they cut our bangs so short, and how did the line turn out so perfectly straight? Someone should have edged the flower bed behind us even half as crisply.

We are standing in the front garden of the house we lived in until I was nine, and it is May — obvious from the eruption of chaotic color behind us, even if the decrepit cardboard Kodak slide mount, now loose from years in various basements and attics of my life since then, is not stamped in little letters and numbers as such. It is 1961, and we are mod, colorful, practically groovy even — or would be, if we were old enough. If the garden around us is any mentor, the lessons are these: Azaleas are apparently better in not just one color but when every known shade cohabits; likewise tulips, which apparently were purchased as "assorted." The more the merrier; a riot of color — all of it supplied by flowers, incidentally, as I don't recall one plant in the place with non-green foliage. Springtime in the postwar suburbs of the

Northeast, as subtle as a neon sign.

Things didn't get any more subdued when we moved to the next town. While school friends were tucked into their bunk beds in gray capes and brick ranches and sensible white colonials, our old-fashioned grown-up headboards — probably finds of a junk-store-obsessed grandmother — were parked in separate rooms in a pink stucco house with an orange Spanish-tile roof and stained-glass windows. The Mediterranean villa, as it was called, had been built far from the Mediter-ranean in the 1920s by a rich businessman for his mistress — but apparently not quite far enough out of sight of his wife, who had the last word on his misadventures, and his finances.

Before his ruination, I bet he was a dandy, for this is the kind of scene he set as back-drop to his antics: In brilliant bits of leaded glass, Saint Joan of Arc (on her white horse) and Saint George (slaying his dragon) over the staircase; parrots and all manner of flow-ers blooming year-round in the big sunroom panes; Spanish galleons sailing in the din-ing room. A coat of arms in one living-room window provided a motto suited to plant or person, and has stuck in memory all these years: *Cedendo tempori glisco* — roughly translated, I think, as "I grow with the passage of time." How continental; how dramatic. (How embarrassing to live in such a decidedly crochety and non-mod place when little friends came over to play.)

It was not a house for the faint of heart, and then my mother's mother, Marion — the decorator in the family, and the one who'd found the pink elephant of a home in the first place and convinced her only daughter that this was *just the place for you* — took things up a notch. An amoebic-shaped, dyed-to-match pink patio was poured under a pink-flowering American dogwood. The dining room was soon painted a red the color of tomato bisque — or rather Campbell's condensed soup, which you mixed with milk instead of water — and it just went on from there. *Lord, have mercy.*

Whether from nature or nurture or a combination of the two, then, I have a high color tolerance (except in my personal attire, where I idiosyncratically prefer just black for every layer). There are few places where adults can act out and be applauded for it, where we can color outside the lines with impunity, but the garden — your own backyard — is a haven for outlandish behavior. What goes with what? Whatever the proprietor deems appropriate. Screw everyone else; this is my place.

That said, I admit I cringe for just a moment when I see my current front yard in its late-May moment, all purple (from *Geranium phaeum,* various alliums, self-sown dame's rocket, or *Hesperis matronalis* — yes, an alien invasive blown in from the roadside that I allow its moment, sorry) against that most shocking yellow that only freshly colored-up gold springtime foliage can provide (in this case sheets of *Sedum* 'Angelina' and a giant old *Cornus sericea* 'Sunshine'). Have I gone too far? Probably. But then I quickly shake off self-consciousness and nearly clap my hands together like a child because it is so unrestrained — the embodiment of the giant scream I want to let move up and out my throat about all the times in my life that I'd silenced myself. *Not here.* A soul has got to shout sometimes, no? It's all very Rilke: "Everything is blooming most recklessly; if it were voices instead of colors, there would be an unbelievable shrieking into the heart of the night."

According to such poetic thinking, I suspect I am defying the local noise ordinance on occasion, but so far nobody has reported me to the town board, not even for the hot-orange trim on the house and barn, not for any of it. Occasionally such effusiveness backfires, even to my mostly immune eye, and lately I am very aware that the gold-foliage thing needs stern-handed subduing. It was just daring enough when it began perhaps a decade ago, this attraction to and adoption of plants with yellow leaves. Gold really roars, but once enough gold things grow in, it can start to be not just noisy but also look a little clownish, like a circus has come to town. I seem to have issued a permit to the full three-ring version.

"Who has the shovel, Margaret, you or the plants?" Marco would ask if he read that sentence, then, because he has also seen some of my other overgrown "issues" here, perhaps adding, "and who has the loppers and the pruning shears?" Put it on the list, then, duly noted: *Whack back size of gold features in front yard.*

(Preferably before any groups of spring-time garden visitors arrive.)

You'd think by now, after fifteen years of hosting garden tours, I would have my opening lines down. But even with all that practice, I start each round of welcoming of visitors not with a hello, but with an apology (read: excuse): *If only you'd come last week* (when the big rhodie out back was peaking); *if only you'd come two weeks before that* (for the lilacs). *If only you'd come a month from now* (when faded spring is finally overtaken by real summer; yes, it really will revive).

I feel compelled to remind them of the record snowfall or ice storm or deluges or late frost or recent drought or whatever else befell me *that isn't my fault, but I'm terribly sorry for it anyhow.* Such crazy thinking. Other gardeners would certainly understand; it probably affected them, too. I deliver the mea culpa infused with every manner of excuse, anyhow, and then for good measure, set about to make sure that besides factoring in the mishaps, they will otherwise see things my way. I do everything short of holding their hand to guarantee it shall be so.

"Start here, in this little circular garden near the door, and then work roughly clockwise around the house," I say. This is how I send each arriving group on their way on open days. They arrive one cluster after another, till the last stragglers make their way up the path, where I wait to greet them as I have all those who have come before since I slid the gates open at nine that morning. "It's a big clockwise," I say next, facing up the hill and toward the back of the house, my back to the newest newcomers, emphatically waving my right arm in a sort of spiraling manner, as big as it can wind, around and around and around again for emphasis. I am the conductor; *follow my lead.* "You'll end up back here in the front yard," I explain, turning back toward them and pointing to the north side of the little house. "I'll be here if you have questions." Such choreography; such lines, though I mean it all from the heart, simply wanting to give them the insider's story if there is any way to.

I suppose I have said this thousands of times by now, never changing the script. But I want them to see the place through my eyes — even if I can't invite them indoors and upstairs, to climb into the shower with its clear curtain and see how bold the low, thirty-six-inch-diameter terra-cotta bowl-shaped pot of orange pansies on the patio looks from *up there* (like a giant sun in a sky of gravel behind droplets of faux rain), or to sit in my chair at the dining table and watch the powerful light etch the flaming edges of an afternoon. I just don't see the garden counterclockwise, front yard first; I just never walk that way. To me it would be like telling a story backward, and it — *this* — is my story. To me that vantage point just does not exist.

Each group is sent forth indoctrinated into the Margaret Method, and except when someone falls in a frog pond (true) or I sense any other form of havoc, I stay put at my post near the house, answering questions — or should I say the same question, as if on instant replay. Depending on what time of year it is and what looks particularly showy, the list: What is the perennial that looks like a pink Queen Anne's lace (*Chaerophyllum hirsutum* 'Roseum'), or the tree with over-sized, silver-blue leaves (the rosemary willow, *Salix elaeagnos*)? What are the big dark blue fruits on that shrubby little tree (drupes of the female *Chionanthus virginicus,* or native fringe tree — and with that answer, you get a bonus tip: the advice never to choose a fringe tree at a nursery except in fall when you can see how good her fruit is, as every female is different). In every season, the wine-leaved cultivar of *Physocarpus opulifolius* called 'Diablo' gets a lot of questions, not because it's rare, but probably because I've let one of mine grow so big that it confuses people. They might be asking about *Angelica gigas* if it's late summer or early fall — the *Little Shop of Horrors* biennial with its giant, unearthly buds and maroon-red umbel-shaped flowers on eye-high stems. Or they might be asking about common old rhubarb in springtime, because I grow a very hefty swath of it in a prominent spot as if it's something fancy, some real prize among bold-leaved plants — maybe like it's another healthy, lush stand of *Astilboides tabularis* like the one across the yard in a shady spot, which they also ask about (and like the *Petasites* blunder I manage to fake as if a conscious choice I made as well, clever me). But sometimes a rhubarb's just a rhubarb.

Inevitably, these efforts at complete crowd mind control will fail, and an individual or group I don't recognize approaches from the backyard. It's obvious from their direction that they've never heard the orders — slipping covertly, albeit innocently, inside the gate down by the road and at once turning right (counterclockwise!) before they even reach my welcome post. *Sneaky.* I shudder to think what it looked like from that perspective, but manage to contain myself and stay silent. At every tour I also catch a glimpse of someone pointing out something to their companion, or taking a photo — but in a spot where hard as I try, I cannot conjure what's in the intended frame. *What are they looking at?* I wonder to myself. I have never stood in that place and seen anything; I'm fairly certain — yes, I'm absolutely sure — that there's nothing there. *Nothing; no way.*

As if my naysaying is audible, they soon trot over with their camera-phone image to offer up the evidence. "What's that?" they want to know, pointing to the LCD, or, "I love how you put these things together over there." Over where? *It wasn't me,* or: *Where is that?* sound insincere, and confusing, but how can it have been my hand at work? I am a stranger to that perspective on the place, a total and complete stranger. I cannot stand far back enough to see it, or of course to see any other so intimate an aspect of myself.

The visitors are gone, but someone whistled at me from beneath the front porch just now, and I have a strong suspicion that it was not a gentleman caller — not a frog-turned-prince or any such manifestation of love-ever-after or other promised happy endings. I know with absolute certainty that nobody's whistling in praise or flirtation at how good I look right now, two hours into grubbing out crabgrass and dock and such from the weedy plant community I mow so I can call it lawn. The only "hot" I look is sweaty; nothing steamy here.

I was really getting into my new spiritual practice — a moving meditation aimed specifically at dandelions, a ritual that brings me into touch with my own powerlessness, and also my own power. It's a three-step program (not twelve, thank you very much — just *insert tool, rock it, pull*) and all are welcome. Required gear: a half-moon edger to cut into the ground very close to the offending crown of *Taraxacum officinale;* your foot (which I assume is always at the ready, preferably armored in a good boot with a sturdy shank), and a tip bag or bucket or wheelbarrow to collect all the pulled-up bodies in.

But just as I am really starting to feel the rhythm of devotion, there it goes again. What bird is calling out from under the porch?

And then it registers: *That's* why they call it a whistle-pig.

Marmota monax is no friend of mine, and despite the flash of his impressively white teeth (atypical of other rodent species, whose smiles are dingy yellow) I am not smiling, or whistling, back.

What's not to like about an asocial, diurnal, territorial, (mostly) vegetarian? Sounds like someone I should closely identify with — someone just like me, no? — rather than harbor homicidal feelings toward. The woodchuck is where I draw the line about inclusiveness and love thy neighbor; he's the one ingredient in the food chain whose presence I just cannot digest. From the beginning of my time as a country gardener, it was the woodchuck who got to me in a way I could not seem to control; this hairy beast (his hair like mine these days, a grizzled mix of brown and silver) is my perennial undoing, the Road Runner to my Wile E. Coyote.

Other than a deer there is no more formidable opponent in the garden, since a woodchuck's hunger is inexhaustible, making the table manners of rabbits look positively dainty by comparison. There is often a second chance to save a crop after a rabbit nibbles, but a woodchuck leaves little on my plate when he is done sharing my supper. Once that taunting sound tuned me in to his presence, I knew just where to look for damage, since woodchucks like nothing better than peas and beans, and mine were well up, all nice and tender after growing steadily in the sustained coolness of this moist spring.

Apparently *Marmota monax* had read Emily Dickinson ("How luscious lies the pea within the pod") and, feeling moved, lumbered down from the hill to have his way with them. I will try again when the timing is right for those crops (my succession-planting theory is on page 181), but *shit*.

It wasn't the first attack on this juicy target: His lesser cousins the eastern chipmunks (*Tamias striatus*) had at them, too, though they didn't wait as long — they'll devour seed straight out of the soil in March, before it sprouts, or even dig for it, as the befuddled gardener stands looking at a row with no signs of life, wondering why: outdated seed; foul weather; kidnapping; or is there still hope for an ascension? But once I'd replaced the missing seeds from Round 1 of sowing, I'd covered my updated row with agricultural fabric until the plants were on their way. They took, and it would have been the best crop in years, after several springs that had heated up too fast for peas in particular, but sure enough, every plant had been savaged, not trimmed carefully at a forty-five-degree angle rabbit-style.

"Good eating, you know," says Herb, as he and I beat the underbrush a little while later, after I had phoned for help finding the holes so that traps can be set, and pronto. Herb in his droll New England humor did not mean the succulence of the fallen legumes that are on my mind, but the flabby-looking beast we are pursuing. Somehow the prospect of turning Whistler into a roast or stew doesn't take the bite away.

Woodchucks — maybe ten or even twelve pounds here in body weight by late summer, after a season of gluttony, though arising from deep hibernation much slimmer — are the king of squirrels. They make the other local Sciurid family species (the flying and red and gray and black ones, and also the chipmunks) seem positively insignificant in size or impact. Woodchucks can climb, swim, and most of all oh, how they dig — especially in well-drained soil like mine. Why bother with some rocky or clayey spot? *There's plenty of prime real estate over at Margaret's; you coming?* Rabbits, skunks, raccoons, opossums, fox, weasels, other ground squirrels, otters, chipmunks, voles, shrews, mice, snakes, and even arthropods will use an abandoned woodchuck hole for shelter — over the winter, for instance, or in some cases to bear young — and I am hoping to forcibly evict the current incorrigible tenant and make one such domicile available immediately. But where's the doorway to success?

And then I see it: A large patch of the common blue violet, *Viola sororia,* a wild thing I mostly just let self-sow in the beds and lawn, has been mown down to stem-only stubble, no leaves or flowers in evidence. Just beyond the ravaged clump, other plants and even the soil look slightly matted — is this an active runway, a path that will take me to the burrow? I drop to my haunches for a closer look, and there it is. It is the main entrance, dug from the outside; the pile of loose soil and stone beside the hole tells me that. Subsequent exits — and there can be a total of five, my best guidebooks tell me — will have been carved from the inside out, the debris falling inward, unseen.

"I found it," I call out to Herb, who gathers the needed gear.

Thou shalt not kill? Oh, really? Well, we plan at the very least to go ahead and try.

The day is sunny and clean, but then, as if it heard me harboring a death wish, the daylight is extinguished. The birds go quiet as a storm flies in from nowhere. As quickly as it came, it goes; the chorus resumes. All is well in the world again, and nobody but me seems to hold on to this momentary fright. Why do they call them birdbrains when they are so smart and know to forget what is not worth recalling? They don't grasp on to a dark moment any longer than the sky holds on to a particular dark cloud.

When it is not behaving positively biblically, the garden instead feels like an Al-Anon meeting or some other Twelve-Step gathering, where solace can perhaps be found — or at least sought — in sayings:

ODAAT (as they say in the steps): One day at a time.

And easy does it (otherwise you won't be able to walk tomorrow).

First things first. (Don't plant until you prepare the ground properly.)

One of gardening's fear factors (except to those who've totally mastered it, which doesn't include me) is pruning, the way to get our woody plants into shape and keep them that way. The pruning method set forth here is so pared down that anybody can do it, even without the kind of artistic vision that turns boxwood into crowing roosters, or reshapes a badly storm-damaged tree so well that nobody notices it was ever hit. All that's required to rate as a B-plus pruner are these simple steps:

Take out the three D's anytime they occur. The D's are *dead, damaged,* and *diseased* wood — and why wouldn't you want to do this? (Some people say there are five D's: *dying* and *deformed* being added to the list, but I'm trying not to get us over-whelmed.)

Take out all suckers and "water sprouts" as often as required. This means that mess at the base of a grafted shrub or tree that looks like a thicket of shoots surrounding the trunk. It also means those things that shoot straight up vertically off a branch at a ninety-degree angle or thereabouts, very common on fruit trees, say, or old magnolias. Look at the architecture of these shoots: If you left them on, what would they turn into? Nothing very useful, or well engineered. Don't wait until you have a mess that such shoots are the making of. Gone!

Similarly, if anything's thinner than a pencil or turning inward in a way that looks like trouble, off it must come. Rubbing against another branch is no good, either. (Those are probably all in the jettisoned "D" called *deformed*.)

Perhaps we'll get to the advanced intermediate stuff and maybe even some advanced stuff in time, but for now, can we just agree to be vigilant about those few simple steps? Our shrubs and trees will look all the more beautiful if we do.

This too shall pass. (And so will the next flower, and the one after that. Ephemera, all of it, and us — living until it is living no more. *This means you.*)

Live and let live. (Well, except for weeds and woodchucks.)

Act as if. (As if you can get this mess completely mowed, weeded, edged, and mulched before you drop dead or snow comes again, whichever happens first.)

And, most important: Keep coming back. (Because the wild raspberry canes, poison ivy, and garlic mustard plan to.)

I'd like to add another maxim, even if they don't use it in "the rooms": The more you prune, the more you prune (a horticultural variant of "no good deed goes unpunished"). I have never seen more water sprouts — the vertical shoots coming off branches that are common to old fruit trees and magnolias and some of my viburnums in particular here, shoots that can never serve a purpose because of their poor architecture, but when cut off seem to stimulate the development of more, more, more such sprouts. The more you prune, the more you prune? Yes, apparently, in some cases; in fact it was an initial pruning cut (or another injury not caused by my shears) that got things all stimulated hormonally and in the mood to sprout like this in the first place. The trees find late-winter pruning invigorating, since they have all that dormant energy bottled up and just looking for an outlet. (My pruning primer is on page 210.)

Every year I promise myself to try summer pruning of water sprouts and suckers, similarly vigorous shoots emerging from the trunk or from the base of grafted things, as the later timing is said to reduce the plant's inclination to pay you back so generously.

That all makes sense, of course, but here's the thing: I just can't look at some of these another minute.

A garden's edges soften over time, as things placed *just so* and with a little wiggle room start using up that and then some, and spilling out of their original bounds. I love where good-for-edging perennials — such as various carpet-type sedums and perennial geraniums and European ginger and ornamental grasses and *Heuchera* (especially the near-evergreen recent *villosa* types such as 'Caramel' and 'Citronelle', in their surprising colors) — have come into their own and started to spill out onto the path, breaking the heavy-handed hard edge of human intervention with a sign of independent life, of botanical self-determination.

My edges have softened, too — not just at the midsection, where I remember a tauter surface not so long ago, but more than that emotionally. I noticed this the other night while I was talking to my brother-in-law on the phone, when my sister was out of town, and I suddenly became aware of how this kind of conversation, a relationship of our own, had outgrown various false starts, times when it was more forced and didn't quite take. Hearing myself — hearing both of us — at such ease, I thought how *we didn't used to do this;* how I, at least, was more resistant, and standoffish, staying inside narrower lines, like those too-small beds I'd started with.

Now we have grown together, and I spill all over him — at least as much as I do with anyone. We have grown into a family, filling the empty spaces that were at first gaping between us, spaces left after losses or other bumps and bruises dug in and left their marks. I heard him using the basic code words of the language Marion and I had together as children, a dialect of made-up, mashed-up sounds and phrases that nobody else who was there then with us, nobody but we two girls, had lived to recollect.

Though it means work to keep them from overtaking one another completely, or someone from getting lost, I am all for plants, and people, that once they get their bearings, feel comfortable enough to talk, touch, and even tangle. There is a standing joke among my kindred gardeners about the *other* camp — the ones who worry when all the perennials grow in and start touching, when no delineation in the form of mulch remains between their precious, distinct babies any longer. Like the best families, the best garden pictures happen after a time, when the mingling begins, I realize, though I say this knowing that I can be the type to leave a safety zone — an emotional ring of mulch — around my own sometimes-prickly trunk.

CHAPTER 3
FIRE (SUMMER)

Hearken; Behold, there went out a sower to sow: And it came to pass, as he sowed, some fell by the way side, and the fowls of the air came and devoured it up. And some fell on stony ground, where it had not much earth; and immediately it sprang up, because it had no depth of earth: But when the sun was

up, it was scorched; and because it had no root, it withered away. And some fell among thorns, and the thorns grew up, and choked it, and it yielded no fruit. And other fell on good ground, and did yield fruit that sprang up and increased; and brought forth, some thirty, and some sixty, and some a hundred.
— PARABLE OF THE SOWER,
GOSPEL OF MARK 4:3–8

It is the cusp of summer, and — *congratulations, it's your lucky day!* — suddenly as hot as hell. Special delivery. I will turn fifty-seven at ten till high noon, and I am having a positive swelter of a birthday, not from some hot flash (one symptom of climate change that blessedly skipped me) but something heading more in the general direction of heatstroke if nobody intervenes.

This is no time to stop, though, and besides, there is no air-conditioning or swimming pool, anyway, to stop in. Garden hose over the head, anyone? After an hour or so of chores I am so overheated that I drag myself back inside and up the steep, narrow enclosed staircase into the furnace atmosphere of the low-ceilinged second floor, because I have it in my head — where do such ideas sprout from? — that I may find

217

relief in some very old jeans and a big pair of scissors strong enough to cut through their industrial-strength twill.

Off at the knees go the twenty-year-old pant legs; off come my baggy, well-worn khakis; on go the newborn — or are they reincarnated? — shorts.

In thirty years of gardening, I have never worn shorts. I do not own a pair, a fact that made this latest improvisation necessary. First impressions as I head down the front path: Outdoors feels cooler with half your trousers missing. So far, so good.

"Nice legs, Marge," says a carpenter friend, Harry, on his way up the walk at the same time to tackle the latest in this old house's unending life list of repairs. To be clear (and in the name of retaining a modicum of self-respect): There is nothing unshapely about my legs. They are perfectly acceptable legs, a matched set, basically, and in good working order. What Harry is commenting on is that after several decades under wraps, they have adopted a cast that could very well be counted on to glow in the dark; they are the light-deprived white asparagus or Belgian endive of lower limbs. If legs can be said to have a pallor, mine do. I should consider it a compassionate act that he didn't sing a few bars of "You Light Up My Life" — though

I *was* carrying a shovel, and was perhaps considered armed and dangerous. Should I have self-tanned in preparation? (Do I seem like someone with the patience for that? Do real gardeners self-tan?)

But today I am fifty-seven and I am busy and burning up. Following the ricocheting style of logic I specialize in, it could be predicted that a solitary person such as myself, one who can even lean toward periods of hermitlike behavior, would love the sun. The word "solitary" is positively sun-filled, springing from the root word *sol;* and "hermit" comes from the Greek word *eremia,* for "desert." Are loners really hot stuff? Not in this outfit.

I hate the heat.

Neither the chores nor the temperature promises to relent, so I have deployed my own countermeasures in the face of them: I shall set about gardening in short pants.

I grow old…I grow old…

I shall wear my cast-off denims cut and rolled.

No, actually, I shall *not*. The experiment lasts a quarter of an hour or perhaps a half. I feel ill-equipped for the work at hand, and positively naked; back up to the furnace for my trusty khakis. It hadn't taken long for bare knees to bear an intaglio of each leaf of grass — or worse, gravel — that they confronted or for the vivid orange-green juice of members of the Papaveraceae — the celandine poppy (*Stylophorum diphyllum*), the plume poppy (*Macleaya cordata*), the ephemeral *Hylomecon japonicum* and the volunteer *Papaver somniferum* youngsters, the ones we call breadseed poppies because the vice squad or DEA will come get us otherwise — to all leave their marks. Their abstract paintings are more hideous for the color of the canvas I provide with my tender flesh. Into the psychedelic poppy sap some soil gets ground here and there like another pigment on the palette, forming blotches that look like a bruise that is aging nastily — and is that smear of something viscous and shiny on my right shin perhaps the aftermath of a slug who failed to inch away in time? *Ick.* I never garden without two entire legs' worth of my various adopted long pants for good reason, all of which have rallied round to remind me in appropriately short order. I need a shower, and after this ridiculous experiment, the recent swell of heat is the least of the reasons why.

A rush of childhood memory — winter sick days spiced with swigs of terpin hydrate and slathers of Vicks VapoRub — overpowers me as I dig out a formidable congestion of mint runners from just-soaked, cooperative ground. I should not be in this position — on my knees, in service again to the genus *Mentha* — after spending a good deal of my advanced-beginner garden career working to get the last bit out. I should know better; I should have behaved. I had promised, like any sinner does in one of those negotiation-type *I'll never do it again* prayers: "No more mint, at least not in the garden proper, if you'll *please, oh please,*" I said years ago only a few yards from here, "just let me get the final trace of this stuff out of this bed where other, unsuspecting plants wish to live in peace."

But here I am, and here the fragrant but devious Gorgon is, all because I got a taste for homemade curries topped with mint-laced raita, and goaded by my hunger away from prudence, I veered yet again, plant-ing a harmless-looking three-point-five-inch nursery pot of *Mentha piperita* (peppermint) and another one of its richer-tasting cousin *M. spicata* (spearmint). In just a single season they have infested a square yard each, and neither observed the boundary set by a ten-inch-high, five-quarters-inch-thick board of rough-hewn local locust that encloses a raised vegetable bed alongside the spaces I'd chosen. Horticultural Houdinis; *under and in we go.* As I pull — not too roughly, eyes closed and *feeling, not thinking,* in search of the sweet spot and hoping to get the most-intact lengths of white roots with every haul — I review in my head whether technically these are roots at all, really, or rhizomes. Yes, I think that's it: rhizomes, a kind of special stem that runs horizontally at or just below ground level. I am having it out today with a giant tangle of stem tissue.

Along each unearthed length are so very many growing points — little enthusiastic knobs that are mints in the making, each a tributary to a whole other potential pipeline of mint. *Mentha* will never be caught short without a backup plan against adversity; it is never unprepared for the need to divide and conquer — ever ready to scramble the op under pressure, bivouac briefly, then march again. How can I outcompete such intensity and intelligent design?

As frustrated as I am for not having paid closer attention before now, at letting things get this far, there is the pure sensuality of the moment, too: the fact of being surrounded by a cloud of volatile oils, as if undergoing a particularly robust form of aromatherapy. If there were only one class of fragrance per customer in the garden, I'd trade in all

222

the sweet ones — all the lilac and *Viburnum carlesii* and mock orange and daphnes, too, as delicious as they are — for the brisk, aromatic stuff, the underpinnings of men's colognes, not the cloying style of women's eau de toilette or parfum.

Bring on the citrus and conifers, and the sharp green notes of the herb garden, of not just mint but sage and artemisia and all the rest, the plants I cannot pass without reaching down to brush a hand against each one, then quickly moving the impregnated palm past my nose. These bracing members of the garden don't depend on some short moment of flowering for their scent the way a rose or *Narcissus poeticus* does — they always smell good. It's all just molecular chains of carbon and hydrogen, organic compounds formed into terpenes and other terpenoids, but it sure smells like something more artistic that that. Oh, dear; I can see where this is going: Maybe I can replant *just a little piece* of each mint in the ground, to be surrounded by and surrender to like this another day?

Earth smell. Gotta get me some of that. In 2007, chemists at Brown University published a paper in a scientific journal that explained how geosmin (which translates as "earth smell" and is the organic compound giving soil its scent) is made. That geosmin existed had been known for more than a century; where it came from, not. A so-called bifunctional enzyme — a protein with a two-part action — was found to be at work.

I am interested to see that geosmin is, chemically speaking, a terpene — like all those other good smells I like so much. And I'm also happy to now know why beets smell, and taste, so good to me: geosmin's at work in them, too, as it is in carrots.

I keep reading that microorganisms in the soil — specifically the bacterium *Mycobacterium vaccae* — can make you feel better emotionally, akin to using antidepressants, by activating serotonin-releasing brain neurons and also immune cells. Those original findings were also published in 2007, by a British neuroscientist, but the media reprises it regularly. Each time SOIL THE NEW PROZAC? headlines come around, I say to myself: *You had to do a study to confirm that?* I've been happily huffing dirt for decades, and have no intention of stopping until I can inhale no more.

We have not spoken of it, but each lengthening afternoon as we slipped toward the solstice together along with all other living things, Jack has tested me, and himself. Jack the Mama's Boy has been reprising his role as Demon Cat, stirred into expanding hours of stalking and slaying by the force that pulls at all things. On this the year's longest day he showed back up just as crepuscular denizens such as the gray fox are calling it quits and the nocturnals (raccoons, possums, and more) are on deck, readying themselves for the overnight shift. In his mouth hangs a limp chipmunk; he brings it to his ritual space beside the door, his killing fields. According to his usual butcher's cut — ass end remaining — he dressed it quickly, expertly. Off with its head, a fast, crunchy snack consumed before he agreed to rejoin me safely inside a moment ahead of when real darkness, once his place of power and dominion, takes hold.

The ceremonial spot where Jack left the now-headless chipmunk is a patch of gravel, part of the foot-wide band of peastone circumnavigating the house foundation so that backsplash from the gutterless roof has a friendly place to touch down. *Thanks, Jack,* I thought, then silently agreeing with myself in the way that those who live alone do that "we" needn't pick it up just yet; some other creature will probably take it away for "us" by morning, anyhow. Yes, that's right: Nature wastes nothing. She's a good eater. No need to use a trowel or the pooper-scooper on this one.

When we next went out, at dawn, the half-munk had moved a foot from where it had lain twelve hours prior; Jack and I both noticed. *Who moved our cheese?* By midmorning it was gone — or was it? No, wait; are those two feet and half a tail poking up from the crumbly soil between the heavy paving stones? (*Who buried our cheese?*) Jack and I both do a double take, and I'm not sure who is more startled. Even he knows something has gone tremendously wrong.

And then the special effects begin. The upended thing moves, and starts to shrink and descend a little more — like the Wicked Witch in Oz, as if it's melting into the ground. *Melting?* Spirits of the underworld? Or, it suddenly dawns on me, as if it's being pulled under, perhaps into a hidden, hungry mouth. But whose? Not the millipede's that I notice slinking along nearby (that strange-looking arthropod is a herbivore); not the colony of ants I see, kneeling to look closer at where body meets soil surface — the ants are just opportunistically getting in on some bigger action. Maybe it's carrion beetles? I have to think this through; I can't just crouch here and watch all day, though it is riveting in some completely horrifying way. It is finally dry enough to mow now, and I must get on with the to-do list. I get my gear and stop briefly to note the progress of the Case of the Disappearing Halfmunk one more time before heading to the barn for the push mower. When I open the door into the chaotic, chockablock space — a tangle of tools and wheelbarrows and carts and mowers — somehow the only thing I can see despite all that visual noise is a big old snake, who thinks he's made himself invisible in a tip bag I use to collect garden debris — hiding in hopes of snaring an unwitting chipmunk or mouse himself.

Which answers my first question of the day. Of course: Garter snakes and milk snakes like the environment under the patio stones, and also eat carrion. *A snake moved our (dead) cheese.* Case solved. Now on to the next question: How can I convince the reptile in the barn to please move aside so I can get to the needed machine?

There is no escape, but we try to find relief from the year's relentless wet, and now from its unexpected and exorbitant offering of heat, too. "I see your eyes," I say to the otherwise-submerged frog in the seasonal trough by the kitchen door, a big glazed oblong vessel more than three feet long and two-thirds as high. She thinks she has made her slick green self invisible in the velvety, verdant surface of floating pondweed, but her amber eyes are a different luster and color from the tiny plants of *Azolla* and *Lemna* she bobs among. They glint, those eyes do, and I am there to catch it. She needs to know I see them; nobody's fooling me. *I see you, flocked frog.*

We are all festering, even the amphibians. Nobody's on deck for anything at all; enervated, we are immobilized in the deep end of this summer together.

Sleepaway camp — though I hated it, as I recall — would be good about now. Two weeks in the cool, deep woods. I could write not-so-revealing postcards home, like the ones in the chest in the living room:

Dear Dad,
How are you? I am fine. Camp is fun. I have new friends. I miss you.
Love,
Miss Smudge

Neither when digging nor at the dinner table am I a fork person, far preferring spoon- or shovelfuls of goodness to lofting the intended prey on sets of prongs. I like my sustenance in dollops, and if it were not for a sense of etiquette instilled so early as to be irredeemable — yes, blame my prudish grandmother for this detail, too — I'd ask for a spoon when I go out to supper, the way I reach for one at home.

A tablespoon to be specific; that is my preferred implement, for the generous proportions it delivers. Yes, I like shoveling food into my mouth (and spooning delicious compost into planting holes and onto beds).

When there is cultivating to be done, as there is today, since I am sowing peas for fall harvest, I have to force myself to bring a spading fork — the one with four nearly flat tines and a short T- or D-grip handle, not to be confused with a pitchfork or manure fork, whose working parts are somewhat curved and sharper, and whose handles are longer and also unadorned. From the hooks on the barn wall I want instead to grab my long-handled shovel, which is so much more my style, though admittedly not the right tool for the job, any more than my tablespoon is right for eating baked potatoes once you get down to the delectable skins. (Thankfully, fingers are, and I admit to sometimes digging with my hands when only a seed or small transplant needs a home.) When there is soil to be turned, the shovel makes for heavier work. When there are plants to be lifted, the fork's the better choice, too, since a spade or shovel will chop needlessly through more roots than a tool with prongs.

Never eat more than you can lift, Miss Piggy admonished — an etiquette that would certainly entitle me to remain spoon-fed, at least. I am right-handed, and though my left shoulder gave out recently, refusing to let me do many of the simplest things, I am plenty adept at feeding myself, with the garden as my helper. No surprise that I prefer a bowl to a plate — a banked course that helps keep the meal's players within bounds as I chase them around its surface at high speed. *Gobble, gobble.*

But I should have adapted and applied a sliver of her porcine wisdom to my gardening, that much is clear. The day my favorite shovel — specifically a long-handled, round-point one — snapped mid-handle, things got messy, and have never really righted themselves. The cherished tool was a tag-sale find that gave me a dozen years' good service, but when it finally broke — because I used it when I should have been using a fork, admittedly, pigheaded person that I am — I didn't really think through the consequences, and failed to save the parts. It never occurred to me that the combination of its light weight; a well-worn, not-too-thick ash handle; and a just-big-enough head affixed at the ideal angle for smooth tossing of the contents would prove irreplaceable.

In five years of trying, I have amassed what could stock a shovels-only tag sale of my own, each one too-something for my liking and now on the tool wall in the barn, beside the other rejects that have arrived by UPS or in the back of my car. They are mostly far too heavy; their handles are too beefy to grasp, and not at all tapered nicely or smooth to the touch. From twenty-something dollars to more than one hundred apiece, they represent no small total investment, and each time a new one is discovered and ordered I become momentarily elated: *This may be the one!* Sadly, blind-dating of shovels has gone as well as the other version, the only difference being that the unsuccessful candidates in this case are still all hanging around.

I don't know how the female oriole learned to weave the socklike pouch she hung and nested in way up in that big oak, or why some tadpoles metamorphose much faster than others of the same species, or how the lily leaf beetles found my little stand of lacquer-red *Lilium martagon* 'Claude Shride'. The reason that my tomato plants lived through to harvest in 2009, the year that late blight (caused by the fungus *Phytophthora infestans,* which led to the nineteenth-century Irish potato famine) ravaged farms and gardens throughout the Northeast, eludes me, too. I know a few things, and will have to remain content with that.

Thankfully, I'm clear on the most important piece: that nothing about gardening is easy, instant, nonstop, or guaranteed — no matter what it says on the label stuck in the plant you're holding with an eye to purchase, or on the bellybands, boxes, bags, or hangtags touting the merits of nonliving gadgets at the garden center, either. Some brands of pruning shears will make each cut kinder on the hand, yes, so I invested in a good and comfortable one — but there is no device that makes the job of pruning go away.

I can say with a certainty born of summers of frustration that there are few truly "self-cleaning" annuals, at least not any with sizable flowers, no matter what the grotesquely oversized plastic labels of the modern era say about "deadheading not required." An example: Hybrid verbenas that are between blooms are pitiful creatures; the faded flowerheads don't get better-looking anytime fast. Some are less messy and faster to rebound than others, thanks to advances in breeding, yes — but they don't come with their own pair of clippers and the instinct to clean up after themselves. That's my job.

Petunias have improved substantially in recent years, too — no longer do hanging baskets turn to little more than stringy, flowerless stems by July, the way their predecessors did. But with the double-flowered types, or with any petunia in a wet year, even the best-bred varieties still need human intervention. No matter what the cultivar, a rainy year is no time to grow petunias, and I wish I'd sited the big bowl of them under the sunny-but-safer south-facing porch overhang instead of out in the open, but it's far too heavy now to move. The delicate, flared fabric of their flowers is stuck together like my sweaty legs and the slip Mommy made me wear even on the hottest summer days. At heaven's bidding, I find myself the constant caretaker of a very large, low pot of some near-orange ones — a delicious break in the genetics of the color palette for petunias, so how could I resist? — but they've simply looked like wet trash all season long, despite my nonstop tidying. That said, perspective reminds me that a year when there is no rain is more painful than any number of collapsed petunias.

Now I start to veer from semi-fact toward

mere opinion: I'm adamant, or perhaps rabid, on the fact that contemporary plant names — particularly faux, soundalike genus names invented by a bunch of marketing people sitting in a room with whiteboards and PowerPoint and boxes of doughnuts and too much coffee — should be forbidden. There are no "Potunias" or "Superbenas," except in a database of registered plant names or the rolls of the patent office. (I suspect the same consultant types of inventing words such as "Gro" and "Lite.") Why can't we teach taxonomy to gardeners instead of what sounds like the cast of plant superheroes in a botanical cartoon series? Poor Linnaeus. Poor us; no wonder we suffer as a civilization from Nature Deficit Disorder. I am happy for breeders to have legal rights and profits from their developments, but wish it weren't all tangled up with imposing these stupid names — and also that the rush to market (read: money) didn't push so many not-quite-ready things into the garden centers before they were properly worked out and stable: good, *garden*-worthy subjects and not just things that could be coaxed into looking all cute and colorful and compact in a nursery pot in peak spring for easy sale.

I am likewise sick of plants with varietal names so unattractive that I wouldn't want them in the garden: a dwarf, fragrant lilac patented as 'Bloomerang', for instance, when something slightly more poetic might have better told me its welcome supposed reblooming story. Instead, all it seems to say is that the shrub may sail on by at any moment, and then come back to haunt you. I don't know what I visualize with the recently patented floribunda rose called 'Ketchup & Mustard', but as arresting as the flower whose red petals have a yellow reverse might be, I cannot stomach the conjured combination of condiments in the garden.

Somewhere between rant and reason, my eye tells me that mulch is not something you should need swatches or color chips to select. If it looks otherwordly, as if it has been custom-dyed, excuse yourself from the transaction and carpet your beds in some other material. (What to use as mulch and when and how much to apply begins on page 236.) I prefer my twine to be neutral tan in color, and the same with bamboo canes for staking. Hold the green dye they both are so often soaked in (which is an ungodly hue that never would occur in nature, anyhow, and rubs off on your hands). I don't like white plastic anything — pots, trellises, birdbaths, chairs, tchotchke — in the garden, including plant labels, and I hate myself for trying to

Q. What is the purpose of using mulch in the garden?

A. Mulch serves several purposes. It will suppress weeds and slow moisture evaporation, but should also break down into the underlying soil gradually and thereby passively improve the soil's texture and encourage the community of soil life. A layer of mulch helps moderate soil temperatures. It serves as a buffer from soil compaction caused by rain, and helps prevent the crusting-over of bare soil that can sometimes prevent moisture from being absorbed.

Q. What makes good mulch?

A. This can be very confusing, particularly because what's sold as "mulch" in many cases isn't really very suitable for performing the full range of duties I expect from it. Briefly, I look for a material that is:

- An organic substance (meaning deriving from some living or formerly living matter)
- Fine- to medium-textured so it will

break down into the underlying soil...

- ...but substantial enough to stay put
- A material that has been aged — composted — before I use it, to minimize the risk of bringing in nuisance fungi and pathogens, and reduce the chance of depriving plants of any nutrients while the mulch decomposes in place
- Dark in color (if for the ornamental beds)
- Available locally at a good price, preferably in bulk delivery, unbagged
- Not a source of contaminants, pests, or diseases (again, precomposting will help with this in some cases, though not the contaminant aspect)

Technically, plants can serve as a sort of living mulch as well; hence the term groundcovers, but here we're talking about the nonliving kind.

To elaborate: Any mulch I use in my ornamental beds must be fine-to-medium textured and a shade of deep brown (read: natural, like soil), so it looks good but doesn't show off. Forget anything that's going to sit there and never break down, such as big hunks of bark (which I call "baked-potato mulch" because they look like giant spuds, or worse, as if an order of potato skins from the local bar menu is sitting on the ground). Forget anything that's bright orange. No dyed mulches.

One caveat: Very fine-textured materials such as sawdust do not make good mulch (except maybe for low-fertility acid-lovers such as blueberries) because they cake, preventing water from permeating, and then fail to decompose.

I used to use bagged mulches, including cocoa hulls and various bark products. I have since switched to local materials I can have delivered in bulk, sans plastic bags (and minus all the fuel used in processing and trucking of bagged stuff across the nation to my local garden center). Environmentally, it's essential to buy locally when you can, especially with bulky items. Become a mulch locavore.

Q. What do you use for mulch in your garden?

A. On my ornamental beds, I use a composted stable-bedding product — a local agricultural by-product from horse or dairy farms that has been allowed to age first. It's simply wood shavings (not too fine, not too coarse) that farmers spread on the floors of animal stalls to absorb manure and urine, and then muck out and compost afterward to recycle it. Find a local source via your county cooperative extension office or a nearby nursery.

Leaf mold (partially rotted and shredded leaves) would also be great, if your local landfill offers it, or start a leaves-only compost pile in fall if you don't live in a municipality that gives away composted leaf mulch.

In my vegetable garden, I use straw (which is of course not dark-colored), preferably chopped. In rough areas such as along the roadside outside my fence, I will use wood chips from the power or phone company, or from a fallen tree. I will also use wood chips or bark chips on utility-area pathways (behind sheds, between vegetable rows). I pile up wood chips and let them age before using them, but even once they have aged, I would not use them in my garden beds proper.

Q. When do I apply it, and how much should I use?

A. I mulch my perennial and shrub beds in spring, but not until after the soil has a chance to warm and dry a bit. I am also conscious of areas where I want biennials and other self-sown plants to have a chance to do their thing; mulching these too soon may prevent successful reseeding.

You want a two- or three-inch layer, generally speaking, and if you use the right stuff, about half of that will work into the underlying soil before you go to replenish it the next spring. Keep the mulch a couple of inches away from trunks of trees and shrubs; never pile it up, volcano-like, against them, as that can invite pests and diseases.

Anytime I work in an area and disturb the mulch, I add a bit more rather than leave bare spots. I apply mulch to new beds whenever I plant.

Mulch is sometimes also used in winter in cold zones to help keep newly planted things in the ground, or to shield tender plants from damage (such as the graft union on roses). For that temporary purpose, materials such as evergreen boughs (which would not normally be good for mulch) may also be used.

Q. Do I have to move the mulch before adding compost and fertilizer?

A. If you use mulch that has the correct texture and has been composted first, this should not be a problem. I simply "topdress" (spread compost and all-natural organic fertilizer right on top of last year's partly decomposed mulch), then replenish the mulch as needed.

The problem with most mulches, even bagged shredded bark, is that they haven't been composted before they are sold and/or are too coarse, so they don't break down very well, but rather form a sort of coating on top of the soil. Good mulch, on the other hand, breaks down — not in a week or a month, but over the course of a season or two. If you have a thick layer of mulch that's not breaking down nicely, and the layer is just getting thicker and thicker each year, rake some away and then add your amendments and start using a new, better-quality mulch this year on top of that.

Q. Are cocoa hulls good for mulching?

A. There is no cocoa-processing plant nearby and hence no local source of this recycled product — meaning it would not meet my requirements. Cocoa hulls can be very high in potassium, which can be a problem for some plants in some soils, and they may be toxic to pets (particularly dogs) if they are swallowed. So those factors added to the "buy local" environmental argument puts them on my "no" list.

Additionally, cocoa hulls are hard to

spread, sometimes blow away, or clump together if the bag gets wet (sometimes they can be moldy in damp weather, too, right in the garden). However, they have many of the qualities I want in a mulch: They are dark in color and fine textured and look good on the beds, so if you happen to live where they are processed, and do not have a dog, you might regard them differently.

Q. Can I use bagged mulch made from recycled tires?

A. To me this seems a real environmental no-no — yet another wacky thing that is being tried out on unsuspecting consumers. Yes, it's a tactic for reusing worn tires, but putting them into the landscape, and nature, in shreds is as bad as, or worse than, piling them up at the dump whole. They don't break down and become incorporated into the soil, so they're no good, and even dangerous. Remember that animals and much smaller living organisms interact with and inhabit the soil — I don't think a worm wants to process tire shreds while making worm castings, or a robin wants to rustle around in the tire litter — though they love the leaf litter.

My first rule of mulch, repeated for emphasis: To be a mulch, it must be organic (a living or formerly living material) so it can decompose over time and return to the soil, not taint it. The one exception to the organic rule, to my mind, would be some stone materials, used in certain zones and certain types of landscapes.

Q. Is black plastic or landscape fabric a good mulch?

A. Black plastic can be used to heat up an area (such as for sweet potatoes or pumpkins in the North) but should not be left in place, as it prevents moisture from entering the soil and otherwise interferes with soil health. Roll or fold it and reuse the sheeting year after year. Landscape fabrics, or so-called geotextiles, are not a substitute for mulch. They should not be used in ornamental garden beds, though they may have a role as a weed block beneath gravel of pathways or patios, for instance. I don't even use them there, personally, preferring not to bury such man-made materials in the soil.

Q. What about Ruth Stout's mulch methods?

A. Long before phrases like "lasagna garden" were making the rounds of the as-yet-uninvented Internet, Ruth Stout (author of *Gardening Without Work,* 1961 — highly recommended though it will have to be scored on the used-book sites) was layering all her organic materials on top of her soil — sheet composting, as it might be traditionally called. Her tactic served to thwart weeds, reduce the need for fertilizers, conserve moisture, and spare her the work of composting in a conventional heap with all the toting and turning of materials.

Her approach to gardening starts with the foundational principle of applying mulch, mulch, and more mulch, and then simply moving it back a tiny bit each year a bit to make room for a row of seeds or seedlings, rather than all that turning and tilling (and weeding). She said the "aha" moment came one spring when the plow man hadn't come yet to till, and she was eager to get planting. She saw that the asparagus (a long-lived perennial vegetable crop) was already up and growing, right through the layers of fallen leaves and such. "I walked over and said to the asparagus, 'We don't have to plow for you; why do we have to plow for the other vegetables?'" Stout said. "And the asparagus said, 'You don't.'"

Where do you get all that mulch? The garden creates it, or at least some of the raw material that becomes it: spent cornstalks and uprooted pea vines and the like, to which Stout added fall leaves and also brought-in straw or hay ("spoiled" hay was fine, and cheaper; don't worry about a little decay, she said).

Q. Do you mulch your pots and other containers?

A. I do apply mulch to the soil surface in

containers, particularly the large ones, to help keep roots cool and moisture in the potting medium. Depending on the type of plant, I may use composted stable bedding, or even a small peastone if I won't be repotting the plant regularly. The latter looks great with succulents, for instance.

conceal the occasional one out of laziness in a bed or border when trying to plant everything all at once in the rush of spring. *Go get a proper small wooden label, Margaret.*

I wish we could all agree that the color blue in horticulture is best reserved for *Meconopsis* (though I can't grow the Himalayan poppy), or the so-easy-as-to-be-thuggish forget-me-not (*Myosotis*), or maybe one of those sky-blue grape hyacinth varieties (*Muscari*) — but not under any circumstances for fertilizer. Fertilizer — better thought of as food for the soil rather than as "plant food" — is best when brown and smelling like something dead, or perhaps like some herbivore's composting toilet. The good ones are recycling at its best, whether the casualty was animal (some leftover from another industry, such as blood meal) or vegetable (compost or alfalfa meal, for instance). We could add the all-important *mineral* to the list, too, in the form of rock dusts, but they are neither brown nor particularly odorous. One more issue I have with fertilizer, while I'm at it: I'm frustrated that modern bedding plants (such as those renamed petunias and verbenas) are bred to perform on life support — blue chemical fertilizer, and lots of it, and also lots of water — or otherwise limp along after we get them home (and off the equivalent of the IV they were on at the greenhouse they were propagated in).

Despite my list of such harsh, old-fashioned prescriptions and intolerances, I'm also absolutely sure that there is always the possibility of getting away with a little bit of fakery: A clean-cut edge and dose of fresh mulch masks a multitude of sins in a bed or border; a couple of brightly painted chairs moved into a place that might be just past peak seems to set it into bloom again.

The cutbacks never stop, and even as we enter the most intense battering days of summer — and even after all the rounds of reduction that came before — we stoop and crouch once more, moving from one end of each bed to the other with a tip bag sliding along with us, extracting debris. Certainly the garden and its coconspirators never tire of creating more for us to winnow out: a chewed-on leaf gone limp; another that had torn, then browned as a result; a fallen branch or stem that perhaps gave way when some mammalian plunderer or other stomped through under cover of darkness. Left in place, it is an invitation to another edition of trouble, and the weather metes out enough of that.

A friend is working maybe twenty feet away, and I hear her say, not to me exactly but just a proclamation, "I want this," and put a handful of something into an empty quart yogurt container that she has positioned in her trug to hold such goodies — pass-along plants that are part of what we kiddingly refer to as the excellent "benefits package" for working here part-time all these years. I watch more carefully across the haze of perennials between us, and then I see: She is cutting off the succulent, fuzzy seedpods of the celandine poppy to take home. For more than a dozen years she has been carrying such things away from here, and yet our gardens could not be more different. Our marinaras and pestos and even our egg salads are different, too, come to think of it; same ingredients, perhaps, but a whole different sense of texture, taste, and proportion.

It is the worst play I have ever seen: *Marmota Monax: A Dramedy in Six Acts*. The tragedy, which I have seen far too many times, goes something like this:

Act 1: The Peas Are Gone (May)
Act 2: Where's the Parsley? (early June)
Act 3: Anyone Seen the Green Beans? (late June)
Act 4: Leafless Sweet Potato Vines (July)
Act 5: Seeking Professional Help (July)
Act 6: Seeking More Professional Help (August)

You fat bastard. I see now that I have been kidding myself to think that my powers of persuasion worked on you; that just because I'd invited you to leave (sending Herb to deliver the message personally — remember?) that you had RSVP'd "yes." If not for an unintended high sign just now from a wild turkey, I might have let you go unnoticed even longer.

I was on the phone, staring out in the blank way I do to provide myself a neutral backdrop to such conversations or if I am simply thinking, when some movement caught my eye. Far uphill, I could see a turkey inside the tall wire fence, where the small field that is essentially the extreme edge of my backyard meets the woodland that is the state forest surrounding me. *Binoculars.* It was a hen, pacing back and forth with the fence at her shoulder: first left six or eight feet, *about-face,* then right, *about-face,* then left, then right, and so on, as if on some drill, preparing perhaps for maneuvers or maybe a full-dress parade. She became more possessed with each fast lap, as if she would not stop till she dropped from exhaustion. Stuck in this perceptual rut (*been there, done that* — though mine was in the city and my former career) she wouldn't move far enough from the impediment to get a clear view of the sky; she thought she was trapped, when the route to freedom was right there waiting for her to stop panicking and notice it all along. *Oh, Big Bird, I know; I know.*

I walked up halfway, staying to one side to try to stay out of sight, then stopped to call out, fearing I'd spook her by coming much closer. My opening line:

You having a bad day?

I'm not sure she got my chick humor, but the approach worked; the distraction caused her to look into the field at me instead of per-

Flat-leaf or Italian-style parsley is a year-round ingredient here, and even though my plants behave technically as biennials — living through the winter and even usable then if covered with an upside-down leaf-stuffed bushel basket — it's hard to get to them in winter. Rather than shovel snow or pay a couple of dollars a bunch from December to April or so, I harvest in summer and fall and freeze the rest of my year's supply: some as "pesto" cubes, others in "logs" of leaflets pressure-rolled tightly inside freezer bags.

The log technique (so easy, and probably the only cooking "Good Thing" I ever contributed to *Martha Stewart Living* magazine in my years there, though my record with gardening ideas was better) can also be used for chives. (I haven't tested other herbs this way, but I am planning more experiments.) When you need some, just slice a disk from one end of the log.

Parsley pesto, frozen in cubes, is great as an ingredient in soup or stew or defrosted and spooned on top of a bowl of minestrone with a drizzle of olive oil and some cheese — like conventional basil pesto. Almost any green herb will take to being frozen as a pesto: garlic scapes, sage, rosemary, chives, cilantro, oregano, marjoram, thyme, chervil.

Your pesto style may simply be a thick slurry of parsley blended (or food-processored) in a tiny bit of water. Some cooks simply chop the herbs, pack them into the ice cube tray sections, pour a little water over, and freeze. Or they can be prepared similarly in olive oil, or go all the way and add raw garlic or nuts (pignolias or walnuts) or Parmesan-type cheese before freezing. Either way, knock the cubes out, once frozen, into labeled and doubled freezer bags (every flavor will look alike — I mean it when I say to label), with the air expressed. If made with the extras, such as cheese and garlic and nuts, herb pesto cubes are a real treat on crackers on a frigid day, or tossed into pasta: a mouthful of summer, just when you're most in need.

Making Parsley Logs

My "parsley logs" are simply tightly packed rolls of parsley foliage that you can slice a wedge off anytime. I grow flat-leaf Italian parsley, specifically 'Gigante' or 'Giant of Italy', leaving the curly stuff for use as edging of garden beds and even in pots with annuals, where its frilly greenness is a season-long visual treat.

When I'm harvesting, I take the oldest (thickest) stems each time, because throughout the summer new ones are being produced from the crown of this biennial. My parsley-preserving gear is so simple I'm almost embarrassed to reveal it: a colander to wash the harvest in, a salad spinner to dry it (wet foliage deteriorates when frozen), and freezer bags.

Once the parsley is washed and spun dry, pick off the leaflets (leaving the stems behind to compost). You may prefer to take the leaflets off first, then spin; your call. Put a lot of clean, dry leaflets in a freezer bag, and then start compressing the mass into a log shape at the bottom. Packing densely means that even one slice from the end of the log will yield lots of parsley. Gradually squeeze out the air as you go. The log should be firm; you can really pack a lot in. Secure with elastic bands or bull clips and freeze. Yes, it looks like some Cheech and Chong stash of weed when you're done, but what would I know about that?

ceiving only the claustrophobic limitations of that fence, and it broke the cycle. With a burst of beating wings, she was gone into the woods beyond, from whence she came. *Sayonara.* (I don't talk turkey, so my single word of Japanese will have to do.) Turning to start back downhill, that is when I saw what you have done: more missing plants. *You fat bastard.*

And then as if on cue, here you dare come right toward me from the patio, probably intending to slip back underground for a nap now that you're full, continuing in my general direction until you see me — *uh-oh, uh-oh, it's her again, that crazy woman!* — and then you make your own about-face and hurry away, low-hanging flesh swaying vigorously side to side worse than Jack's own ample dust ruffle. I give chase, and as I quicken my steps I start screaming, too, for good measure: *You fat bastard.* And then it hits me, literally — a hornet or wasp of some kind hits me right in the forehead and violently deposits a stinger, as if to say, *Keep it down, won't you? Some of us are trying to work here.*

What things have come to: Fresh from an attempt at conversation with a turkey, while chasing a woodchuck whom I'm shouting at, I run right into an angry insect, who attacks and also scolds me — the utter exclamation point on my complete undoing. This is war; shades of Winston Churchill, who told the soldier and poet Siegfried Sassoon that "war is the normal occupation of man," but then amended that to say, "war — and gardening." Hard to tell the difference, when one's backyard is always under siege.

With Herb gone for the summer, I am thinking it's time to call for alternate backup. Some of these *Animal Planet* moments culminate in crossroads I cannot navigate alone, I know, from early years spent innocently setting the roots of a tree on fire (when a proper pest-control smoke bomb shoved down a woodchuck hole backfired), or waking up to find live cage traps filled not with frightened rabbits but with very large and aggravated skunks. The peas are long lost, yes, but now the beans — the flat-podded Italian- or Romano-style ones I rate as an essential ingredient of any summer — are heading in the same direction, and so is the row of hefty

'Gigante' flat-leaf parsley plants (more on growing and storing a year of it on page 252, plus why I skip the curly stuff). Likewise, the twenty-foot-long raised bed of sweet potatoes looked better last week, when it still sported some leaves. I've read its foliage is edible — tastes like spinach, apparently (no, not chicken, or woodchuck) — but so far only the waddling marmot, who's definitely behaving as a hostile witness, could offer any firsthand feedback on the succulence of this year's crop.

"Hello, Mike, it's Margaret Roach, over by the state park, with the gardens; remember?" My voice sounds sheepish; almost apologetic, I know. I should be able to handle this myself, I am a big girl now, but then the vintage image of the flames shooting from beneath that tree beside the woodchuck burrow — too far for the garden hose to reach, of course — regains its spot in front of mind. Never again; no way.

"Had any rattlesnakes yet this year?" he says in reply, apparently remembering me very clearly. There have been none in the garden proper lately, none of what a blog reader mistyped to me as "rattlesnacks" in her Freudian-style empathic e-mail, as if she meant to help me find the details of gardening in "rattlesnack" country all very happy-go-lucky and comic-strippish. *Whee!*

It quickly becomes a summer of can-you-top-this episodes, with the licensed nuisance-wildlife control operator as my witness and my 911. On Visit 1, he leaves enough traps behind to qualify the place as Margaret's House of Havaharts, if I were the type who wanted to name her garden — or perhaps sign a promotional contract with the manufacturer to supplement a sagging income. On Visit 2, when they are filled with an impressive haul of skunks and raccoons, he rebaits patiently (and somehow misses getting sprayed). On Visit 3, when the catch of the day is three raccoons at once: "You've got more things going on here than the Catskill Game Farm," he says — and that's before Visit 4, when on the way up the path with a new supply of cantaloupe wedges and a jar of trapper's fruit-paste lure meant to sweeten the ante, the first glimpse of the backyard includes a magnificent red fox making himself right at home in plain daylight. He must be on the scent of the same woodchuck — oh, could I be so lucky that the fox will handle this for me?

"That's the biggest one I've seen in years," says the man who makes his living noticing such things. "He must be four or five years old." We stand motionless and silent, reverentially watching the handsome canid as he circles like the family dog in his own safe-feeling living room and curls up for a snooze. These stolen moments and sights are the bonus rounds — prizes awarded even though I lost the earlier stages of the contest, and really never figure to win more than the occasional point. Not just second chances, as in the rower's repechage, but actual prizes, apparently awarded for what I'm getting very good at: losing complete and utter control of everything.

As frustration increases with the weeks, a lot of time is spent beating the bushes once again for clues, and we find that by now there are three open woodchuck holes, not just the one discovered in late winter. Days pass and it seems as if every chipmunk, squirrel, raccoon, and skunk in the region has sampled the bait in one cage or another and gotten trapped — but not the woodchuck. I study for ad hoc apprenticeship: learning to let out the squirrels and chipmunks (a try at freeing a raccoon was met with demonic cackling and outstretched claws not extended in any friendly greeting; I never tried again). I close the live traps before sundown and reopen them after dawn to focus on our diurnal target, not his crepuscular and nocturnal neighbors, the raccoons and skunks; I look for flies around an open hole (the sign of an occupied burrow, apparently), and check holes and their immediate surroundings at dawn, midday, and again at dusk to try to figure out who's where when.

Finally: *flies!* Mike bombs one hole, presumably with the elusive woodchuck in residence (and without any three-alarm backdraft). Three days post-bombing, I am dismayed to see the burrow active again.

"Cover it," I am instructed on the morning phone call that is becoming pretty regular. "See if anybody opens it." Dutifully, I do just that, then follow up throughout the day to see if we still have any takers. Post-it notes on the counter remind me: The last thing I must do before bed and the first thing in the morning is to check the hole. At dusk: still closed. At barely dawn: open, but a smaller opening than the previous day. Disappointed again, I call in my latest findings. This is apparently progress, I am told. *Progress?*

"A fox probably smelled the woodchuck in the hole and dug it up to eat it," he says. "Then after you recovered it, a chipmunk smelled the fresh soil — and they just love to dig in that."

I see. Everybody around here smells opportunity of one form or another, everyone except me. We are apparently working our way through some new flowchart of mammalian genera and their relationship in the food chain — some new twist on the connection of man to woodchuck to fox to chipmunk, and who knows who will be next. *Rattlesnack?*

Knowledge is power, the saying goes, and so for extra credit in my summer animal-control internship I am madly reading up about my opponent and his habits. But the research proves wildly un-empowering; it sounds hopeless, since apparently these bastards do everything but fly. It's not enough to fence them out with a four-foot-high heavy mesh barrier unless you continue it, buried, a foot underground — and better still, add a strand of electrified wire maybe four inches outside the fence perimeter and the same distance off the ground. Yes, I read about the single strand of rope sprayed with bobcat urine that kept these beasts out of some cabbage patch somewhere — but between the price per quart of bobcat urine (not even considering where it comes from, and what cruelty the animals producing it experience), and the image of myself maintaining said rope barrier, I think not.

Thankfully, I also learn this: I'm not alone in my plight. While I'm in the throes of all of it, letting the presence or absence of flies dictate my mood for each arriving day, I hear that the farmers down the road shoot fifteen woodchucks in one field after massive crop destruction. Then my old friend Herb, back for a mere three days to check on his house, finds his vegetable garden plundered, and traps out five adults in no time. Five of these supposedly solitary creatures in one hole back-to-back: unheard of. We are all fighting the good fight, comrades-in-arms. I don't have the heart to tell any of them — the farm family, Herb, even Mike, the trapper — the data from a study I read about from Pennsylvania State University, in which 1,040 woodchucks were removed over the course of four years from a six-hundred-acre agricultural site. The impact on the population: *nothing significant.* Apparently all the intervention did was help prompt increased birth rates, juvenile survival — and invite nearby animals to *come on over, dinner's on,* and best of all: *the coast is clear of competition* (well, at least the four-legged kind, for this is not my summer's only infestation by any means).

We have a mostly anonymous relationship, and for years I liked it that way. Though they are my closest neighbors on every side and we live all but intertwined, I know few of my weeds by name. Confession: I cannot remember the names of some of my human neighbors, but thankfully in either case, I never forget a face, and therefore manage to behave semi-appropriately.

Mowing and many other chores are all but halted now, in these conditions, but ever since it thawed this year, the soil has been consistently conducive to one task — weeding — to coaxing up and out all unwanted rootlings that compete with garden plants and plans. Audacious and brilliant English gardener and writer Christopher Lloyd spoke of the "soothing monotony" that weeding holds for some of us, myself included. In the process of implementing the latest upheavals, I have been studying my outtakes more closely than usual, taking my time to set aside samples of any I cannot identify and look them up so that I can finally address *Alliaria petiolata* (garlic mustard) and all the others with the proper (dis) respect. And there are a lot of "others," I realize now, having compiled a rough list these last weeks, adding to it after every routing session. Maybe I simply never made a tally because I knew it would make the garden chore that can never be completed — which is how I think of weeding, really — even more formidable, but never mind. Now that I have started to force myself to surrender to this practice of *naming* the unwanted plants, I will treat it like the excellent meditation tactic it can be.

In various spiritual traditions, practitioners name the stuff that comes up during a meditation session to try to take its sting out, to release the hold that the invasive thoughts that surface from the stillness — *my leg is asleep,* or *shit, I forgot to pick up the dry cleaning* — might otherwise have. We silently name the thoughts and hope by doing so that they will just slip by, cloud-like, untroubling. *Nonattachment.* Let's hope that naming works on weeds, and proves a powerful mental herbicide.

The list so far is diverse, and the harvest here is therefore always ample: There lives among those I can now identify the likes of bedstraw (which my friend Marco charmingly calls Sticky Willie), bindweed, bittersweet, broadleaf plantain, bur cucumber, Canada thistle, carpetweed, chickweed, common burdock, crabgrass, dandelion, foxtail, *Galinsoga,* garlic mustard, greater celandine, ground ivy, heal-all (a kind of *Prunella*), honeysuckle, jewelweed (or touch-me-not), lamb's quarters, mugwort, oxalis (at least three species), pigweed, prostrate spurge, poison ivy, pokeweed, purslane, ragweed, *Rubus* of some kind, sheep sorrel, stinging nettle, wild grape, and wild lettuce. I don't include violet or dame's rocket (*Hesperis matronalis*), because I don't weed them out of most beds, likewise leaving any clovers and hawkweed right in the lawn where they appear. On a given day, I can practically guarantee finding at least one example of any of those in the list, with the presence of many, many multiples the far more likely scenario. A positive stampede, really.

I wish I were blameless on all counts for such variety, but it's simply not so. Yes, some came with the place: the Oriental bittersweet; the wild grape; a shrubby Asian honeysuckle; thorny, suckering canes of the wild bramble that's probably some kind of blackberry. I was greeted right from the start of my days here by stiff, sharp Canada thistle and deceptively benign-looking stinging nettle — not exactly the Welcome Wagon, those two prickly personages (though the latter is an important element used in biodynamic farming and gardening). Poison ivy in its most mature stage was in the inherited mix — a woody vine, wrist-thick around, that shall forever climb most every tree along my perimeter and along the roads nearby. At least it's an important wildlife plant. I had never seen garlic mustard before I came here, but its abundance locally has more than made up for any deficiency earlier in life. And there is one I cannot find in any book or other reference — not showy enough to be a garden escape, but a fleshy, tall, bright-green self-sowing summer annual that seems to reproduce almost nonstop, and grow upward even faster once there is some heat. No wonder that asking someone to help weed is so tricky: The assistance is always needed, but how will they tell — if I can barely keep track myself — what is to stay and what's to go? A cookie sheet with a sample of each targeted offender should be handed out to overnight guests upon arrival, I figure. *Find me twenty of each, and earn your supper.*

I remember where some others came from — accidental immigrants from the gardens of friends, appearing here shortly after some horticultural treasure they'd shared with me had made its way into my ground. You have to take the bad with the good, and I am willing, if not happy, to pull up *Galinsoga ciliata,* with its little yellow flowers, in payment for the unusual and treasured plants I got from one generous person who never intended the unfortunate bonus. Sadly, creeping red wood sorrel, *Oxalis corniculata,* came with some more mundane nursery annuals, and now loves the cracks and crevices in the stones here, as does spotted spurge, *Euphorbia maculata,* which in a case of double-trouble reached my doorstep with a garden *Campanula* I thought I wanted, but that has proven hideously weedy itself and that I'll never be able to extirpate, either. Both the spurge and the oxalis hug tight in the cracks as if there's to be no letting go, no matter how moist the soil is, proving a job for the discarded kitchen bread knife or the Japanese tool called a *hori-hori.*

People write regularly to ask how to get rid of ground ivy (*Glechoma hederacea*) in the lawn, and my true answer is "I can't." That would be where herbicides come in — or biocides, as Rachel Carson more appropriately called all pesticides, since they are indiscriminate killers — and even with them, it's not a sure thing. Of course *Glechoma,* the most successful of my many lawn opponents, would prove to be a mint relative — in this case a low-growing perennial species. Mint? This can't be a good prognosis; my track record with mints sucks.

Weeds are cleverer than I am, that much is clear, with strokes of built-in genius, such as barbs and hooks that grab on to an animal's coat (or a gardener's) for the ride to some new plot to plunder, or plumose hairs and other umbrellalike attachments that act as sails, to send them off onto the breeze. Some set so much seed — even a single plain old dandelion plant can produce more than two thousand — that it's actually quite exhausting to contemplate. And then there are the real evildoers you can never quite get out: the ones that regard my incessant digging at them as a form of propagation, those capable of regenerating from the tiniest bit of underground root left anywhere on earth, and perhaps beyond. When I lecture, I refer to these as the "under-the-bed plants," as in: They'll probably even grow under your bed if you toss them there, they're that insidious.

Weeds generally have all the good qualities I like in people — they're un-fancy, enthusiastic, adaptable, and display constancy. They can be counted on, when all else fails, which is why Shakespeare said they "make haste" (compared with what he called "sweet flowers," which are slow). So shall I try to keep my sweet friends close and my hasty enemies closer? Is that the only plan I can offer after all these years — that and layers of newsprint or recycled, unprinted corrugated cardboard topped with mulch, in the worst situations where total erasure by smothering is required? Better yet, keep your weeds at this time of year out of the ground and deposited into a substantial plastic bag set up as an adjunct to the compost heap — a sort of very inhospitable waiting room, where they can cook to death for a while before gaining entry to the main pile. Such pretreatment is essential with anything bearing seeds, as so many are right now, or with rhizomatous roots that can sprout a new plant.

"Cultivate your weeds," a blog reader told me she had written on a slip of paper and pinned up in plain view, an admonition to smooth some of the gnarly bits that we each face now and again in ourselves. But as for cultivating garden weeds, other than the occasional crop of dandelion greens for the sauté pan, I think not. And so with each handful or forkful these moist mornings in the garden I'll be saying this instead: *Who are you, my familiar strangers,* and also: *What's your secret to success?*

Except with weeds, where I work hard to be as inconsiderate as they are, the strands of good-neighbor DNA are so ingrained in me that things like this happen: I awaken at five thirty, and my first conscious *be-up-be-doing* thought is that I need to mow, but I put it off (inconveniencing myself, and sometimes facing quick-rising heat) until a "reasonable hour." A child of the suburbs, I am incapable of making early-morning noise — or actually any unnecessary sounds that anyone else could hear and be irritated by, except for this little detail: Nobody is close enough these days to really be disturbed. My neighborhood is too spread out. Nevertheless, the mower remains quiet until at least nine; ten on a weekend day.

"Neighbor." The word has been pushing ever upward in consciousness as I've settled into being a small-town one since relocating, which by the most literal of definitions completely changes who, if not what, the term conjures. Once used more widely to connote the biblical-style "one in need" or "fellow man" (deriving from Matthew 19:19, *love thy neighbor as thyself*), it is typically the Anglo-Saxon derivation, the literal translation of "near-dweller," that most of us hear today when the word is spoken. Oftentimes, "neighbor" seems more a matter of geography than evocative of an outpouring of goodwill — the literal "person next door," or at least quite close at hand. Close, indeed:

We may need to travel to see our families for the holiday meal, but our neighbors are always right there. (*For better or for worse,* some would say.) Even if we barely know their names — even if we can't tell their kids apart — we can describe their routines. Wherever we live at any given time in our lives, we are one, and have at least one. Being a neighbor is one of those things you can't escape — even by moving. An understudy awaits at the next location, ready to fill the role.

Necessity is the mother of neighborliness, as my nearest near dweller, Robin, and I have come to manifest lately in our particular enactment of the word. "Do you need anything?" one will ask the other if she must go out on a slippery winter day, or her near-dawn e-mail of, "I called the sand truck; they'll be here soon to do both our driveways." And then we have this special bond: the daily digital data swap, to record the body count after the latest respective rounds of mouse patrol. "One in the shed, none in the cellar" is trumped by, "Three in the garage." Women who live in old houses can't be squeamish.

"I want you to be concerned about your next-door neighbor," Mother Teresa of Calcutta taught, asking, "Do you know your next-door neighbor?" Well, I know that she and I both need some more serious carpentry repairs or these unwanted, unneighborly invasions will simply never stop. Maybe we can get a twofer on some hours with the neighborhood handyman?

Words I love: Oh, to be a geophyte, ready to carry on (albeit in hiding, or at least in a good disguise) even in the worst of times, rather than stand up and face everything inhospitable that comes along — a sudden lack of resources, for instance, or someone gnawing at you. Geophyte: "A plant growing with stem or tuber below ground, usually applied to bulbous or tuberous species from arid lands." So says Mark Griffiths in the *Index of Garden Plants*.

Tulip and daffodil bulbs were the first things I planted here, arriving as I had in autumn after the closing on the house I'd found that summer. (My approach to using mostly animal-proof ones is in the sidebar on page 273.) Even now, with an overstuffed garden, I tell myself there is always room to layer in more bulbs. In my first years of acquiring houseplants I displayed a natural proclivity for geophytes, too, or, more specifically, for caudiciform plants — ones with fat "bottoms," whose shortened stem tissue lives just under and/or at the soil surface, often dressing up not as stem at all but more like a rock or piece of craggy bark, or in some cases like a bulb but sitting aboveground. Is drought

It won't be time to plant most hardy bulbs here until fall, but ordering in summertime means getting the best selection — and often an early shopping discount at some of my favorite sources. Because many flower bulbs can be animal bait — an expensive disappointment — I recommend species that are resistant to pests such as deer, rabbits, and squirrels.

Daffodils, or *Narcissus,* are poisonous, and therefore seem to have all-round resistance to nibbling or digging by animals. The ornamental onions (genus *Allium*) have a built-in repellent as well, with that onion-y smell of theirs. I can attest to many years of experience with nobody bothering those, as I can to the apparent animal-proof nature of *Camassia* and most *Fritillaria* (though I have had skunks dig up the small ones many times while rooting around in the beds here; funny that they'd dislodge skunky-smelling *Fritillaria,* those skunks).

Hyacinths and foxtail lilies (*Eremurus*) are also rated as deer-resistant; I cannot offer any firsthand insight, only friends' reports (and those in catalogs and books).

Do not even think of growing tulips or true lilies (*Lilium*) without protection if you have deer. I am fenced in against those large predators, and grow tulips in one raised bed near my vegetables, specifically for cut flowers, and nobody digs them up. I have them planted extra-deep, which is also said to help the bulbs perennialize (that is, come back for more years than some tulip varieties do under normal planting conditions).

Among the minor bulbs, animal-resistant choices include snowdrops (*Galanthus*), snowflake (*Leucojum*), winter aconite (*Eranthis*), glory-of-the-snow (*Chionodoxa*), Spanish bluebell (*Hyacinthoides hispanica*), *Ornithogalum, Scilla,* and *Muscari* (grape hyacinth). The so-called autumn crocus (*Colchicum*), with its late flowers, is also apparently not tasty.

I have had good success here with all those, but almost complete failure with the genus *Crocus,* which squirrels and chipmunks here adore, though extra-deep planting and a sprinkling of blood meal on the soil surface as they pop through is said to deter the incessant digging. One year I planted 4,000, and by spring there were perhaps three flowers (and 3,997 divots) where the imagined swath of them had been. Last fall I succumbed to catalog and reference-book promises that the species *Crocus tommasinianus* types, in various shades of purple and in white, are more animal-resistant. Come spring, the thick little shoots stuffed with unopened foliage and flowers lay like fallen soldiers on the battleground. I now officially surrender to the genus *Crocus,* and to its Rodentia masters.

Some gardeners enclose delectable bulbs in hardware-cloth "cages" that they fashion as underground dig-proof protective devices, but the wrinkle there: Once your bulbs multiply, the clump can't really spread past its cage. Unnatural-looking, to say the least.

or fire or cold — or maybe even hungry, nibbling animals — headed your way? Drop any vulnerable greenery and go into hiding, the caudiciforms say, living off the water and carbohydrates in the ingenious storage organ your species evolved to meet such adversity. These plants make survivalists with well-stocked bunkers look positively unprepared.

For nearly twenty years my two most prized and carefree roommates have been *Bowiea volubilis* (it resembles a pot full of big, thin-skinned pale-green onions that sit on the soil and sprout a feathery-looking vine; every bit is poisonous) and *Bombax ellipticum* (which would be a thirty-foot tree or taller in its native range of southern Mexico to Honduras, but here is more like a large rock with a pair of five-foot branches that leaf out if and when they want to). Neither has been repotted in a decade or longer, nor do they seem to care. They follow their own calendar — and all I have to do is be respectful, meaning even here in the captivity of my little house they seem to have made the perfect life, no? — living as they wish, among those who display tolerance in return.

Another good word: allelopathy. Being allelopathic would take things a big step further than geophytic, not just outsmarting would-be neighbors with now-you-see-me, now-you-don't hide-and-go-seekery, but outright repelling or killing off those who tried to sidle up to me, or at least making things pretty inhospitable. I suppose that's going too far, but there have been days — which I suppose is what the big metal gate at the end of the driveway and caller ID are for.

Allelopathy, says the International Allelopathy Society, is "any process involving secondary metabolites produced by plants, algae, bacteria and fungi that influence the development of natural and agricultural systems." This takes into account that not all such effects are necessarily negative, though the more generic and commonly used definition might be that allelopathic organisms — plant or otherwise, with the black walnut being the most common example among gardeners — inhibit the germination or growth of certain other species by some chemical action. These characters, the negative allelopaths, mark their territory, and most everybody obeys the boundaries. But looking at the fuller range of potential impact on other members of a community — both upside and downside — might even explain why invasive alien species that were not so troublesome in their home environment so forcefully take over a new home. The sometimes-pushy neighbors of their native turf aren't there to keep them in line — to enforce building codes and other ordinances, so to speak — and so the new guy on the block just has at it, quickly becoming the aggressive developer type whom everybody hates. The neighborhood? Ruined, or at least altered forever.

"I have created a monster," Page, an enviably talented garden friend, said the other night. It was the latest of many true-confessions phone calls I find myself having these days on whispered matters ranging from slack body parts and surging awareness of mortality, to shrinking bank balances and no retirement possible ever. "Why did I do this?" she continued, and in case there is any confusion: This monster is not some prickly interpersonal relationship gone wrong, but her too-big garden, the one that has been a mainstay and compass of her adult life and identity the way my very own monster has been of mine.

I love my monster but *love-spelled-loathe* the grip it has on me, and as we talked about what we plan to do — erase this bed, simplify that one, recruit that ever-elusive local teenager who'll work really cheap — I mentioned a few of the nothing-special-but-very-"can-do" plants around here that suddenly are looking really good to me, the onetime quasi connoisseur.

"Thank God for *Geranium macrorrhizum*," she said, reading my mind, and we laughed together, in that instant imagining our two very different places — her beast of many formal and informal "rooms" makes mine look easy to manage — with nothing remaining but the "bones," the shrubs and trees, and under every grouping of them that most cooperative of herbaceous perennials, the big-root geranium. That's it: The answer is a monoculture of what is basically just a living mulch — the next phase of our gardening lives will look like that (echoes of the wisdom of Marco, who is always one step ahead). The hell with needy, too-precious-to-be-practical things.

"Remember wanting absolutely everything — growing everything that came along?" she said, and oh, I do, I do, and as we compared best-of lists from fleets of botanical creatures between us who have come and gone, we couldn't help but notice how relieved we both sounded.

"I think the monster's trying to tell us something bigger than just about gardening," I said eventually of our shared predicament. "You know: How you can't be everywhere at the same time, or everything to everyone; how you just have to let go of some things, or everything suffers — especially ourselves."

A moment of silence, and then yes, we

agreed, there are other aspects of our lives that could use some pruning back, some weeding (or a lowering of the bar?), which then ricocheted to this last thought:

"Do you have mile-a-minute weed yet?" she asked, referring to a 2006 accidental introduction to the United States from Asia, *Persicaria perfoliata,* a barbed and aggressive annual vine whose acquaintance I have as yet been spared. Mile-a-minute, I thought, which is how fast the days seem to go now, how fast whole new years appear and then — *presto!* — elapse. Just what we need when our clocks are running faster and our bodies slowing one bad shoulder at a time: a new opponent in the form of something known as "mile-a-minute weed." Perfect.

We have both known some sexy beasts, Page and I, the ones you'd never cast out, no matter what. It's all a matter of taste, of course — or is it some kind of chemistry that explains an indescribable, elusive sense of attraction? I like screaming, outsize foliage; another person might be inclined toward tight little rock-garden miniatures. Maybe that's all there is to it: to each her own, and no understanding why. Whatever the source of the attraction, a new one always makes good fodder for gossip.

You know the way a best friend wants to hear all the details of your latest intrigue, based on whatever the friend likes most about objects of intrigue herself? (Forgive me, gentlemen; just swap all the personal pronouns in this passage to suit.) "How are his manners?" she'll ask, and "His sense of humor? His smile?" Or, "How are his hands, his shoes?" if those are her particular fetishes. *Do tell.*

Here's what I'd ask if I were your best friend and you had your eye on someone new, especially in the perennial or shrub department at the garden center: *How are his leaves?* It's leaves, after all, that dictate a plant's character, hanging on as they do longer than most any flower can.

When you go plant shopping or seek an introduction to someone special from a knowing garden friend, be sure to ask the all-important question: How are his leaves? A perfect example, even now, after months of aggravated meteorological assault: *Geranium phaeum* 'Samobor' (named for a city in the former Yugoslavia, where it was found), that perennial geranium out front with chocolate-purple chevrons on every leaf, is a real dandy. It hasn't put out a flower since May or earliest June, but it has nothing to worry about in my way of thinking, because really, who cares if such a hottie ever comes across and blooms?

They shag and bonk, but no snogging first — the hell with foreplay, huh? *Just do it.* I live in an amphibian Plato's Retreat. Love is in the air, baby. Frog love. The backyard is an equal-opportunity brothel these days, not some prim, prom-like get-together in white gloves and dyed-to-match pumps, but a full-on, naked orgy for one and all.

A big female bullfrog, her left eye clouded over and probably blind, her jaw always just slightly ajar and no longer quite plumb in its hinge, had arrived and quickly claimed her stone at poolside early this spring, hopping a ride on a downpour of a night with another bull or two from wherever they'd spent the off-season. She would be well cast in a movie featuring sorcery; she is no beauty. No matter; there is someone here for everyone. Just across the pool on a diagonal, the one who adores her has his own stone, and each day they take their places, motionless and stone-like themselves. Despite the damaged eye, the misaligned jaw, and her sagging, freckled white belly, she is the one for this boy bull. They sit. And wait, and with at least three of their four collective eyes, watch each other while remaining in a state of readiness for the next meal to crawl or fly on in — their version of a dinner date, I guess.

The males of various species make all sorts of impolite sounds all mating season long, but every so often I hear a froggy little gasp I know is a female voice that I imagine is saying, "Here we go again," or maybe something slightly more romantic like, "Hey, little guy" (no size-joke insult intended; in some species the male is the smaller of the two). I look around, and sure enough: There she is, the latest one to get grabbed into the embrace called amplexus, when the male clasps the often-larger female around the back. There is no intercourse, exactly, but rather she releases eggs and he releases a fluid to fertilize them. This goes on for some time — frogs don't know from "nooners" or "quickies," apparently — and they also don't seem to be one bit shy. The first public display of affection of the season (as always it was a pair of wood frogs) began in April right out at poolside, where fifteen other frogs of various species were sunning themselves, before the happy couple finally retreated into the shrubbery onto a bed of pine needles. A couple of weeks ago, Lady One Eye gave it up for a daring young bull, not her longtime admirer after all, and barely half her size. The latest: two green frogs in the glazed terra-cotta trough by the kitchen door this week. Twenty-six hours after the moment I heard the little lady's telltale gasp: still there. Not that I'm the kind of pervert who times frogs having sex or anything.

Another weird common thread — or should I say "filament," since their threadlike cells are connected end-to-end — is running through this soaking summer, as I find myself hosting a positive world's fair of fungi. Those all-important neither-plants-nor-animals have the power to make the world go round, but also to bring some plants (think Dutch elm disease and chestnut blight); animals (currently bats suffering from white-nose syndrome, for example), and even humans to their knees. Mushrooms and their kin in all forms, sizes, and colors are appearing here as if from nowhere, and as with weeds and certain insects, the first reflex: *Get that thing out of here.* And then I calm down and try to discern what each one is telling me — to see if I can find the *why*.

I needed to brush up on my scant grasp of mycology: A mushroom is the sexual fruiting body of a fungus, but not all fungi have sexual states (nor therefore do they all produce mushrooms). Fungi don't have chlorophyll, so they cannot make their own food (like plants do), nor can they ingest it (like animals), except through absorption from their surrounding environment. Most fungi are saprophytes, meaning they feed on dead or decaying material, such as the leaf litter of the forest floor — or the debris in the compost heap. Their second critical role: Most of the plant kingdom depends on symbiotic fungi called mycorrhizae, which inhabit plants' roots, to live. Of the 70,000 species of fungus, says Tom Volk, a personal hero of mine who is a biology professor at the University of Wisconsin–La Crosse and proprietor of tomvolkfungi.net, 250 are edible, 250 can kill you — and the rest, well, funky business or just plain *blecch*.

The winner of all so far this summer: a two-foot-wide colony of something so fluorescent orange you could see it across the yard. I'm fairly certain it is *Omphalotus olearius,* the jack-o-lantern mushroom, but silly me: Though I mowed around the glistening, glowing community carefully for weeks, I forgot to photograph the underside — to see if there were any keys to identification, such as true gills beneath the cap, or how the stem and cap attached to each other — and it disappeared before I realized the oversight. Next summer?

In nonmushroom fungal news: Cedar-apple rust is having a banner year. So what do you do when you live with warring roommates? In the case of the back-and-forth skirmishes between a towering eastern red cedar (*Juniperis virginiana*) in front of the house and all the apples and other rose-family plants, nothing. Well, I do watch in fascination in spring, especially at the stage when orange, almost gelatinous "telial horns" (tendrils of spores) are developing where the cedar galls were the previous fall and winter. If you didn't know, you'd think the conifer was flowering (except that such ancient creatures, which evolved before the angiosperms, don't). I don't intervene, despite the havoc this fungus causes, particularly foliar damage and defoliation of Rosaceae relatives. It prompts the shadbush, or *Amelanchier;* the blue-leaved *Rosa glauca* (the best rose for combining with perennials), and my oldest of apples to lose their leaves so early each year. Its presence is also the reason I don't even try to grow hawthorns. Quince, crabapple, and pear are among other Rosaceae members similarly affected, host species that can pass some kinds of rust back and forth with the juniper.

Much darker, and far more ghoulish: Bats have been disappearing in terrifying numbers, in a pattern first noted close by in 2006, near Albany, New York; it has since spread through New England and the Northeast, and at this writing has reached as far as Tennessee and Alabama, out into Missouri and up into four Canadian provinces. The losses are probably because of a fungus that is known as white-nose syndrome, previously unknown to science but now named *Geomyces destructans*. (That second word, or species name, in the Latin binomial — *destructans* — is another example of a spot-on specific epithet. *Destructans* indeed.) Without bats, we'd face not just a booming mosquito population (among other pests), but if the syndrome were to continue its spread into warmer zones, farmers would be without one of the pollinators for avocado and plantain, and missing the only creature that pollinates agave.

Selfishly, the last few summers I very much miss the little brown bat who tucked himself into a crack in the beaded spruce roofers that form the ceiling of my unenclosed back porch, right above the door frame. For decades, from the end of one *Myotis lucifugus* hibernation period to the start of the next, every day at home was a game of chicken between me and the year's bat-in-residence. Who would flinch first: him (by waking up and either dropping from his holdfast into flight or drawing up farther and literally disappearing into the woodwork), or me (by using another door, rather than risking such an encounter)? It got so that nobody minded the other one — in fact I came to like to stand below his spot and watch him sleep — but despite how hard we worked on our relationship, we meet no more.

We have it here, too, that *light in August* that Estelle Faulkner commented on to her husband, William, as they sat on their Mississippi porch, staring out into the cusp month, the one that offers a glimpse forward. August and its uncanny light teases the first taste of fall in a changing angle of the sun and a few cool nights — but then flip-flops us all right back to the here-and-now of high summer: of heat, humidity, harvest, and usually havoc in some form from hurricane season. The Faulkners' South has no corner on the phenomenon — and it's not just the humans that take notice. The rodents seem to know first, burying food and exploring potential shelters long before I need to think of taking fall and winter clothes out of their cupboards for more easy-reach spots, or to choose an option (spin the roulette wheel?) for the year's heating-fuel payment plan.

It is not autumn, technically, not even close

yet, but by the more important standards I can see and smell it coming, and hear it in new movements. There is a sudden, measurable shift in animal behavior; spring and summer's primary mandate, sex — and with it all the battles in defense of the kingdom — has suddenly lost its appeal. There are no hours in the day when the grass is truly dry, even in a drier year than this sorry one; a changing of the guard has begun among the birds, who are molting and disappearing and will soon be replaced by other friends not seen since spring came on.

Last night was the first blanket night since May, and this morning: *so much dew*. The gauges are practically empty, but water drips steadily from the roof as if it had stormed, and hard at that, and all the paved surfaces are dark and slick. The moon is out in the morning, high in the west. I go out to pick up the ritual wheelbarrows of windfall apples and pears, none of them ready yet, but the doe who has summered in the cornfield across the road will eat them, anyway. Behaving like my trained fish in this one moment of our daily interaction, she lumbers up the field when the first barrow-load drops by the roadside, *thud thud thud thud thud thud thud thud,* so many imperfect, unfinished fruit touching down and rolling over the embankment to congregate again — *reunited* — in a hollow that serves as her dinner bowl. On the way out to the task, my shoes get soaked through, as they knock off and then absorb the silvery bead of water from the tip of each and every grass blade I disturb. Outward bound, I leave a dark-green trail of beadless blades in the otherwise light-green, glistening lawn. I try to stay within the lines on my retreat so that, once back inside, I can look out to see the strict, defined mark of my latest imprint on this piece of land.

I pull down the latest round of nearly ripe tomatoes, another daily late-summer routine that tries to keep me just ahead of the pressure from chipmunks and raccoons, and today also of the tropical storm that's due any time now. As I write this, a wild woman called Irene is hurling herself up the nation as if to have at the many tropical plants I dare to grow in defiance of my zone. Not that I take things personally.

On the way back inside with my semi-red haul (how to ripen a tomato, page 291), I notice that six frogs are huddling together two feet aloft in the bough of a dwarf white pine, presumably testing their emergency-preparedness plan in case a move to higher ground is called for. The cradle would fall if

Oh, the juicy joy of a ripe tomato — if you can nurture one unscathed to that perfect shade of orangey red, that is. Chipmunks (who demonically begin taste-testing at about half-ripe) and raccoons usually drive me to picking early and ripening every fruit indoors — which might not be such a bad thing, it turns out.

What Is Ripening, Anyhow?

"Ripening" sounds a lot like a midlife crisis in retired professor Brian Capon's little masterpiece, *Botany for Gardeners*. His section on the topic, called "Hormones and the Aging Process" (!!!), outlines the biochemical events involved in what we hungry gardeners and cooks regard as a fruit reaching perfection. It's actually the beginning of the end. It's all part of a bigger plan: Green chlorophyll breaks down, and other pigments surface — which, along with increasing softness and rising sugar content, serve to attract animals (who will in turn serve to disperse the seeds inside). And the beat goes on.

The flavor change comes from the decline of tannins (whose pucker-up taste cleverly staved off those same beasts until the seed was ready). Chalk the softening up to ethylene gas (present in increasing amounts in aging fruit), which helps break down cell walls and membranes.

How to Hasten Ripening in the Garden

If you're worried frost may beat your crop to the finish line, a few tactics can induce hurry-up mode. One is called root pruning, and couldn't be simpler. Simply insert a spade just six inches or so into the soil in a circular pattern, circumnavigating the plant one foot away from its main stem.

Should cold nights threaten, be ready with fabric or plastic to keep frost off the vines. Even in cold zones, first frosts are often followed by another warm spell, and you'll eke out more vine-ripe fruit.

When to Give Up and Go Indoors

I already suggested two instances: Do your ripening indoors whenever animals, or prolonged cold, threaten to get to the crop before you do. But intense heat can take its toll, too, says the Illinois Urban Extension, which recommends picking "pink" fruit when temperatures are over 90 degrees Fahrenheit.

Alice Waters (in *Chez Panisse Vegetables*) isn't alone in suggesting ripening indoors as a regular practice, picking when the shift from orange to red begins, reportedly to maximize sugar and acid content. But what to do with the unripe tomatoes once inside? Here's where it gets interesting — as in mixed advice. I confess to being a windowsill ripener, which apparently isn't so bright (tee-hee).

Most extension services recommend some kind of darkened space instead, achieved by tactics including:

- Sorting the haul into categories: those showing some red, full-size green fruit (called "mature green") and other green, and then...
- Wrapping each fruit in newsprint to place in trays with others of a similar stage of maturity, or...
- Placing similar-condition fruits in

brown paper bags closed loosely, not stacking fruit upon fruit but in single layers, and ...

- Sometimes putting a bit of apple peel inside to up the ethylene, or ...
- (If there's no getting past oncoming weather) getting drastic by cutting down entire plants at the base and hanging them, fruits attached, in the cellar or garage ...
- With all of this ideally happening in a cool, dry spot at 65 to 70 degrees Fahrenheit.

Sorting by ripeness stage allows you to check on each batch by opening just a few test wrappers. Mature green fruit (see below) should reach ripeness in about two weeks.

Everyone agrees on this part: no refrigeration (unless you simply must keep fruits you plan to cook in a day or so from decaying further). If I can't use them now, rather than use the fridge I prefer to freeze fruits whole in doubled freezer bags at peak ripeness — a substitute for canned whole tomatoes in recipes.

Some Will Never Ripen, Nohow, Nowhere, No Way

There are always holdouts, those who won't cooperate even if given the TLC above. Immature green fruit, for instance, can't turn red — no matter how you coddle it. How to tell which can and cannot? Get out your knife. A tomato must be at least "mature green" to ripen off the vine, and if you're not sure if yours are at that stage yet, sacrifice a representative fruit.

Slice it open, and look inside: If it's gelatinous, it has a chance of ripening after harvest. You may also notice some color change on the interior, perhaps a yellowish tone — another optimistic sign that similar-sized and colored fruits will get there in time. If not: Find a recipe for pickles, or green-tomato mincemeat or chutney. If life deals you lemons, you know what to do.

Jack and I jumped on this bandwagon; better have our own Plan B. I put out extra rain gauges, which can't hold the forecast of ten inches, anyhow; I'll have to dump them at least once mid-storm. I drag anything that could be hurled around into a building for safety, and then basically behave petulantly until bedtime, like someone put-upon, when still no rain of any significance has developed to justify the efforts.

And then I toss: from two to three in the morning, thinking not of sump pumps but of shoveling snow — of trying to carve the path to freedom from the kitchen doorway down toward the street with my increasingly bum left shoulder. I am reminded of how bad it has gotten each time I roll over onto that side and hear it scream at me in response. Not sure I can heft shovelfuls one-handed, the way I have been mowing for weeks and weeks already. Feeling defenseless, I daydream into the night about snowblowers. The tropical storm hasn't even been reckoned with, and I am worrying about the threat of winter. By morning, though, all thoughts are back to rain: We are at seven-point-five inches, six of which are in the cellar, where my impressive collection of mousetraps — mechanisms of death — float like tiny life rafts on the tide, life rafts each stocked with a ration of peanut butter. *Anchors aweigh!*

Jack is eager to get out, once the rain slows by afternoon, and makes his rounds of the fieldstone surfaces surrounding the house, the landing pad that seems to anchor the building into the landscape, added a piece at a time over the years. Like a bar-bound sailor in a familiar port, he knows each stone intimately, and which holds the best drink. The puddles that form in their distinctive depressions are of a nectar far superior to any I could pour into his red enamel bowl inside the mudroom. There is no finer water, apparently, and he drinks from each of his favorites on this aftermath morning of way-beyond-plenty.

What's wrong with this plant? Ken the physical therapist asks, pointing to a green plastic nursery pot on the windowsill while I sit swaddled in an ice pack after our twelfth session in little more than a month, and that's not including all the other kinds of appointments this uncooperative shoulder has cost me so far. I still can't buckle my seatbelt, get long-sleeved garments on and off without tears, rub-a-dub-dub my back dry with a bath towel, let alone face the fall cleanup that approaches. But objectively he measures a few degrees' more range than when we started, and so on we go.

All I can think of as I examine the increasingly crispy *Spathiphyllum* that just doesn't look like its roots are properly connected to the soil any longer: I hope it doesn't look this bad inside my joint capsule, but I bet it does. *Ouch.* I don't have the heart to tell Ken to toss it (and thankfully he seems to be sticking with me and my sorry wing for the duration, too). Maybe we will both get lucky.

Only thirteen days have passed and now the rainfall total for that short span is at fifteen-point-five inches. I've fallen (more than a little) behind on the mowing, weeding, and deadheading — but I'm way ahead on the watering, I tell myself, cultivating a succession crop of homegrown garden humor, at least, as the other crops suffocate and decline from too-wet-too-long root systems and all the general hammering. If there had been any real flame to this summer, it is certainly extinguished now for good. The sounds of August, enormous swells of tiny insect voices (can you call them voices if they come from legs or wings being rubbed, not out of throats or mouths?), try mightily to compete for attention with the pounding of the nearby brook, now double-wide and extra-violent. There are so many mosquitoes — not a creature I typically see many of here on my hillside — that I need to add to my tool bucket what my niece in childhood referred to as a "fly swapper" and a can of "bug propeller." The storms have washed away the summer's fire, and even my burning desire for the garden is seriously dampened, and almost put out.

CHAPTER 4
WIND (AUTUMN)

How is it with the reed? All the winds come and blow against it, and it sways to and fro with them. When the winds have been lulled, the reed resumes its normal position. Wherefore the reed has been deemed worthy to provide a pen for the writing of a scroll. The cedar, however, does not remain in its place. As soon as the south wind blows, it uproots it

and overturns it; and what is the end of the cedar? The cutters come and chisel and carve it, they use it for covering the houses and the remainder they throw into the fire. Hence it was said: "Let a person be as soft as a reed and not as hard as a cedar."
— AVOT DE-RABBI NATHAN, CHAP. 41, A MINOR TRACTATE OF THE TALMUD

The weather can't decide what it wants to do any more than I can at the moment. We fuss and pace and ponder the possibilities, or pretend to when perhaps we are simply both procrastinating, with spurts of this and that but no sustained anything of consequence. Positive spin: In my ineffectiveness and indecision, I am one with nature. I am — we are — stalled. Only certain among the birds are decisive, and starting to move along, to catch a current, capitalize, and take it to the next step.

On these neither-summer-nor-fall days when bouts of swirling energy intersect just so with the declining angle of the sun, I watch the typically shapeless, transparent air take shape — as if it were suddenly liquid, and not gaseous at all. Aeroplankton, a bubbling, luminescent soup of tiny living things, ride the lowest slice of the atmosphere, showing up, and off, against its dramatically backlit currents. Like its better-known undersea counterpart called plankton, it's a congregation of creatures, not some exclusive community of sameness. Small insects and spiders and seeds consort with spores and (although I cannot see them) bacteria and pollen, too — or definitely ragweed's, at least, if not the wholesale pollen assault of the earlier end of this wet, wet growing season. Back then on the most prolific days, the air showed itself in thick billows of yellow instead from nearby sugar maples, oaks, birches, beeches, pines, and black walnuts.

The element of air is having its way with all these little life-forms, who surrender any pretense of volition or self-propulsion and just go with the literal flow. Bigger creatures rock and roll in the 3-D, HD, DNA-loaded plasma screen in front of me, too, enjoying the ride but strong enough at these relatively tame wind speeds to be able to determine their own courses still, to dive-bomb and argue over the deed to the best flower or watering hole — or maybe they're just showing off, who knows? Dragonflies and damselflies and a band of ruby-throated hummingbirds surrender to the rhythm suddenly, too, and all manner of bees and wasps — everyone appears to be wanting to eke out another meal or two as if they know summer's picnic is in a precarious state, about to pack itself up into the hamper of fall and disappear.

Except when seasonal peaches or blueberries became a bubbly dessert, the word "crisp" hasn't been in the local vocabulary for what seems like forever now, but if the wind manages to kick up and sustain itself, perhaps we will feel that, and not exhaustingly heavy and limp, again some day.

Like young surfers riding the waves, bobbing around at once competitive and playful, the hummingbirds come in a few at a time, as if each swell of air is washing them ashore here. I know it's all about them being hungry travelers, though, and that their numbers will increase for a spell now as early migrants from farther north stop by to fatten up for the next leg of the journey, before continuing onward. None of the newcomers, presumably from just slightly up the airy pike and that much farther from the species' wintering grounds, will stay long, but I enjoy my fleeting visit with them, as I do each bird who flashes into view on any day of any season (how to make a bird-friendly garden begins on page 304). Each fair afternoon, time is set aside to go stand in the self-sown stand of oversized *Nicotiana* to the west of

I know what birds like. Boys, perhaps not so much, but birds — well, there I've got the knack. As many as sixty species that I can identify visit me each year here in the garden, which was originally planted for attracting them (see more on my overall approach on page 47) and seems to have succeeded. Fall is a perfect time to add some bird-friendly plantings, since many are woody plants happy to be transplanted now, and also to provide for the most important thing of all: water. Big surprise — it's all about keeping them fed, watered, and sheltered in every season. The essentials:

Water is required twelve months a year, preferably moving water; curious birds cannot resist a drip or spillway, such as the little waterfalls in each of my two small garden pools. Even when those are shut down due to the deep freeze of December through March, I keep part of each pond unfrozen with a floating heater originally designed for keeping stock tanks open for farm animals, like a buoyant hotplate. Smaller models are available for birdbaths.

Less mown lawn means more botanical complexity, which fosters more bird food in the form of insects and seeds. Many years I leave a section above my house unmown each year, but here's something even better to figure into your landscape, perhaps where there currently is mown lawn:

Edge habitat, the place where field meets woods, for instance, is where the action is for many birds: It affords a place to hide, and for some species to nest, providing an often food-rich jumble of shrubbery and vines. Think hedgerow; I use a lot of winterberry holly (*Ilex verticillata*) as a backbone for all such islands here, and various viburnum figure in heavily as well. *Aronia,* or chokeberry; bayberry (*Myrica*); and twig dogwoods (such as *Cornus sericea*) are just a few of many other fruiting choices. Add this transitional zone somewhere in your garden, perhaps along the road or along another boundary, or create an island shrub border of bird-friendly plants (ideas below). Mix it up (thorns, evergreens, vines, fruit, seedheads, nectar-rich flowers) to make a multiseason destination.

A brush pile in some out-of-the-way corner is another great hiding place, especially in harshest weather, though perhaps impractical for the small garden (making the brushy "edge habitat," above, even more important).

Evergreen cover is an aesthetic and wildlife-friendly element of any garden, providing shelter from weather, nesting sites, plus seed-rich cones or other fruits, such as those of the eastern red cedar (*Juniperus virginiana*). Spruce (*Picea* species) and firs (*Abies,* such as the blue *Abies concolor* and *Abies koreana,* with its wildlife-friendly purple cones) seem to get a lot of bird action here in particular; which species of foods prove most desirable will vary by region and bird populations.

Nest boxes are a great addition to the garden, especially where there are no big old trees, since cavity-nesting species, such as eastern bluebirds or tree swallows, won't build a nest on a shelf (like flycatchers will) or in a brushy thicket (like some sparrows). Think about whether you have all three kinds of nesting places to attract a diversity of birds looking for a place to raise a family.

A chemical-free environment is essential; birds (like frogs and snakes, among others) are canaries in a coal mine (sorry) for toxic elements, and their favorite foods are even more vulnerable. Don't taint the habitat you create; get off the lawn-care regimen and see a vast increase in worms and other soil life, the favorite food of robins and flickers, among others. Bugs are bird food, and most birds are at least partly insectivorous, so obsessive antibug campaigns impact the quality of your habitat. Use least-toxic methods, such as your hose-end sprayer of water, hand-picking, row covers, or soaps and oils, to thwart the ones you must, but not chemical insecticides. Ditto with lethal herbicides and fungicides and even fertilizers, of course.

Clean feeders regularly, if you offer seed this way: To prevent disease, thoroughly wash and sterilize your feeders regularly with a dilute bleach solution (1:10

bleach to water) or just hot, soapy water. Allow to dry before refilling. Purchasing a long brush suited to the task will encourage more and better cleaning. Even a twelve-month bird feeder (many people feed only in winter) is no substitute for food-rich habitat; in a successful wildlife garden, birds will come year-round even when there are no feeders, though feeders will bring them closer to the house, where you can see them (as will that number-one item up top, water).

The right diversity of living foods: Plan the landscape for a combination of seeds (such as from grasses, composite or daisy-like flowers, fruiting plants, and conifers); fruits for each season, including not just the sugary, watery ones of summer, but some high-lipid ones that hang on as hollies do into winter. Large numbers of native plants, even in a garden like mine that includes many nonnatives (such as the fruit-laden Kousa dogwood, an Asian species), prove highly appealing; go heavy on them. Nectar-loving hummingbirds will appreciate trumpet vine (*Campsis radicans*), honeysuckles (*Lonicera* species), and flowering sages (*Salvia* species), among others. And remember: Most everyone wants insects for supper, so discriminate in your bug killing, please.

My garden's top bird-attracting plants from a food standpoint (by no means a complete list, and again, it varies widely by region):

Trees and Shrubs

- Elderberry (*Sambucus canadensis,* also great for jelly and jam)
- Blueberry and raspberry (*Vaccinium* and *Rubus* species; plant extra for birds)
- Chokeberry (*Aronia arbutifolia* and *A. melanocarpa*)
- Dogwoods (especially *Cornus florida; C. mas,* also some twig species such as *Cornus sericea; C. alternifolia;* and *C. kousa*)
- Oaks (for their acorns, attractive to some woodpeckers, jays, and grouse)
- Spicebush (*Lindera benzoin,* for fruit)
- *Viburnum* species (couldn't garden

without these)
- Crabapple (*Malus* varieties)
- Apple and pear (orioles like the blossoms; many birds peck at the fruit and its seeds, even when mummified in winter)
- Sumac (*Rhus typhina* 'Laciniata', the cutleaf staghorn, and others for their fruit)
- Hollies (*Ilex verticillata,* or winterberry, and others)
- Eastern red cedar (*Juniperus virginiana,* for fruits and shelter)
- Spruces (*Picea* species, for seed-rich cones, shelter, nesting)
- Firs (*Abies concolor* and *A. koreana;* cones, shelter, nesting)
- Shadbush (*Amelanchier,* summer fruit)
- Spikenard (*Aralia spinosa,* and *A. cordata* and *racemosa,* for fall fruit)
- Roses with good hips

Vines
- Honeysuckles (*Lonicera sempervirens* and others)

- Virginia creeper (*Parthenocissus quinquefolia;* long-lasting fruit; not showy, but eaten by vast numbers of birds)
- Grape (I let wild vines remain at the woodland edge here; a cultivated arbor would be more attractive)

Birds like to be watched: Join Project FeederWatch to support and help in Cornell Lab of Ornithology's program, or eBird (a collaboration between Cornell and the National Audubon Society), and learn more about your local birds as a bonus. OK, so maybe birds don't actually care if we watch them, but aware humans make better companions and custodians for songbirds.

Reduce danger of window strikes: Certain windows, because of glare, may prove to be the site of strikes by songbirds, many of whom die from the impact. Place feeders and birdbaths either within three feet or more than thirty feet from key windows; birdhouses even farther. There are also various ways to reduce glare, including UV-reflecting decals; taut, springy

5/8-inch mesh stretched on frames several inches outside the glass; special stick-on fabrics like those that bear ads on bus exteriors, or exterior "curtains" made of nylon cord stretched vertically four inches outside the window.

No marauding cats is what birds like most of all. In the residential environment, cats are a leading cause of death for songbirds (with fatal crashes into windows the top killer). Estimates for the number of songbirds killed annually by feral and domestic cats range from a few hundred million to one billion. Keep your cat indoors during the daytime in particular, and especially during nesting season. Let them watch the Bird TV Network through a window or a glass door instead. It's Jack the Demon Cat's favorite channel (when he's not asleep, which is most of the time).

the house and let the birds swoop around me at will in the process of sipping madly — *zzzzzt, zzzzzzzt, zzzzzzzzzt* — each one- or two-tenths of an ounce of hyperkinetic motor power barely missing my ears.

On the best days this time of year, there are six or even nine of them going at it right by the patio, more than at any other moment. None has a red throat, though they are all *Archilochus colubris,* the ruby-throateds. The showy adult males left for Central America or thereabouts in August — the advance guard, as they will be again on the trip back across the Gulf and up the nation come spring, arriving here as a big, inherited bleeding heart someone left all those years ago in the front-yard soil for me — *for us* — does its thing.

Is the males' ahead-of-the-pack timing some kind of evolutionary or divine ornithological FIFO algorithm: First In, First Out, as if programmed that way, but by a higher power than a computer-science graduate? I suppose so. That means the ones who are here are all — or at least they look like — females, though some are actually juvenile males whose ruby-ness hasn't blossomed yet, female impersonators. Whatever their chromosomal arrangement, I simply think of them all as "the girls" each encroaching autumn — *the little women,* whose men have all gone off to war. So much energy, these little girls.

The winding down has begun, but rather than being a slower time yet, the approach of fall is a quickening of the pulse, a *hurry, hurry* stage. *Beat the Clock* — whether to the tropics, or just to get your tender plants into the cellar before it's too late. *Hurry.*

"When do you think the lawn will dry so I can mow again?" I say to a friend who stops by, looking out together at what looks something like a wet hayfield in certain spots despite the sun and breeze right now and my dogged attempts to mow some section or other any time conditions allowed it the last weeks and months. Mostly I just knocked it down and pushed it around a lot, the worst thing I could do from a lawn-health perspective, but the way we often behave when we can do nothing but simply must *do something;* irrational, insistent, domineering. "Maybe next spring," she replies, not evidencing even a hint of a smile. I suspect she may be not just serious but also correct. Even with the teases and wisps of wind, the wettest of summers is not going to be sopped up easily, or anytime soon. It's hard to steer around heaven's schedule — and especially to steer a mower around it.

Some plants have just said *screw this, I can't go at it any longer,* and begun to drop their leaves. I wish the lawn would do just that: drop every last blade down to a close self-crop, military-style. Self-mowing turf-grass? I could make millions on it. A few leaves from someone — a birch, I think, but they are spinning and floating too far above my head to be sure — catch a current and join the air-force aerobatics; the flying scenery is warming up for another show.

Though I have no eastern sycamore trees in my yard, I know I will soon be raking up the distinctive-looking *Platanus occidentalis* leaves, as I do each fall, along with the maples and oaks and magnolias and dogwoods I do grow. Of course the not-so-mysterious reason why is the power of the wind, which helped dry and then carry the giant, multilobed brown leaves from the woods and delivered them at my doorstep down the road.

Wind, which most simply described is the motion of air molecules — the air in motion horizontally — brings us more than just extra leaves to contend with. It is a powerful pollinator, through a process called anemophily. Why is it that all the good words — this one literally translates as "love of wind," from the Greek *anemos* for "wind" and *philos* for "love" — are held in secret in the scientific realms, such as museums' "study collection" areas that nobody but the occasional academic sees? The United States Forest Service says that about 12 percent of the world's flowering plants are pollinated by wind, along with most conifers and many other trees (some estimates put the total of all types of plants that are wind-pollinated near 20 percent).

Grasses (including corn) and cereal crops are the most common wind-pollinated types among the flowering plants, and since they don't need to attract animal pollinators, those flowers have no need to come in flashy colors or to smell good or to provide nectar or even to have petals for anyone to land on. Imagine beets and chard and spinach — also wind-pollinated — when they come into flower. Not much to look at, are they? Think about it. This is just another example of the ancient, secret deals brokered between plants and animals that draw me to gardening in a deeper way than just the mere aesthetic. Perfect fits; no energy or pretense wasted on frilly lingerie or even party dresses.

The wind can move not just pollen but also seeds around to some extent, and more significantly, it moves birds. Its force (or lack of it) at a given time helps them chart courses and attain their destinations (or not), impacting not just everyday flight but also their migratory efficiency. The birds, of course, in turn move seeds, replanting else-where as they digest and disperse (to put it nicely), and the grand plan has seen to it that sprouting doesn't take place inside the inhospitable darkness of their guts. Sometimes the mechanics of bird digestion — such as the gizzard's action, and various digestive acids — are actually critical in the scarifying, or abrading, of tough seed coats (such as native blackberries and raspberries) that allow germination to happen at all. Quid pro quo, nature's master plan.

Its generality probably renders this next statement grossly imprecise, but I'll say it anyway: Without wind, we would not have weather change. It is my understanding, rudimentary though it is, that when the pressure gradient (the difference in pressure over a given distance) between adjacent high- and low-pressure areas is greater, the wind speed is greater, too — and *whoosh,* in comes different weather, moving from the high-pressure area toward the low. The National Oceanographic and Atmospheric Administration or weather.gov, which I respectfully prefer to call the Almighty NOAA because I look to it so heavily to steer my days on earth, explains it far more scientifically, and with charts and maps, but what I just said is as far as I can manage to go mentally in grasping the sternest of the elements, and that's enough. Even though I usually cannot see it — except on days like today when there are all these madcap floaters out there on parade — it's the element I fear the most.

Among its other powers, wind is also responsible, in some environments, for serious soil erosion. Another potential impact is evidenced when wind meets up with water, such as the dramatic weather they create in concert near the coasts. Where I live, I'd have to count wind — not cold, despite my Zone 5Bish climate, where theoretically the temperature can get to minus-15ish degrees Fahrenheit, but doesn't seem to any longer — as the most destructive force in the garden, bringing down or splitting apart woody plants when it roars; desiccating evergreens in winter; generally making plants thirstier faster, in a world where water is in ever-shorter supply. Particularly when it combines with or follows drought, as it did all last growing season and does most years in dry stretches in late spring and summer here, it's the force majeure. Sometimes, all that means is a few stray sycamore leaves, but normally it has nastier tricks in mind. I am not the wind's lover, no anemophiliac, if that's even a word; not me. It isn't time to batten down the hatches quite yet — but soon. I am watching, and listening.

■ ■ ■ ■

Chugging up the steep path from the car with too many bags of groceries (including more white vinegar for another batch of refrigerator pickles, on next page), I see botanical Swiss cheese over the corner of one sack. I am not even home and unpacked yet, but someone is already eating, and the delicacy this time is my favorite canna, the one I know as 'Grande' but that is a lookalike or maybe the same as *Canna* 'Musafolia'. Its very tall, thick stems are tinged purplered, and its extra-large, banana-like foliage is edged to match. Apparently the flowers would be reddish and somewhat small, but I have never seen them in all the years we've spent together — and besides, I only grow cannas for their leaves. My regular practice is to disbud those that do show the inclination to bloom before they go all garish and gaudy on me. Call me a contrarian, but hold the flowers, please.

A furry, black-and-white-patterned creature is systematically erasing the foliage I favor, but he has timed his actions well. It is September, and I am feeling less protective than I might in May, when the first real heat of the year coaxes the rock-hard but frosttender, beet-pink-tinted rhizomes that slept

DAN KOSHANSKY'S REFRIGERATOR PICKLES

I first ate these pickles, which have proven to be the single most popular piece of content on the A Way to Garden website, more than twenty years ago, at the Long Island home of retired Long Island Rail Road conductor Dan Koshansky. Did I mention it was breakfast time when he served them up to me? Dan's refrigerator pickles were a hand-me-down recipe from his mother, and the "recipe" couldn't be simpler:

Wash jars: Run gallon canning jars through the dishwasher, or hand wash thoroughly. Smaller jars can be used if desired; I use half gallons, and adjust the proportions of spices accordingly.

Prepare your brine: To each quart of water that has been boiled and brought to room temperature, add ¾ cup of distilled white vinegar and 4 tablespoons Kosher salt (Dan would say "heaping tablespoons," and I would add the caveat to use Diamond brand; Morton is much heavier and saltier, so if that's your brand, you will want less). Estimate how many quarts of this brine you're going to make based on how many jars you will pack with pickles. Note: Do not use reactive pots (such as aluminum) for making brine. Stick with stainless and glass equipment for pickling tasks.

Wash and pack small cukes (or green tomatoes or peppers) into clean glass jars, into which fresh dill has been layered on the bottom first.

Add 1 tablespoon of pickling spice and lots of chopped garlic. (Trust me, I can still recall the garlic-for-breakfast experience. It's up to you how much. And frankly I never chop it. Creative license!)

Add a dash of crushed red pepper flakes, or 1 or 2 small hot red peppers slit open lengthwise, plus more fresh dill. I love having the flowerheads from a variety such as 'Mammoth', instead of just the foliage of 'Fernleaf' for this task, but you'll want plenty of both.

Cover with plastic wrap and let stand out on the counter until soured, perhaps a couple of days, then refrigerate with lids on.

I think of these unprocessed pickles as a seasonal treat, so I make enough for two or maybe three months only. If you want to store pickles all year, use a recipe that calls for water-bath processing (meaning vacuum-sealed lids). It's not that refrigerator pickles go bad, but they lose that special quality and get soft and too sour. It's the crispy freshness that makes Dan Koshansky's Refrigerator Pickles so fantastic, a real rite of the harvest season, so enjoy them summer-into-fall and then (as gardeners know how to by necessity) start looking forward to next year.

naked all winter in the cellar to push up their first energetic shoots. I put the shopping bags inside the kitchen door, get my camera, and go outside to sit and watch, an exercise in restraint.

The enemy. All too often gardeners — including myself — are revolted by the sight of a caterpillar. The immediate instinct is to *kill, kill, kill* these seemingly voracious eaters who are the larval stages of various moths or butterflies, members of the order Lepidoptera. Everything unknown or misunderstood that we cannot see as beautiful according to our filters, everything we don't see as *serv-*

ing us is a potential victim. But how many besides the tomato and tobacco hornworms (the latter love my *Nicotiana*) or gypsy moth (hardwood trees) or eastern tent caterpillar (apples, crabapples, and other Rose-family relatives), do I — supposedly an "expert" gardener — really know by name? How many can I identify by their favored diet, I ask myself as I watch the inch-and-a-half-long beast continue his enthusiastic chewing. He seems to like what I have cooked up for his supper.

There is something to be said for allowing pure fascination to take hold, for suspending judgment and just being, not doing (which in this scenario translates to observing, not squishing). The story of the caterpillar's workday is a parable in itself: Is he really a thief and a scoundrel, or simply a devoted worker who knows that his intended higher purpose lies just ahead if he stays on his unpopular course, against all odds? The negative space of the leaf he's working on enlarges quickly, and I realize that I am grateful to this moth-in-the-making, happy to share a portion of the fading summer garden with some hairy little beast in the name of awareness and tolerance. Rather than a rush to crush, it's a time that I asked who's who — and also, again: *why?*

I don't learn until I am inside and have put away the groceries and started searching on the computer — how can I not have a caterpillar guidebook, but I do not, at least not yet — that I have been passing time with the larval form of a hickory tussock moth, whose usual diet is ash, elm, oak, hickory, maple, willow, and other trees.

Though he looks velvety, I'm glad our budding relationship has stopped short of heavy petting. It's a case of look but don't touch, apparently: The long "lashes" of *Lophocampa caryae* are hollow tubes connected to poison glands, and can give susceptible people a stinging-nettle-like rash or other reaction. The rest of the bristles, or setae, on his body may also be irritating. Apparently this hardy visitor will spend the winter in a mere silk cocoon under tree bark or on the ground — how can he survive that way? — then work his way gradually next year to moth-hood.

He's the cousin of two other recent arrivals, I realize after sitting still long enough to allow things that had been only semiconsciously noticed prior to really register themselves. A small yellowish-tan caterpillar I saw the other afternoon might be the Virginian tiger moth (*Spilosoma virginica*), which apparently feeds on both herbaceous and woody plants. I found that one in my house, actually, on a piece of garden gear I'd brought inside, and relocated him, I recall, now that I am slowing down, and concentrating, and able to connect the dots. How long have I been oblivious, playing at master of the universe instead of fellow traveler with this guy? He had apparently been parasitized by some wasp or other — a cluster of white eggs, such as braconid wasps lay, jutted from the larvae's chenille body, and some had fallen off when I moved him back outdoors.

Both of my recent finds are cousins of the familiar woolly bear or woolly worm (*Pyrrharctia isabella*); all three are in the taxonomic tribe *Arctiini* (the tiger moths). Since they're not deforesting the entire region or anything, I'm just letting them be — and eat — and frankly, it is pretty entertaining. Cheap thrills, I know, but we just don't understand enough about all of nature's tiniest creatures to go blindly rampaging against them, do we? That's the E. O. Wilson-esque question I keep asking myself. What do caterpillars even *do?* When I shift perspective and let go of the arrogant, ignorant, and egocentric view that they are simply *pests* and *eating my garden,* as if all has been assembled to do either service or harm to me — the weather, the animal and insect visitors, all of it — this is when it gets really interesting.

Caterpillars do some semi-obvious things I have witnessed in the garden or in books: They are a favored food of birds, especially good for feeding to hatchlings; when they become moths and butterflies (many of whom have roles in plant pollination in certain habitats), they feed another range of birds (including flycatchers and martins, for instance) and also bats. Some caterpillars make silk; other species work to break down the litter of fallen foliage and fruit and even woody plant parts. (Digression: I have come lately to treasure my yard's impressive population of size-XL millipedes for this reason, too, after being repulsed for years by the six-inch-long taupe and orange beasts with all those crazy legs. *Narceus americanus,* sometimes called the worm millipede, does a similar job as its common namesake, digesting leaf litter and such debris, meaning that, like earthworms, they are detritivores — eating detritus. Nature's composters. Like the Lepidoptera, millipedes are arthropods, with a hard exoskeleton, a segmented body, and many pairs of legs, the way a scorpion or a lobster is armored and armed.) And then — *back on point again, please, Margaret; public service announcement on behalf of millipedes complete* — there is this:

Caterpillars force plants to take measures against being eaten alive, says Dr. David L. Wagner of the University of Connecticut, author of the *Caterpillars of Eastern North America* field guide that finally filled the gap in my bookcase, once I'd met my fourth member of the *Arctiini* in little more than a month along that same path from parking spot to kitchen door. (I figured all these caterpillars were trying to tell me something: *Go buy a book.* I also figure Dr. Wagner must have sent them, in a clever and sophisticated biological marketing ploy, but so far that's merely an unproven theory.) With their incessant chewing, Wagner explains, the hungry and plentiful larvae have long put pressure on plants to develop built-in chemical controls against predation by herbivores — substances such as latex and alkaloids and tannins. Caterpillars are masters at inventing noxious and just plain crafty tactics for thwarting their own predators, so it makes sense that they are good mentors in tactics of self-defense for the plants. Besides the poison setae, there are caterpillar species who outsmart foes with crypsis (camouflaging themselves to look like anything from a twig to part of a flower or leaf to the leaf litter itself), and others boldly marked in a defensive warning coloration who just go along calmly eating what they please right out in the open, as if to say: *You'd have to be nuts to take a bite out of someone wearing this outfit.*

At this time of year, we usually start to notice the woolly bear, or Isabella tiger moth — looking to see how much black versus rusty banding circles its fat, fuzzy body to try to predict the coming winter. The idea goes that more brown means milder and more black fiercer, but this bit of folklore-cum-superstition doesn't hold up to science as a forecasting tool by any means — though it probably makes this caterpillar the one species we don't go squashing reflexively as if it is a known enemy. Me? I'm forecasting an early onset to winter based on equally sketchy notions, such as the fact that several species of feeder birds who usually don't bother with me again until serious fall properly sets in are already hanging around the hopper looking for a handout during the last week. All efforts to ask them what's up were met with the usual chatter, but nothing I could decode. Perhaps the next time I really sit still, it should be with an audio guide to birdsong connected to a set of earphones.

Headphones would be good right now, actually. Wheeze, rattle, and roll. With each ragged breath, I try to make my peace with the wind inside, and with the more forceful one making itself heard this late day beyond the house walls, too. I am talking silently to my own weak, asthmatic airflow — *calm down now; in and out, in and out; there you go; quieter now, that's right* — but I can still hear every wisp of air passing through angry bronchi and bronchioles on its way to those all-important alveoli and the needed gas exchange meant to keep everything firing over here.

But my breath, my damn breath, with which I have fought for control since my twenties, usually losing, can be so loud sometimes — such as right now, on this increasingly windy afternoon. Even with the strengthening force of the inspirations and expirations kicking up outside — with the kousa dogwood beginning to rub and slap the corner of the building like an improvised drum set paced by wire brushes and a hi-hat, and other early warning signs that it will be one of those nights — all I can hear is the sound of high-pitched wheezing of my own tight spaces and sibilant rhonchi, as the doctor would say, though thankfully not rales, or crackles, the distinct noises when fluid, and not just inflammation, is giving the passages a test.

We are in for a wild ride. It's really one of those "Houston, we have liftoff" weather days (though NASA, in its wisdom, wouldn't launch anything into this dervish of a sky). Looking for something crispy and delicious, titmice manage to fly in the face of it, darting in and out of fluffy big *Hydrangea paniculata* heads, now dried to match the cornfield full of cow food that stands withered and awaiting harvest across the way. Our collective hunger mounts as fresh stockpiles dwindle. Suggestion box: Weather should come in metered doses like the puffs of my inhalers — never more than you need, or less. Perhaps I'll write that wish list item in a letter to Santa Claus (or maybe NOAA?); I have been good, or at least I have tried my level best, despite various provocateurs, meteorological and otherwise.

May the wind take your troubles away. Jay Farrar of the alt country band Son Volt wrote and sang that, but for me the wind *is* the trouble: finding a place of equanimity with a bigger breath that knows no confinement to its territory, a free-form force that has no tight passageways to reckon with or be restrained by. The wind knows how to breathe deep — and oh my, can it ever exhale.

■ ■ ■ ■

So that's what the recent wind is about. We had our double tropical storms, and now the way-too-early forecast is for frost or thereabouts. The phrase "adding insult to injury" is one every gardener quickly becomes accustomed to, but this year it is simply insult after insult after insult, the resulting fractures all proving to be of the compound type. I'm not ready, and neither are the soggy nonhardy plants — the big *Brugmansia* I bought on half-price closeout a few falls ago; the tuberous begonias such as 'Bonfire' and other *boliviensis* types; the fancy-leaf begonias and clivias and various forms of bromeliads and other "houseplants" that winter inside with me (tactics for storing many kinds of tender plants are covered in the sidebar on page 332). And so begins the first fall fire drill: calculating where I can offer things enough cover to face whatever comes, all the while knowing that with this short notice, somebody won't get there in time. Russian roulette.

I am looking at the updated forecast and doing mental dress rehearsals for next year's garden without the big tropical things — pretending this one or that one is gone, that it didn't make it into the lifeboat, asking

331

A threat of frost always sends me scurrying to haul in the houseplants, and though sometimes it's a false alarm, at some point in September here it's time to make plans for them and for other tender things such as cannas and bananas, cordyline and a favorite pelargonium or two, in hopes that what I call these "investment plants" (not perennial on their own, but carried over year to year with extra effort by me) are still around come spring.

First, my general thinking: No two gardeners' potential places to stash such treasures will match in temperature or humidity, so when I say the basement works well here, someone else's cellar might not. I have identified my best spots by experimenting, and by killing many things in the process. But every year I score another victory or two because I don't let failure stop me. (Isn't all gardening like that?)

And this: If I don't have the right spot for a plant — often a combination of high light but cool, 50ish-degree conditions (which is why I am adding more shoplight hoods to my basement, to brighten it up) I find trying to force dormancy or semidormancy preferable to forcing it to limp along somewhere warmer. If you have nonhardy plants you've tried keeping as "houseplants" in your heated home with you, only to see them go wretched and leggy, think about letting them rest, or close to it, next time — watering very sparingly and keeping them cooler.

The additional grow light or fluorescent hood will run for about fourteen hours a day in my cool basement to make a so-so storage space into a really good one for many more things that keep their foliage, such as phormiums, *Farfugium,* and cordyline. Some of my specific tactics, by plant type:

Houseplants

Fancy-Leaf Begonias: After a summer in the high shade of trees near the house, in come my rhizomatous and cane begonias, such as 'Little Brother Montgomery' and 'Marmaduke' (two favorites among many you can get at Logees.com or Kartuz.com). But first, as with all my "houseplants," they get a physical: a checkup in the wheelbarrow or on a tarp, one at a time, which includes a trim of any battered leaves, a gentle removal of endless spiders and the occasional tree frog trying to hitch a ride, and a wipe down or rinsing off of the pots. Best to get all the houseplants in before the heat is on indoors, to make the transition less abrupt. These guys are tough, but most of them resent drafty, cold spots. Keep them from dropping below 50 degrees, and closer to 60 is better. I try to find enough bright but protected places, but each fall the plants are bigger, and the house seems smaller as a result.

Bromeliads: Bromeliads are show-offs in the shady garden all summer, and great in the house all winter. I have had some of mine for close to ten years, have only occasionally repotted, and simply keep their cups filled with water all year, occasionally remembering to water the sparse amount of potting soil they're tucked into for support. Talk about an investment plant.

Clivias: This Zone 9 South African relative of *Amaryllis* asks what many plants from that area do: Let it go dry and cooler in late fall in order to trigger the late-winter bloom cycle. I simply stop watering both the yellow-flowered and orange ones for two and a half months, and deliberately grow them in the mudroom, where the temperature shifts noticeably with the season; 50 to 60 degrees is perfect.

With all houseplants: Give them a physical, as above; even then, you'll import some bugs, but it's no big deal. Take care not to overwater (certain death) and do not feed in lower-light months, except orchids that are out of bloom, which I feed alternating weeks or (as the saying goes) weekly, weakly. (In other words, use an extra-dilute fertilizer if you want to include it with each watering.) Avoid placement near heaters or too close to what will be ice-cold or drafty window glass in cold zones. Pebble-filled waterproof trays can add humidity to an area, as can clustering many plants or running a humidifier.

Bulbs and Bulb-Like Plants

Agapanthus: Traditional evergreen varieties (usually hardy to about Zone 7B) want that tricky combination of conditions that a cool greenhouse provides better than a heated home: bright light, and mid-40s or so, or as close as you can get. Perhaps an enclosed porch, mudroom, or windowed basement (or bright garage if yours stays in the mid-40s or a bit warmer) can provide this. They also want just enough moisture to keep them from desiccating, but not ever to be wet. Go easy. Those that are non-evergreen (they will have less-thick leaves than evergreen types), will go dormant; place pots in the basement or another cool spot; no water required.

Amaryllis: I start withholding water in August or September, and get the plants out of the rain, to dry them off for eight weeks or thereabouts, leaving the pots in a closet in the dark. I'll take them out in mid-October or November, top up the soil if needed, and water once, then place the plant in a bright spot until it wants to grow. No trying to coax a sleepy amaryllis with repeat waterings, which can rot the bulb. Wait a few weeks before trying again; only once a shoot of some kind appears should you begin to water regularly.

Begonia 'Bonfire': The *B. boliviensis* selection called 'Bonfire' — a favorite "annual" of mine for summer color in pots — is a tuber, and wants to dry off and rest awhile. I put mine in my 45- to 50-degree basement in the dark, pot and all, remove the withering foliage, and just let it sit, no water. Watch in late winter or earliest spring for hints of awakening: tiny pinkish bumps that sprout from the tuber or at ground level. Don't water again until you see this signal of readiness, and in truth: If it comes alive too early, I torture it, withholding water a few weeks longer until closer to when I know there will be stabler temperatures and longer light, in May sometime. Otherwise it gets slack and stretches too far for limited sun. Bring the pot into the light then and water carefully until fully awake. Rot from overwatering (sometimes made worse by too-deep planting) is the easiest way to kill one of these in any season, but especially when just emerging and when it's petering out after a long season and wants to take a nap.

Canna: In Zone 6 or colder, cut back frosted foliage to about six to eight inches (or just do this in late fall if no frost happens), then dig the rhizomes. Shake off the excess soil or rinse if you prefer. Divide into clumps of three to five eyes if really large, and place in the basement (or somewhere that's 45 to 55 degrees) in plastic bags left slightly open or perforated for air. If the fall is too hectic, skip the dividing; I usually wait until spring, when I clean and divide the clumps in April and pot up indoors for a few weeks' head start before transplanting them out when the weather settles.

Dahlia: Wait two weeks after a hard frost before cutting stems to six inches above the ground and harvesting tubers carefully. Note: The wait is more important for these succulent tubers than the cannas for them to be ready to store; if there is no killing frost, though, I dig in November anyhow. Wash clumps, then dry in an airy, protected spot for a day or two. Store tubers layered in boxes or crates (but not in plastic) in sand, peat, or vermiculite at 40 to 50 degrees, checking for any signs of decay periodically during storage. Though dividing can be done before storage or in spring, big clumps may be hard to store, holding in moisture that can prompt decay, so at least cut them in half and wait another day or two for cuts to heal before stashing.

Elephant ears: That's the common name used for both *Colocasia* (known as taro; the "elephant-ears" with typically matte leaves) and *Alocasia* (generally, these "elephant ears" have leaves that are shiny). Storing them can be confusing, since varieties on the market vary in hardiness from tough 7B-hardy types to true tropicals, meaning they have very different tolerances. It's also particularly tricky if you live in a cold zone, where the tubers often don't get enough summer heat to really size up. Some new varieties don't produce big tubers at all. Small tubers don't have enough reserves to survive, dug, all winter long, so are best potted up (or left potted up) and stashed in a cool basement. Better yet if you have the spot: overwintering these newer types such as my favorite, 'Mojito', indoors in 60-plus degrees and bright light, as "houseplants." This is another example of where those shop lights or other plant-type lights on timers will come in handy. Larger tubers of other kinds can be dug, the leaves cut back to the bulb, and allowed to dry until dry to the touch before placing them in the 45-to-50-degree spot; some people put them in containers of peat or vermiculite first.

Gladiolus: After the foliage dies, harvest the corms and store dry in mesh bags with good air circulation at about 40 degrees, such as hanging in a basement. Check a couple of times over the winter for any signs of decay.

Other Tropicals

Bananas: Container-grown bananas can be cut back to about six inches just after light frost and stored, pretty dry, in a spot that's about 45 to 50 degrees, such as a basement. I always check things I'm keeping dry to make sure they don't desiccate in storage; sometimes in January or February, I need to give a little water. Bananas that were grown in the ground must be dug up before frost, which disturbs the root system, so do not cut back the top growth as well in fall in that case. Instead, wrap the dug root ball in a plastic bag and bring the whole plant into the same kind of cool, dark spot as above, allowing it to dry off at its own pace, cutting it back before watering and growth begin in spring. Blog readers have told me that they simply lie their plants down on the cellar floor.

Brugmansia: In areas where *Brugmansia* isn't hardy, the best tactic is to let the angel's trumpet go dry and dormant in a 45ish-degree spot, such as the cellar. Mine is so tall I now just lie it down there, or you can try to cut it back partway to even get it into storage. A reader of the A Way to Garden website from Zone 6 blog recently told me she stores hers right in her house this way; cut back by half, and resting, in an out-of-the-way corner, leafless just as mine in the cooler basement will be.

Hibiscus: Many people in cold zones know to bring these treelike plants indoors in winter, but then try to keep them growing. A more effective tactic, if you have a cool spot, would be to encourage them to drop their leaves by letting the plant go dry (like the *Brugmansia,* above), then store the dormant plant in a 40- to 45-degree location. Check every other week to see if a little water is needed to prevent desiccation.

Pelargoniums (including fancy-leaf, scented geraniums, or even zonal types): Many experts say that taking softwood cuttings to root in August, discarding the parent plants, is the best way to have the freshest plants for next year. But you can also grow them as houseplants if you have bright light, or cut them back hard before frost (to perhaps four inches) and store them in a bright but frost-free spot for winter, where they will need only enough water to keep from desiccating. Or do as my grandmother did: She dug or unpotted them and cut them back to stumps, let them dry a bit, and then put them in paper bags, which she pinned to the basement clothesline, barely alive. Pelargoniums with any hint of weakness or disease should be destroyed.

Cordyline and *Phormium*: These are really pricey plants, and get so much better when big, so I've been trying storage tactics for years with mixed results. I usually get a few years in my imperfect conditions before pests become a problem. Bright and cool is the key here (like high 40s but lots of light; little water), hence my adding a grow light to one area of the basement this winter to accommodate my ever-larger plants better than the two tiny windows can now. Keep a careful eye out for insects, particularly in late winter, and be prepared to trim off dried leaves come spring, when they can go out early.

Just-Tender Woody Plants

Small trees and shrubs that are just slightly more tender than your winter conditions allow can be grown as pot subjects, the way I do my Japanese maples, and a nearby garden friend does a collection of spectacular hydrangeas that don't perform well this far north. I have five Japanese maples in very large faux terra-cotta pots that are technically hardy, but hate the ice and wind, so I wheel them, pots and all, into the unheated garage for the winter once they have frosted off and are leafless and sleeping. They stay there until sometime from mid-April to early May (to avoid late frosts on tender emerging leaves) and require water once or twice in late winter so that they don't dry out once the potting soil thaws.

There is very little light where I store them, and none is needed, since deciduous plants would be leafless while in storage. Every third year they must be potted up or root-pruned.

myself: *Is it really a big deal?* This is how I practice for dramas that promise to cull the herd, my herd. Usually it's a gradual, orchestrated march toward winter quarters: first to somewhere such as the porch overhang or the garage, where things can dry off enough so that whatever strong helper I am able to recruit and I can even think of being able to lower them down the staircase into the basement, or carry them into the house and up the narrow, steep stairs — somewhere, anywhere, into protective custody. This is no terrain for wheeling things around easily, but we must get out the handcart and genuflect a few times for good measure and go at the task.

I will certainly meet my death on the downhill side of the two-wheeled, screaming yellow carrier, flattened by one of the various giant pots that slips off its not-big-enough step. The thigh- and nearly hip-high containers far outweigh me, and the operation each spring and fall has long put the laws of physics to the test, not to mention pushed my luck, and that of my sorry left arm this time around. That will be it one day: RIP Margaret Roach, who died trying to ensure that her potted plants lived to see another spring.

Birch leaves, some early abandoners gone yellow and crisp enough already to drift downward, skitter across the lawn that will not dry today nor any day in what remains of this year, no matter how much patience is exercised. As I mow, I send the nearly triangular leaves spitting out the chute and then aloft again, one more joy ride per customer. *Hi, ho.*

Frost is coming — this time for real, and of more than a few hours' duration, I think. At each hard turn or reverse of gear, the tractor tires tattoo the soft soil with an imprint that will not fade, a dark scar that we both regret, but I push on.

Frost is coming.

Eastern chipmunks perch on every promontory — every gate finial or post or bit of ornament — reducing magnolia pods to mere husks, holding them ever so delicately like corn on the cob in those tiny, slender toes (just four on each front foot, not five as on the back ones). I have cursed these cutest of rodents all season long, wished them dead, for all the tunneling they have undertaken and crops they have undermined, absconded with, destroyed. Compared with the recent and approaching storms, their mischief now seems so trivial, I almost wonder why I was upset.

Jack, who until the high-summer half-munk episode would typically knock the occasional one off for sport and lay it before me whole — *not good eating* — has lately regarded them as sushi, with the head a particular delicacy over and again. Maybe he has heard, or worse watched, as I knelt like a madwoman and screamed into the crevices in the stone wall, or into all those little holes in the ground, about the vegetables they upended: "I'm warning you, chippies!"

(Cue sound of chorus of rodent and feline laughter.) Maybe he is trying to settle the grudge, or maybe it is simple feast or famine because he seems to have knocked back the population of his favored prey, the weasels and flying squirrels, to the very slimmest of pickings. Maybe like I do, he eats whatever the garden serves up, a locavore in his own right.

A falsely optimistic last row of bush green beans, and another of peas, planted in late July and just starting to bear, have escaped animal predation so far. As I roll on by on my orange machine, I can see them, tucked beneath a white drape of insulating fabric that I hope will not prove to be their shroud. Hurry up; tuck in and tidy now. *Or else.*

Today, just for a day or two, I live in Oz, where the road — I'd expect the darkest slick brown dirt on such a dew-soaked morning — is golden, paved in kernels of dent corn. The fat little tiles join with leaves whose job is also done into a gleaming, if ephemeral, mosaic.

Across the way, a slit in the clouds bathes just a clean-cut slice of earth in a startling shaft of gold light. Nearer to me, along the road bank, and again farther beyond in the distant woods, another color of light altogether stains things an intense slate blue, so from where I stand, it is as if the one spot-lighted sliver of just-harvested cornfield, now a luminous khaki stubble, is where the Yellow Brick Road will lead: into the welcoming, warming glow. *Follow, follow?* Things are changing fast now, moment to moment; by the time I get there, across the street and halfway through the field, will the shining spot still be what it seems to promise?

Both the kernels and the leaves of birch and maple have lost the connections to their mother ships, but neither was a sorrowful parting; it was time. Two days of a farmer's combining have felled the giant grassy corn-stalks, grinding them to bits while separating the grain. For nights and days before the massive machine pulled in and laid claim, the local raccoons and squirrels had been doing their best to *get there first* — to plunder the field, one ear at a time. The squir-rels would run across the road to my side, over and again, to stuff the cartoonishly big prizes they carried inside a hollow old apple trunk, an improvised silo. Now the source has been erased, with only spillage to pick over. *Bargain-basement sale; get your corn-cob seconds here.*

Looking around, it's hard to know whether to focus on the full grain wagon or the empty field; the light spot or the dark zones; the trees that are already naked or those that are dressed to the nines and showing off. This is the toughest cusp of the year, the one when riotous displays of color presage months of monochrome, a lurid but irresistible peep show before the vice squad shuts the bawdy operation down. Overall, in both the spectacle and the abundance — just-harvested crops in full barns, full root cellars, full freezers — this is the richest time. Yet it's challenging not to seize upon the losses instead, to grab at what's slipping by. Caught up in the distraction of such poignancy, I'm barely noticing that from spent plants everywhere, crops of a great diversity of seeds are bursting forth from pods and seedheads of all descriptions, and staking a future claim. The plants play dead, but don't be fooled: There is life in them, so much life. *En ma fin gît mon commencement.* In my end is my beginning.

The corn needed a nudge to reduce itself to a format my neighbor can easily store, and use to feed his herd, but it took no machinery, nor even any manual tool or bare hand or paw to convince the trees' leaves to set out on their own. Environmental triggers are part of the equation, but not even the wind typically persuades a tree to part with its foliage all on its own. It can carry the leaves off, but under normal circumstances only if there's a readiness on the part of the plants — a willingness to surrender. As with *Homo sapiens,* external prodding and pleading for change go only so far, until we are ready to make the move, though here among the plants, the resistance is chemical. The point of the bond is small, but strong: the abscission zone, at the base of the leaf petiole, or stalk, is controlled primarily by the hormone auxin in active growth months, but as the leaves start to undergo senescence in fall, the cell walls on this tiny sticking point start to weaken, too. A shift in the balance of hormones, particularly the increasing influence of ethylene, makes it all come unglued.

Plants act more intelligently than we do, I often think (and so of course do birds, who know when it is time to go — *migrate!* — and do not overstay their welcome when a situation has played itself out). "What's the difference between humans and other animals," I heard a scientist ask the other day on a radio interview — "what's the difference in the way we think compared with *them?*" I expected him to reply that it must be sentimentality, for though animals certainly have intricate social networks and connections, they seem to put practicality —

survival — ahead of anything unhelpful or even cumbersome, such as nostalgia. When push comes to shove, we do, too — mostly — but oh, the indecision, the lingering to reach that point. How many of our short hours do we spend at that hem-and-haw threshold, the one Sylvia Plath imagined in the poem "The Tree of Life," watching her life go "absolutely bare" while she pondered her course: mother, poet, academic, wife?

Flowers abscise, too, starting to dry and often drop off after they have served their purpose of attracting pollinators or otherwise achieving fertilization. And leaves — well, leaves fall. Why carry the leaf into winter if it is no longer feeding you? Unnecessary bits are let go — even when humans call them our "baggage," we typically keep lugging them around, anyhow. Plants systematically cull the weak, damaged, or unneeded, for the greater good, like my dwarf white pines and other conifers do. My apples, knowing they cannot ripen every fruit that sets in a year that favors thorough pollination, self-thin by dropping some tiny fruit in June (a practice apple growers have mimicked, and taken further than the tree itself would go, with chemicals such as carbaryl, often known as Sevin, to limit the number of fruits in favor of premium-sized ones). Sometimes, such as when an infestation of gall insects or leaf miners takes hold, a plant can send out the chemical signal to its component parts to defoliate early, forcing an early separation, yes, but one strategically planned to save itself and foil the foe. A sacrifice, and also self-preservation. If there is drought or other perceived danger — even when you move a houseplant indoors after a summer outside, for instance, and it defoliates in protest at its changed environment — the plant takes measures to ensure survival.

Leaves fall. If we learn nothing else from gardening, let that be the single lesson.

Sometimes they don't fall in autumn, as is the case with some of the big oaks in view right now, which are called marcescent for this holding-on trait. I have a Japanese-maple lookalike from Korea, *Acer pseudosieboldianum,* a small tree with particularly vivid fall color, that I can fearlessly grow in the ground because it's much less prone to injury here than are the Japanese species such as *Acer palmatum* or *japonicum* or *shirasawanum* (the ones I prefer to protect all winter in the pots wheeled into my barn). The first year the new maple refused to drop its leaves, and I called the nursery I bought it from to ask why — as if there must be something I was doing wrong. No, *it's just that way,* was the answer (one of gardening's most honest explanations, since so often all we know is what we see — unless we run a plant-pathology lab). I have come to accept, and love, this plant for its at first odd-seeming characteristic of withholding.

Marcescence is not well understood: Is it that certain leaves on plants thus inclined (perhaps those at the top of the tree that got the most sunlight) hang on longest? Is it that some species, or populations within species, don't form a proper abscission layer at all for some other elusive reason? Another stash of questions for my ever-growing heap. I simply must come back next time as a librarian, or research assistant, preferably with a large and renewable multiyear grant in place.

Meantime, I can make my peace with a Seneca Indian legend that explains it this way: The oaks defy the winter gods by holding on to their leaves, and the pine trees join them — but not the tamaracks, which shed theirs as if resigned to defeat at the hand of what lies ahead. In fact the foliage of tamarack (*Larix laricina,* also called eastern larch, a deciduous conifer) would gild the roadbed here about now — adding its inch-long needlelike leaves to the ranks of the fallen — if only I had planted one as I have for years intended to. No matter; by the end of a day's worth of farm vehicles and other traffic, the Yellow Brick Road will be turned to cornmeal — but for now, it shimmers. Robert Frost knew: "Nothing gold can stay."

I wait for the wind to stir, as I know it will, as NOAA's radar maps show it has south of here already, tossing snow-covered branches, and trunks following right after them, to the blanketed ground. "Don't leave me," the latter parts seem to say. "We are one; I have separation anxiety!" Even with the still air of the last three or four hours, the freakish storm has dumped eight inches on the October garden, still clothed in its fall foliage, and the destruction has begun. Two pieces of the magnolia by the door — the one the sapsucker has been playing hit man on; the one with all the character that a friend propagated when he began his nursery decades ago, one of his first progeny — have broken off and fallen under the load of piled-up feather-sized flakes.

"What weighs more," my father liked to ask us when we were girls, always the big tease, looking over the tops of his half-glasses at us professorially, "a pound of lead or a pound of feathers?"

These crystalline feathers are plenty heavy, and might as well be metal.

"Nature, the gentlest mother is," wrote Emily Dickinson. I'm not so sure. I think she runs a pretty tough household; we're all calloused and bruised here, that much I can attest to.

During the siege, I suit up again and again, round after round, big rubber-and-neoprene boots and a hat and a hoodie and a hooded waterproof jacket over that for good measure. I venture out to take the snow off every thirty minutes or so, since it is falling so fast — two to three inches an hour — targeting the most vulnerable and the most precious things out there that are within my merely human-sized reach. Unlike the well-practiced drill in winter, when only conifers and broadleaf evergreens have their foliage and appreciate my attention, this unseasonal routine extends to not just the usual suspects but to multiple dogwoods, mature lilacs, willows, magnolias, maples, and even the vast apple trees.

At first, as if they are exhaling and ex-pressing gratitude — *thank you, thank you* — the lightened limbs levitate at my touch, or the extended touch that is mine thanks to my crazy tools: the twelve-foot-long piece of molding that's lain idle in the shed for months now, a couple of brooms, various lengths of bamboo. By the third or fourth round of rescue attempts out to the magnolia 'Ballerina', the Japanese maples, the big dogwood by the front walk, some of the patients are nonresponsive. The branches no longer spring back in a generally upward direction; they grow weary of the load, and of my ministrations. The temperature is too cold now as night overtakes the day, and the limbs are growing stiff and brittle; I risk doing more harm than good, even using the gentlest of practiced upward strokes.

I must simply go inside and watch as they vanish with the last slip of light, as they are erased from view, at least until sunrise — knowing that it may be permanently. On the way in, the old copper beech on the hill catches my eye; I can see the load it is carrying, but I can offer no help to someone of its stature. "Please be there in the morning," I say, before I know that I am speaking out loud into the near darkness. "Please try to hang on." I know that I am too old to grow another beech from its childhood to this size; beeches make you wait. I do not want to be without the others, either — but by comparison with dear *Fagus sylvatica,* their replacements would shape up fast.

I feel like I'm back in Girl Scouts, earning merit badges for proficiency in new tasks

— tasks I never wanted to learn, but that are apparently mandatory to this year's bruising curriculum. This morning — the *morning after* — working in my high boots and warmest gloves, I have mastered Generator 101. It was no picnic, but I did manage to make a tea party, with my electric kettle operating alfresco on a big cutting board balanced on top of the loud machine — or at least I made a cup of hot tea or two to fuel me on into rounds of resumed snow removal of various kinds that will shape my day.

Up and down the road, from nearby town to town, all Friday had been spent getting ready, the spirit of the day expressed in anxious e-mails and calls as if we all feared a levee breach and were filling sandbags, or battening down before the overnight air raids began in another country, another era. There was no optimism, just a sense of "together against the odds" — and I heard no expectation that we'd really be prepared — but you can't just sit there doing nothing, can you? Hope against hope, and mostly blind hope at that. In one silent entreaty after another, I reminded the forces that be that I had already *given at the office;* remember? My common prayer: I'd culled the herd; I'd offered up the bodies of more than a dozen shrubs and trees in earliest spring

— *that was me, you know that, right? Have mercy.* I don't need a double order of *smote,* you know; *one per customer.* I am all smoted out over here.

A few innocent-sounding inches of snow had fallen the night before last, on Thursday, October 27 — before Halloween and even before the clock change and other avowed markers that winter's coming on — and rendered the fifteen-foot kousa dogwood closest to the house into a flattened octopus of splayed arms. I have never seen a field of soybeans standing in snow, but now I have, at the same neighbors' whose lowest-lying adjacent cornfield had been swamped in August's particular havoc. What would a foot or more of additional wet snow, as was forecast for the weekend, do to a landscape with many of its leaves still intact?

Actually, I had an idea. I'd seen this before, and worse, but only once in all the years here, when an October 4, 1987, storm surprised parts of the Northeast. I'd just bought my place and had enough time here on weekends, working ceaselessly to clean it up from its overgrown state in the hopes of making a garden. One weekend night I was awakened from my sleep by the sound of shotguns — dozens of them, all at once — or so I thought. It was my first experience with the sound, in a time when everything nature did was new to me. That night, the trees were not just stretching and objecting to the cold, as I now understand that they do on the harshest of nights, having listened to them groan so many times; those were no mere utterances or mild protestations in 1987. It was the sound of the forest around me collapsing, a tree at a time, plenty of which (including an eighty-foot maple) fell into my "cleaned-up" yard.

And so on Friday I had done what I wish I'd had advance warning to do that long-ago October weekend before the power went off for a week: I cooked up food that could be eaten at room-temperature; filled water bottles (and also buckets for toilet flushing, since the well pump requires power). I filled the portable generator, too — there must be an easier, safer way, some siphon device maybe, to transfer gasoline from the five-gallon can into this beast? — and found the snow shovel again, and my big boots, my secret-weapon molding, the cans of salt and grit; all of it. And when it came, I'd gone out to work — or at least to try to alleviate any sense in the already dreaded and visualized aftermath of *what else could I have done*.

By the time more than a foot and a half of new snow was piled up on top of Thursday's, and on top of giant sections of many garden plants — by the time it was time for tea on the generator, shoveling walkways, and carefully digging out a select few pinned-down limbs with my gloved hands — I wondered why all the fallen had not called out in the way that the trees so often do. It had been such a silent night. They had gone without complaint, as if stoic, or simply resigned to where they were headed, or perhaps wanting to rejoin the friends I'd sacrificed just as the garden year began.

And now the grass needs cutting. I find my safety glasses, ear protectors, and gloves, and I head for the barn, grabbing the snow shovel from beside the kitchen door where I left it after clearing the path less than a week ago. Don't need that today. The white landscape has gone green again, and in its new ensemble it calls out for another form of attention. The garden is my fickle dominatrix; I am enslaved: *Mow me. Shovel me. No — mow me again. I long for your rough, noisy touch, Margaret.*
Vroom.
Or maybe this is just another test of the emergency broadcast system:
"We interrupt this program for a special bulletin: It's not winter yet. Keep mowing,

Margaret. We'll let you know if and when to stop."

But shit, no gas in the tank, and none in the gas can, either. I'll have to go out and get more. It is hard to remember to set aside some fuel for mowing when you are standing boots-deep in snow. Survivalist instincts must have taken over when I dumped it all into the generator, as if readying for a long siege, and now I am siegeless — my siege has up and melted. No wonder: Today we are featuring early September (or June?) in November. *Try that on for size, garden and gardener. Take that.*

Vroom, vroom.

As I buzz-cut the backyard, I see them backlit and glinting on high: various species of social wasps — bald-faced hornets and paper wasps in this case, I suppose, not ground-nesting eastern yellow jackets. They hover in short flight patterns up and down, up and down the surface of the highest strips of clapboard, as if on some invisible track that holds them just inches above the siding's surface. They appear to be scoping out a crack they might slip into, looking, as we all are now, for cover. Can they all be inseminated females — the future queens of the colonies of the coming year? Only the young females, holding in their beings the germ of the next generation, overwinter, I know, with every other current member of the intricate caste system, Class of 2011, perishing at the coming cold.

Looking up to near the ridgeline on the sunny sides of the house, I am mentally calculating how many nests that means next year if things go according to each of these heat-seeking girls' plans. Good thing I am not allergic to their venom; next year may be even more violent on that score than this angry one was, when I seemed to bump into someone at every pass of the mower (or on the trail of every slippery woodchuck), quickly suffering the consequences.

More geese than I can count in time pass overhead in single-file formation, honking. The cat, just now rolling in the warm gravel of the driveway as if it were an exfoliating spa treatment or maybe hot-stone massage, looks up, and wishes he could fly. As if to get with the program, entire flocks of leaves take flight in unison, riding the air currents before alighting in the branch of a tree that is not theirs — or on the ground, of which they will become a part in time. *Swing your partner; do-si-do.*

"Your e-mail said you were going to be outside *meowing*," says a friend who catches me on the phone just as I go inside to get a fast drink of water. "No," I say, "I said *mowing,*" off by just a vowel, and an entire season. "Mowing *snow?*" Nobody understands me, and right now I realize I understand so little.

Vroom, vroom.

After the fall, a body count. The tally is complete, though I avoided facing it for weeks. Herb, with the same small chainsaw that sliced through spring's sacrificial lambs, did the deed: took down the disfigured or otherwise devastated woody plants that the freakish storm had savaged. We walked around the other day, once the initial shock felt less sharp and stabbing, and I'd pointed: *Take the left side of this,* and *This one goes completely.* And then I went out for the afternoon to nowhere in particular, just out, returning only after all evidence of those who could not bend with the wind or bear the latest of life's burdens, all that wet snow, was erased.

Apparently my pleas for mercy — the request that the shrubs and trees I'd offered up onto the pyre as the season began be taken into consideration — went unheard. Parts of big native maples and oaks, now suspended as hangers along the property's edge where the worst damage had been in 1987, were the least of it: This time the garden proper was the target of the vengeance. *Humpty Dumpty had a great fall.*

The lilacs were the hardest hit, and at least three are gone, with that number likely to grow (the word here should be "dwindle," no?) to six mature shrubs next spring, when the temporarily spared, half-standing ones will likely be erased the rest of the way. A 'Gold Rush' metasequoia, one of a group of three up on the hillside where they call to me from way down below with their bright yellow-green foliage, was made to vanish, too, as was half of a big viburnum (unlikely to recover) and one-third of the delightfully gnarly old rosemary willow. Hopefully, it will rebound, but its once-striking massiveness has been starkly reduced. Severed arms of magnolias, dwarf white pine, and the giant rhododendron that has been here longer than I were clean-cut and dragged away; so was one side of an ancient apple. The sassafras is too far gone to save, missing its head and an arm both, a beheaded amputee. Just a few weeks earlier when he was visiting, Marco had said, "Your sassafras is really shaping up into a great tree."

Now he is instead reminding me by phone what he always says about garden losses:

"Bury your dead, and fast."

The idea, he's been reteaching over and again the last two weeks in an emergency refresher course: Erase the evidence of disaster, and start imagining what you will put in the gaping places. That is of course a much better and saner view of all living landscapes, including our interior ones, than to hold on to the empty ache of disappointment and have to stare it in the face.

Akimbo, askew, awry, amiss. That is how it still looks out the window today, even though the cleanup has been done for days and the bodies dragged out of my sight line. Nevertheless, the view is now a wreck, a ruin — a total mess. Was this violence a reminder of our perpetual state of vulnerability really necessary, I ask you, both kind and brutal sir or madam? I promise, that fact was already quite squarely in mind; middle age and an adulthood spent gardening and also, thank you very much, your ceaseless meteorological antics this season will do that to a body.

Is this some "sinners in the hands of an angry God" moment we've been having, because if it is, I don't take too well to such fire and brimstone (despite the fact that the latter, sulfur, does make a good agent against fungal issues, admittedly, and ericaceous

365

plants may also appreciate its pH-lowering effect on soil). Stop with the havoc already.

Yes, yes I know the point: You were just trying to remind me that everything is always falling apart — as everyone from the Buddha to Alan Watts will admonish and enlighten me, too, if I let them, but right now all their wisdom on the subject sounds like small comfort, really. I am pouting again; I want my two big islands of ornamental grasses back, the ones you flattened, forcing me to cut them to the ground in their prime, the ones who have always stuck with me as kind companions across the threshold into another spare winter. I have never been without the gracefully faded wheat-colored stands before, or at least not in twentyish years since I placed the young plants they were then into the soil. Disorienting; after so long, I expect them to *be there for me.*

So does the cat. These days and weeks since, Jack sits by the big *Miscanthus* islands uphill, now down to near stubble, knowing these were his most productive stalking grounds for all his years here, listening as he always has patiently for a rustling; waiting, sphinxlike, for some sign of motion, but with none to be discerned. He, too, finds the garden less than what he'd come to expect. Party pooper, this weather. *Really.*

I want the berries put back on the hollies, not scattered about the way you left them like so many miniature red marbles. Is this too much to ask? Sorry to shout, to rant and repeat myself, but I swear I get it — *I've already admitted it, haven't I?* — that gardening is a contrivance, an imposition on your bigger plans. That *nothing lasts;* that we are all (plants and animals alike) "poor insects of a few short hours," as Coleridge described. Which puts me in the oddest place, at once praying to surrender to inevitability and also fighting back, both believer and heretic. Here I am, trying to find my way to the on-ramp toward *just going along with it all,* but simultaneously resisting, for isn't the very fact of making a garden an act of trying to impose some sense of fixity, that "all set" thing again — that fresh-made bed or fresh-laid dinner table — and trying to put everything in its place?

Forget it, the forces — *you, big guy* — are forever reminding me, or so it seems when you mess up the picture I have painted in the dirt. *You will never beat us at this game, Margaret.* Is that what pissed you off — that I keep trying, cultivating my row of beans, taking a hard hand to the very unnatural but handsome espalier a few times each season when it tries to express itself beyond the bounds of my expectation or desire? Was that the message behind your latest meteorological homily?

"All things with which we deal, preach to us," Emerson wrote in *Nature*. "What is a farm but a mute gospel? The chaff and the wheat, weeds and plants, blight, rain, insects, sun — it is a sacred emblem from the first furrow of spring to the last stack which the snow of winter overtakes in the fields."

What is a garden but a mute gospel, then? Voiceless, but, for better or worse, also the only voice I seem to be able to really hear and pay any mind to.

Well, except for Marco's. Besides regularly reminding me that I am now in my shrub season (with free Tuesday matinee movie tickets and other senior perks not far behind), his voice keeps hinting at mounting evidence that one gets more particular and less flexible as one ages. We grow more controlling, he says, even if of a smaller, simpler realm that's manageable despite an achy, creaky touch of this or that.

There's that word again — "control": It's the foundation principle of horticulture. I want to say first, in self-defense, that compared with many other gardener types, I always thought that I exerted relatively little of it, eschewing chemicals, clipped hedging, or anything much in the way of formality. I managed to piss off some power greater than myself anyhow, though, and my opponent — or is it my partner? — keeps moving pieces off the game board. I wonder how the match went when the contestant was Marco's mother, a true master of the art of control?

"I hated going home because I didn't like what she had done with the place," he says, smiling at the turn of phrase and recalling a time before the exceptional horticultural career he is now retired from was only starting to come into focus.

Before he went into the army, the aspiring young gardener had changed his late father's vegetable plot over to shrubs, including some *Ilex crenata* 'Hetzii', an evergreen littleleaf Japanese holly variety he'd imagined would sprawl in the nicest way, showing off its glossy leaves without expecting much work — good bulk, good filler.

Maybe not. To Mom, it was a piece of marble, a lump of clay.

"I was gone in the service in Germany for a year, and when I came back, lo and behold, she had transformed it into a four-foot-tall handled basket — ovoid, with a concave section and all." Isabella Scissorhands.

A drift of *Sempervivum* he'd looked forward to seeing all grown in? It, too, had been reinvented, subdued into a perfect succulent heart.

The lesson, in his words:

"To the Italianate mind, nature is to be conquered."

Isabella's sense of empowerment was not limited to mere embellishments and flourishes; she even dabbled in daring acts of creation. Son had given Mom a *Viburnum* to plant in the yard, and on one of the visits, her guided tour paused at the former gift, all grown. She said she liked the shrub so much that she now planned to propagate it.

"You can't right now," the good son explained, trying to be patient and also helpful, saying how you have to wait until summertime and take cuttings, when the wood is just right and ideal for rooting, but no, she said, "I'm just going to put a piece of it in the ground."

"No, Mom, you can't." But she did, taking off "a branch the size of a chair leg and shoving it in the soil," he remembers. "And of course: Mother knows best."

When I visit the grown boy's garden lately, there is always some exceptionally well-clipped creature commanding center stage — if not as "out there" as an Easter basket fashioned in living holly, then at least a perfect set of boxwood cubes. Nature? Nurture? Nurturing nature? Or just the way that we must get — more assertive, because we need something, *anything,* to be manageable — in the face of the inexorable fact of our diminishing days?

I call the complaint line. Hello, Doctor? I have questions, so many questions. "The nature of life is to be overwhelmed," the shrink I call Dr. Eric V. Goudard is telling me in the latest of our phone assignations while Jack gnaws, jealously, on my knee for attention. I use that code name for my old go-to reality checker not because I am maintaining my own privacy over here — memoir writing rips that shutter off its hinges — but medical ethics say he must remain incognito and not get proper credit for his wisdom.

You only have to read Ernest Becker, Dr. Goudard the alter ego is saying now, as Jack's irritation at my distraction from his needs grows toothier and more insistent. I learn that Becker, whose work is an interdisciplinary fusion of psychology, philosophy, anthropology, and beyond, won a Pulitzer Prize for his book *The Denial of Death* just months after he died in 1974 at age forty-nine from colon cancer. He sought to understand what makes people act the way they do (good or bad, or even very, very bad) — asserting, nail-on-the-head-style I'd say, among other things that an unconscious denial of our mortality is the ticker inside us, but that it's even trickier than the mere awareness: It's also the knowledge that "when, where, and how?" are "anytime, anywhere, any way," and that there is absolutely no anticipating it, and no control.

And then, as I am taking in that synopsis — *shiver* — the doctor spouts a Becker one-liner:

"Mother nature is a brutal bitch, red in tooth and claw, who destroys what she creates."

Note: This means you — or, um, *me.* Nothing lasts. Leaves fall. Gardeners and their gardens? *Compost starter.*

Watching the aging garden — my life partner — collapse and fade around me these violent days, it's hard not to take it *personally,* too, as in: to sense how perilously close to utter ruination and erasure I am myself (as I have been since the day I was conceived; yes, I know). And yes, I anthropomorphize the garden and give it my own life's seasons — Conception, Birth, Youth, Adulthood, Senescence, and Death and Afterlife — but it works in the other direction, too; I also *botanimorphize*. Am I looking out the window, I sometimes wonder, or looking in a mirror? Hard to really tell. Advaita.

As Dr. Goudard speaks, I glance across the room at my bookshelves and think: I should be a member of the Ernest Becker Foundation (do they take college dropouts? I must inquire). Sure, there are the garden titles, whole walls of them, but also a heavy dose of *wake up, Maggie, I think I've got something to say to you.* Listen to a few stiff spines:

> *Full Catastrophe Living*
> *When Things Fall Apart*
> *What Doesn't Kill Us*
> *No Time to Lose*
> *Going to Pieces Without Falling Apart*

No Becker here, not yet, except a cappella through the phone line, from the good doctor. Here comes another killer (ha-ha) Beckerism:

"To live fully is to live with an awareness of the rumble of terror that underlies everything." Is that another crack of thunder I hear coming my way just now?

So many robins: It looks like my turf is Robins' 'Hood out there at the moment. Flocks of these partial migrants are madly robbing the crabapples, shades of a designer-lingerie sale at the old Filene's, everyone grabbing at the same much-picked-over items in the bin with do-or-die energy. *Save some for later,* I say, listening to their late-season voices — like the collective lilt of rising-and-falling laughter — that stands out on this subdued, padded day of light rain. *Pace yourselves,* you big birds. *Or else.* They'll only save the jumbo, shiny red crabapples of 'Ralph Shay' and that is simply because they are confounded by the fruits' scale, about as big as a crabapple can be without being classified as an apple. Good thing they can't master how to fit them into their mouths just yet; it leaves me something to stare at, one trace of the mostly stolen show I usually associate with right here, right now. By the end of months of freezes and thaws, though, 'Ralph Shay' will soften and yield to the pressure of the first flocks of February, relenting to be had at last.

A winter wren is bouncing around out back, too, blunter in shape and darker in color than the wrens that chatter their admonishments at me all spring and summer; maybe he's checking out the off-season accommodations. I suspect he's always around here somewhere — in the adjacent woods?

— but I never catch a glimpse except as the season shifts, when he comes to the back water garden as if we'd made a *Same Time Next Year* vow, or who knows why. Besides this propensity for the annual reunion, another point of great affection for this aeronautical third-of-an-ounce soul is its Latin name: *Troglodytes troglodytes.*

If a troglodyte is a hermit, or cave dweller, this one's clothed in feathers, not in a fur wrap or carrying a club. He's some wild monkey of a bird, hard to sight but easy to hear while trilling sixteen big notes per second, but even with such antics he's no chimpanzee, despite the fact that the chimp's Latin name of *Pan troglodytes* shares half the bird's. Welcome, friend; perfect timing, this arrival of yours, for we are all heading into our respective caves here soon, whether actual or mental. And then I also love this: My troglodyte friend is the only wren species found outside the Americas, and one proposed explanation for how that's possible bumps right into the reason that the native flora of eastern Asia and the eastern United States have so many same-but-different counterparts, too. The theory in each case, bird's and plants', centers on the former land bridge across the Bering Strait, and possible migrations during an interglacial period, so

I like to think the wren has a vestigial affection and appreciation for my garden that gathers together plants from both places. Perhaps in some ancient way my lifetime's putterings make him feel at home.

I am making vegetable stock (the recipe is on the next page); the windows are steaming up, tucking me in a cloud that smells of the garden harvest. *What's that now?* It's another of the helicopters that have been buzzing overhead lately, as the forest canopy drops a bit at a time, baring more and more of the land beneath. *They're looking for pot,* I tell a friend, and then in today's local paper: six hundred plants seized, seven arrests, myself not among them. My definition of "homegrown" lies firmly within the letter of the law; no worries there — but I do wonder what my garden looked like from above. *What the hell is all that stuff down there?* the pilot must have wondered. *What a crazy lot of work.*

More auspicious signs that this will be an auspicious day: Four of six mousetraps in the cellar are missing when I go down to check in the morning. *Gone.* What does it mean when they walk away, trap and all? (It means they win — because you get to have nightmares about where the traps could be and under what conditions they disappeared

As the garden winds down, I grab the scissors and a bag and out I go: last call for vegetable-garden snippets. Why leave those final bits of kale and collards, parsley and pak choi — tattered as they may be — to winter's ravages? Combined with some onions and a winter squash that aren't in ideal condition to store well in the cellar, among other things, they become stock. I use this as my standard soup base, and freeze small amounts (ice cubes or slightly larger) for use when sautéing vegetables, making sauces, and so on; and I also make it earlier, throughout the season, to make use of less-than-perfect produce that some flea beetles might have nibbled, or that didn't fully develop; or I use the trimmings from other vegetables.

Because I always include winter squash such as 'Butternut' in the mix, the broth is rich-tasting enough to drink hot on its own, perhaps with a pinch of salt. In winter, I often have a cup between meals.

Note: Dicing and sautéing the onions, celery, and carrots (called a mirepoix) in butter and/or olive oil first until they caramelize yields a rich, more traditional style of stock. I skip it, and toss in the squash. No fat, no chopping, less fuss.

My preferred ingredients:

- Onions (peels on)
- Garlic (peels on, cloves smashed with flat blade of knife)
- Winter squash (no seeds, but skin on if grown organically and not badly blemished)
- Kombu seaweed (kelp, available dried in health food stores; maybe two six-inch-by-two-inch strips to start)
- Fresh ginger (just a slice or two, unless you want its flavor to dominate)
- Something green and leafy (kale, collards, chard, beet greens, Asian greens, parsley, or a combination; go easy on strong-tasting or spicy ones like mustard, and even the beet should be used sparingly or it may overpower things)
- Carrots
- Another root vegetable or two (turnip, daikon radish, parsnip, rutabaga)

- Celery (if I have it)

Simply assemble vegetables that are washed but not peeled (assuming that all are organically grown) in a large pot. Large ones may need to be cut into coarse chunks. Cover with water. Bring to boil, reduce to simmer, covered, until everything is falling apart. Let cool; I often leave it overnight to let all the flavors intensify. Strain.

in the night.) Researchers at the Mayo Clinic revealed recently that purging senescent cells in mice — cells that are over the hill, no longer dividing and growing vibrantly — could postpone many effects of aging. I have a body full of aging cells and a basement full of mice. Maybe we can set up a research substation down there? I could use a fountain of youth, instead of just the occasional flood, in that primitive hole in the ground on which the lopsided building and an increasingly one-armed Margaret teeter.

Back on the first floor, I hear it: There is either a dying smoke alarm battery or a cricket in the house that I cannot locate.

Shit. Underfoot outdoors, more beechnuts than I have ever seen, triggered by the stresses of a dry summer the year before, and more maple samaras — *snap, crackle, pop* — and so many hard little wild pears from the mystery tree I inherited with the place, lichen-covered trunk included. The plenitude — excess? — combines to make the right shoe choice seem to be whatever the footwear equivalent of all-terrain vehicle would be. Must I strap on my winter crampons to walk even now?

Bertolt Brecht asked what happens to the hole when the cheese is gone, but at the moment I am busy pondering what happens to the tree when the leaves are gone. (And, as always I'm asking myself this: What happens to the garden when the gardener is gone?)

Grandma sold her garden to try to buy a sense of security. Five years into her widowhood, my mother's mother moved to an apartment from the false Tudor house on a big corner lot that she and her husband had built early in their marriage — the place where every plant that grew there by the time she signed the last paper and said good-bye was one she had delivered into the ground. All "the girls," as she called not just me and my sister but also the gaggle of wives-no-longer who burgeoned as lifelong bridge-club and garden-club friends, likewise outlived their mates, were doing the same — downsizing. One after another, they gradually took up residence in the same new brick high-rise on the main boulevard leading into Douglaston, a late-life sorority house of sorts.

Every Sunday afternoon she'd come to the crazy-looking pink house she'd picked out for us and have dinner. Though it was *just us* — just our tiny but entire extended family at the table, six of us when she and my father's father were still alive, and then *five, four, three, two,* in uncomfortably short order — her jewelry always matched the dress she wore, and at regular intervals, she'd get up to "powder [her] nose."

Sitting on a vinyl-upholstered stool in the corner of the kitchen sipping a Bloody Mary as her son-in-law or daughter prepared the meal, she'd always say the same thing, as if it was from some script we were reenacting. In between snippets of local gossip about the odd little town she'd spent two-thirds of her life in, on whose geographic fringe she now resided several stories aloft because she'd sold her house and garden presumably to feel financially safe, there was always:

"I may be going to the old-folks' home soon."

The sentiment was echoed at least once in each edition of the weekly family miniseries by Grandpa Roach, who lived with us in the little bedroom off the kitchen. His version of the refrain: "I'm going to the poorhouse." (If not for his son's hospitality, maybe he was right: Grandpa was favorably inclined toward the two-dollar window at Belmont and Aqueduct, but it was not so favorably inclined in return.)

Grandma had sold off her most precious possession, but she still didn't feel secure, or so it sounded Sunday after Sunday. In my early fifties I sold off my security — a career that on paper appeared to sustain me — for the chance to live here in the garden, where I hope to drop, facedown, one day while weeding and be done with it all at that.

Grandma died one night in her apartment, falling forward onto one of the twin beds, stricken while changing into her ladylike nightgown. When picking out the dress her mother would be buried in, Mommy saw the old safe hidden in the back corner of the deep hall closet — a safe that had been in the mercantile that Grandma's people had operated back in Wisconsin a generation before. Inside were various bankbooks that did not qualify her as rich, exactly, but would have kept her from the old-folks' home for certain.

Sitting there in the dark lockbox, though, all that these sequestered, invisible proceeds of the house sale kept her from were ten more springtimes in her beloved garden.

When Mommy was born to Harold and Marion, both in their thirties at the time their first and only child arrived, it was early November, and the next month they shopped together at the local nursery for baby's first Christmas tree. It was a live, balled-and-burlapped spruce, not unlike the nastily aging ones I must soon relinquish here, the ones I planted when I first arrived as a weekend gardener. After enjoying the young *Picea* inside, all decorated and glittering, the new parents packed the ornaments away and gave it a prominent place in the yard, probably sheltering it in the garage until the ground was willing to accept the newcomer into the evolving landscape. I suspect the family's very jealous and snappish fox terrier pissed on baby's tree with regularity, besides its many attempts to grab directly onto baby. Before long a little playhouse, filled with child-sized furniture and scaled-down dishes and even a tea set, was built for the newest member of the family in the spruce's increasing shadow.

I don't know who planted the two big conifers that may be nearly as old as the house I live in, one a triple-trunk white cedar of some kind, the other the eastern red cedar I see from my big bed. The former has acquired such a girth that to accommodate the growing trunk over the years, an increasingly widening half-circle has been cut with a Sawzall into the roof overhang of the shed it stands beside. Only two inches' more wiggle room remains before the shed will have to be moved — or perhaps the tree will move it for me. When the wind goes mad the little building does, too, creaking and almost wobbling with the currents as if it's flapping some unsteady, untested wings, but not quite ready to fledge, or fly.

I don't expect that anybody living within its view now knows who planted my mother's first Christmas tree, either, but there it stands to this day, as does her playhouse more than eighty years later. Had Grandma Marion not moved on, I wonder if she would have taken down the spruce eventually, in favor of making room for more exciting things — any keen gardener would have, in spite of the considerable sentiment. I won't cut out the unknown former owner's conifers here, but those nasty quarter-century-old spruces that were my doing: They will be erased before another planting season here begins, that much I know.

I guess I place much higher valuations on other people's treasures than I do on my own, but in the bigger picture of my grandma story, I am still having trouble with the final tabulations, which simply don't add up: She sold her garden so that some bankbooks could sit for a decade in a closet. A not-so-special tree lived longer than expected in the deal.

Late-November days present themselves with peace and violence, often all at once — a peach-melba dawn sky is the backdrop for breakfast tartare. Whose organ meat is that left on the sisal mat out back, Jack? Can you not even wait a moment and watch the daybreak? But no, you are still on the raw diet, the vole-a-day health regimen you set for yourself in spring, and haven't wavered from yet. Impressive; so few dieters stick with it.

Me? (You didn't even bother to ask, oh cat of my heart.) I slept with a cracker last night. No, not some redneck type — I mean no offense to anyone in announcing this latest assignation, or strange bedfellow — but specifically a black-sesame rice crisp, one that had escaped when I devoured its companions in bed before slumping into slumber, salty-sweet black bits between my teeth.

Sometimes we all need a little comfort, and some encouragement. Too many garden losses lately; too much very undelicious, indigestible global bad news. And then, as if the brightening sky heard that I could use a hug that the cat won't offer, just as dawn breaks into fullness and Jack finishes off his last spoils, at least sparing me the cleanup, a giant rainbow frames the west view from right here in my reliable and most-loved chair. Is it actually a double? Yes. Yes.

In some things lonerism backfires, like when the ladder needs steadying to get at the top of an errantly sprouting espalier, or a truckload of eight cubic yards of mulch is dumped by the far gate. A fresh year of catalogs are starting to arrive, and though ordering seeds is not heavy work, it is best not done alone, either; I have always had a companion for the task. My latest one, of considerable years' duration, got it in his head to move to Oregon recently, for greener garden pastures, taking with him not just the in-person dimension of our friendship, but also access to the nearby greenhouse that was, of course, a perfect complement to the shopping we did together all that time.

"I'll buy the tomato seeds if you'll grow them," the conversation with Andrew would always begin, as if he needed my ten- or fifteen-dollar annual enticement, when of course we never really paid careful mind to who bought what or really kept a running tab of our years-long botanical barter. It hardly mattered; what counted was the chance to look together, to compare notes, to react collaboratively to the possibilities — *ooh! aah! ugh!* — and eventually to relish the harvest (or to commiserate when something was a flop and there was no harvest, or to split the yield if only one of us got lucky). It was like one of those dinners out where you share two entrées. Delicious, and far more stimulating to the palate than supper alone at the bar.

I don't get out much. But when I do, it's usually because someone has been persistent, demonstrating more "pro" energy than I can muster "con," typically over a prolonged period. Tod was like this, relentlessly and delightfully so. Thank heaven for the world's Tods; may all sentient beings be visited by one when they are despairing, stuck, or overwhelmed — or when their seed-ordering companion has flown the coop.

He had arrived in my garden a few springs back, as many strangers do, on an open visiting day, with enthusiasm so contagious that I'd offered plants if he'd come back for them, since it was revealed he's a close-by neighbor. He e-mailed, returned, and he went away again with garbage bags of *Geranium macrorrhizum* rhizomes and who knows what else — one woman's trash bag holding another man's treasure. I was even invited some time later to see my outcasts' new adopted home, where they looked very happy but more than that: where I had a sighting of that precious but lately-for-me-elusive state of beginner's mind. It was not because the garden looked beginner-ish at all — it was the spirit of the place, and of the gardener. As we walked around, I remembered the young woman who'd worked each weekend tirelessly, filled with eagerness and free of preconceptions, happy just to toil and try things — *everything* — and see what came of it.

In the visits since, he has told me of his own rites of garden passage: how weeds were the first reality check (especially for a weekend gardener, as he is now), and how the stage that followed was one of exploration — tentative, perhaps — before the letting go began with moving stuff around, suddenly unafraid whether it will die or not, releasing that presumed rather-safe-than-sorry form of exerting influence. Yesterday, we sat at his kitchen table surrounded by laptops and our two piles of paper catalogs and his big, orderly box of leftover seed packets.

"I'm going to get tomato seeds from that heirloom-tomato guy in Carmel, California — or whichever place has 'Pink Accordion'," he said across the heaps in my direction, and I was startled that both halves of that out-loud equation were unknown to me.

"What guy in Carmel?" I said, "and what is 'Pink Accordion'?" Unwittingly by either party at the table, another session of horticultural therapy was being performed on this tired old soul. Apparently at my grown-up age it is not just safe, but also terribly sane, to talk to strangers.

Never stop wanting more plants. With the occasional glimpse of the garden through eyes that are fresh to possibilities, perhaps there is a chance I won't.

Why do I garden? I find myself stuck on that question, especially in the vulnerable hours when darkness grabs the day, and before another one shakes loose from its clutches. But is it really "Why do I garden?" or, stripping away down to the real question: Why did I pick *gardening* as my way of coping with my own "denial of death," or whatever existential expression I label it with, my finitude-infinitude issues — the conversation between a body that won't last as long as the mind attached to it imagines there are things to do-taste-smell-touch and places to be?

I am so happy here and now, and intend no darkness with this subject at all. But I notice that I am not the youngest person in the room anymore (a condition that seems to be becoming more chronic than acute!) and it gets me pondering. In *And I Shall Have Some Peace There,* the book I wrote when I first came to live full-time in the garden almost five years ago, I answered the "Why do I garden?" question thus: *I garden because I cannot help myself.*

The garden is my Temple of Fancy, to steal a name from a nineteenth-century department store in Albany, New York, not far from where I live and grow things today, a place I suppose stole it from the one at 34 Rathbone Place in London, which made a specialty of "genteel products for ladies": prints and cards and such ephemera. ("Ephemera" — there's that word again.) But as I dig, I am not looking for just pretty, fleeting pictures; I am no outdoor decorator; no. I am just another creature looking for the way through.

I find comfort here in my temple, in its reassuring monotony (think: "watching grass grow," or the way that a spring follows each winter, and a summer surfaces after that). I find exhilaration — a reminder I am alive, but in that "waiting for another shoe to drop" way — in its times of total madness, in the unexpected and often unwanted dramas that it lays at my doorstep. I have been privileged to attend many births here, of new seasons, new crops, new creatures, and also many deaths.

I relish and even cultivate the moments of equanimity, of course, but sometimes — *tilt* — I get a little lost, or at least pensive, like the other afternoon, when I said it all out loud as best I could and a voice replied, bringing me back to earth:

"It's why we do *Savasana,* the Corpse Pose, in yoga," my writer friend Katrina was saying now over Skype (the contemporary incarnation of the fifth element, or ether) as I floated back into focus, "to practice the attitude of death, of our final surrender."

Of course — and *bam!* — that's it, that really is why I garden, too: to stare it in the face and fall to my knees, over and again. To keep chewing at the leaf, or burrowing, taking sustenance and refuge, and hopefully offering all the others around me some of it in return.

AFTERWORD, AND
GRATITUDE LIST

*A vine cannot behave olively, nor an
olive tree vinely — it is impossible,
inconceivable. No more can a human
being wholly efface his native disposition.*
— EPICTETUS, *DISCOURSES* 2.20.8

So many voices. The weeks-long-already
swell of the dawn chorus — if not the calendar pages, exactly — tell me that I am
blessed to see another growing season, or at
least the start of one. It is only early April as
I write this postscript and offer up thanks to
those who helped me through to here, to the
final pages of *The Backyard Parables* and the
first days of a spring that's both flash-frozen
and deep-fried — one that arrived in a blast
of near-eighty-degree March weather that
threw me, and the garden, into a mood, and
got us all talking.

As many years as I have bent to the task of
accepting what comes, or trying to — read:

as long as I have been gardening — I am nevertheless only so flexible, and no willow rod whatsoever about some things. Apparently I need more practice, but first, I must add my squawk to the amen:

I don't want peepers when February is barely put to bed, or mourning doves chasing each other wanting you-know-what quite that early, or moths gathering precipitously at the porch light each night to confer madly and then rest, plastered flat on the siding like some wallpaper pattern inspired by an E. A. Seguy illustration. I don't want 22 degrees after 70-something (or worse yet, multiple such hard freezes on tender tips and blooms), and neither do they. But what I want — what *we* want, my companions and I — is immaterial. Ready or not: It has begun, and I must be grateful for the pass to the next showing, even if from the coming attractions I'd say it promises no happy ending.

Our nonwinter is over, the first year in the twenty-five that I've known this house and soil when there was no frost in the ground to speak of, and the back mudroom didn't heave on its footing to effectively lock the door shut from December to March or even April. I am eating fresh-dug potatoes — ones that got away, or almost, when I missed them at the fall harvest. Last month they showed themselves, fat and firm, as I turned nourishing rock dusts and compost into the raised vegetable beds earlier than ever before. (My best advice: Do not ever dare use the phrase "I think I got it all" after a session of digging potatoes, or of weeding. The spud, and the spurge, will rise again; it is hubris to forecast otherwise.) As with all of life's most essential but exasperating searches, large and small — for errant eyeglasses, or maybe even one's true love or a sense of meaning — *Solanum tuberosum* outliers typically reveal themselves by sprouting the next spring, from right where you were looking in the first place the autumn prior. This time, though, with the extreme, ungodly earliness of everything around me accelerating even my personal locomotion and to-do list, I got there first. Dinner, lunch, dinner — and then, suddenly balanced between the prongs of my cultivating fork, *gotcha:* one more lunch.

It is another cusp now, the moment just before the juncos leave and the ruby-throateds buzz back into view. Yesterday, a swirl of six swallows chattered at me on the hillside, swooping and glinting in that blue-blackness of theirs. Between shows of aerobatic agility, they paused to discerningly peer with their pointed faces into the circular door-way of each accommodation I had tidied up to offer for their coming broods. From the humble wooden boxes aloft on poles, I'd shooed the mice who'd squatted inside while we all waited in our respective wintering grounds for our reunion in the here and now. "Welcome home," I screamed an afternoon ago into the summerlike sun, throwing my face upward. *Welcome.* This morning, a less-connected moment: A pair of flycatchers thought a shelf in the barn looked like a good nesting place, until I came in to get one of my various not-quite-right shovels off its respective peg, rudely foiling their plan.

Right now in the year is a sharp but tender edge: bright and warm, but over and done with; fresh and gleaming, but cold and dark. All of us who survived have come out of dormancy battered, not by snow and ice this time around, not like last year, but by the unfinished business when no winter followed spring, summer, and fall — disoriented, an out-of-sorts version of ourselves set against an out-of-sorts backdrop. What signal are we meant to follow in such chaos; how can we catch the beat? I suspect many more souls will perish in the process of trying. I'm moving as fast as I can — we all are — but it's not fast enough, and it makes me more than ever one who keeps wishing for the familiar, for: You go first, *Cornus mas,* but not until the *Hamamelis* are exhausted, and then *Lindera* and *Corylopsis,* starting just before the first of April, and down through the list I think of as *the right order of things,* and not all at once and not earlier, *please oh please,* follow the script, won't you? Of course there is no script in this interpretive dance, and even if there were one, and if miraculously we all followed it, would even that serve to satisfy one such as me?

The familiar — a snowy winter, a spring that starts with rain — is what I crave, but it eludes me. The familiar tried to elude me while I was writing this book, too; maybe it kept getting washed away in all of last year's rains, the irritation or lamentation of that moment, but now recalled fondly compared with this frightening, moistureless entry to another year.

"It's like a fish describing water," said Dianne Choie, assistant editor at my publisher. That might be the nicest thing anyone ever said in the way of describing me — a fish! — and, at least in European freshwater, a Roach is a kind of fish. I had just finished saying to her how this was the hardest thing I ever wrote — a story about something I

397

know so very well, but maybe too well to be able to express without feeling exceptionally self-conscious, or as if I am repeating myself, since the garden has lived inside me for so long.

And then there was this other tricky part, the fact that I was brought up not to talk religion (or money or politics) out loud, in public. Impolite, you know. Makes people uncomfortable, doesn't it? None of my business to tell you about my own version of hosanna-in-the-highest, nor ask you about yours. Save the parables for the preacher man, right?

Thanks to all of you who reached this page for listening anyhow. Thanks to the beloved, delightfully vocal readers of the A Way to Garden website, who put up with regular doses of woo-woo, and to those who visit me in real life on Garden Conservancy Open Days. All of you — virtual or in person — help me see what I cannot see otherwise, left to my own eyes alone.

Thanks especially to my family — the writer and teacher Marion Roach Smith and her husband, journalist Rex Smith, and their daughter, Grace, from whom all blessings flow. I am grateful also to the gifted photographer Erica Berger, family but for blood, and to Marco Polo Stufano, the best fusion of dad-husband-brother-escort ever, and the best tutor, too: of flora, frittata, and assorted finery.

To Irene and Albert Sax for reparenting me with proper dinners and adult conversation that the monosyllabic but dearly beloved Jack the Demon Cat could not provide (and to the Berkshires restaurant called John Andrews for serving as our clubhouse). To Herb and Flora Berquist, my first, and finest, country friends.

To Pam Kueber and Charity Curley Mathews, with their very good compasses that they are always willing to loan, thank goodness. Ditto Kurt Andersen and Anne Kreamer. Thanks to the latter pair for pointing me to ace researcher Stephen Blair, who waded with me early on, unafraid, through the depths of religious texts. He knows his way around a conventional library (and even knew what cello recordings needed adding to my music library). To the constant and clever Dr. Goudard, always there. Thanks also to Bert Halliday.

Gardeners I have shared many springs with, relying on one another over and again: Bob Hyland and Andrew Beckman, John Trexler, Glenn Withey and Charles Price, Page Dickey, Ken Druse.

Close to home: Where would I be without

Mike Todd (answer: up to my neck in wood-chucks, and without a stash of secondhand stories that make the best conversation-starters anywhere, tales that start with things such as the retelling of phone calls beginning with "Hello, I hear you have my pig.")? I'd likewise be nowhere, or in that general vicinity, without Tom Foley, Tod Wohlfarth, Robin Bruce, Brian Boom (everyone should have a botanist as a neighbor), Evelyn Santoro, Susan Ziobron, Andre Jordan, and Robin Hood Radio. Fierce technical support and much laughter provided by Brad Williams and April Heline, Ken Smith — and by WordPress.

The best thing that happened to me since I left my former city life to live here in the garden was that my longtime friend and agent, Kris Dahl of ICM, played matchmaker between me and Grand Central Publishing, and especially the *shidduch* she engineered with Deb Futter, my editor (and more important, my confessor). Her team, including Matthew Ballast, Diane Luger, the aforementioned Dianne Choie, Daia Gerson, and Mari Okuda, provide every imaginable support, and we even have fun. In the extended Grand Central family, I am particularly grateful to fellow country-dweller and author Katrina Kenison, who has proved the best of writing partners.

Whatever we all believe — and again, it's none of my business, really — may we all believe in the natural world outside, and be sure to look at her as much more than just a pretty face. Nature insists that we see not just the obvious but also the little things: the shelf fungi, or conks, growing bracket-like on a great and sturdy-looking tree, but foreshadowing its weakness; the rice-like eggs of future pest controllers that some helpful braconid wasp has deposited onto a tomato hornworm that we were about to kill. Big guys don't always win: If left undisturbed — if nature is left to its own plan — the eggs will hatch into septuplet-and-then-some Davids to the big green worm's apparent Goliath. Nature looks out for those she loves, and who love her. Look again, dig as deep as you can, moving aside the occasional rocks; reap all she has to offer.

ABOUT THE AUTHOR

Margaret Roach is the author of the memoir *And I Shall Have Some Peace There*. She has been an editor at the *New York Times,* fashion editor and garden editor at *Newsday,* the first garden editor for *Martha Stewart Living* magazine, and the editorial director of Martha Stewart Living Omnimedia. Margaret is now a consultant and avid gardener, keeping fans up to date on her website *A Way to Garden,* which Anne Raver of the *New York Times* called "the best garden blog." Margaret is also the author of *A Way to Garden,* named Best Garden Book of the Year by the Garden Writers' Association of America.

THE BAD ACTOR

THE BAD ACTOR

GLEN EBISCH

FIVE STAR
A part of Gale, Cengage Learning

GALE
CENGAGE Learning·

GALE
CENGAGE Learning®

LIBRARY OF CONGRESS CATALOGING-IN-PUBLICATION DATA

Ebisch, Glen Albert, 1946–
    The bad actor / Glen Ebisch. — First edition.
      pages ; cm
      ISBN 978-1-4328-3114-1 (hardcover) — ISBN 1-4328-3114-3
    (hardcover) — ISBN 978-1-4328-3109-7 (ebook) — ISBN 1-4328-
    3109-7 (ebook)
      1. Advice columnists—Fiction. 2. Murder—Investigation—Fiction. I. Title.
    PS3605.B57B33 2015
    813'.6—dc23   2015008331

First Edition. First Printing: July 2015
Find us on Facebook– https://www.facebook.com/FiveStarCengage
Visit our website– http://www.gale.cengage.com/fivestar/
Contact Five Star™ Publishing at FiveStar@cengage.com

Printed in the United States of America
1 2 3 4 5 6 7 19 18 17 16 15

THE BAD ACTOR

CHAPTER 1

Dear Auntie Mabel,

Whenever we're out with other people, my thin friend "De-nise" always finds some opportunity or other to make a comment about my weight: nothing outright nasty, but she'll say that "a few extra pounds looks good on me" or she'll mention a dress shop that I should try where they have clothes for the "larger woman." Maybe I am a bit plump, but I'm certainly not obese. "Denise" and I have been friends for a long time, but I find her remarks hurtful and humiliating. How do I get her to stop referring to my weight in front of others?

Pleasingly Plump in Springfield

Tell her to shut her big, mean-spirited mouth, I thought to myself. Say the next time she makes a public comment about your weight, you'll kick her scrawny butt across the room. My fingers were poised over the keyboard, ready to fire off my answer.

I paused and took a deep breath. That was me speaking, not Auntie Mabel. I could almost see Auntie the way she was, or, since there were no known photos of her and I'd never actually met her, the way I imagined she had been. She settled into the chair next to my desk. She was comfortably large, with soft, pillow-like breasts where a girl could rest her head while she told Auntie all the problems of the day. A woman whose gentle compassion was wedded to a sharp mind, and supported by a

7

lifetime of carefully chewed and digested experience. Auntie gave me a warning smile.

Be careful now, don't let your emotions get in the way of good sense. You've got a responsibility to your readers to show some restraint.

I nodded, and my fingers picked their way cautiously over the computer's keyboard.

Pleasingly Plump,

Although Denise is a friend of yours, she is not acting very much like a friend. You should point out to her that you find her remarks to be painful and wish she would stop. You might also ask her if there is something bothering her in your relationship that she would like to discuss with you. Perhaps after clearing the air, you'll find that you are better friends than ever.

Auntie Mabel

Yeah, right, I thought. And maybe you'll find out the miserable witch was never a friend of yours in the first place and that she's probably been sleeping with your husband. Auntie Mabel gave me one of her "now, now," looks, and I took another deep breath. I have to listen to Auntie Mabel because like it or not, we're a team. I'm the living half and she's not. A less pleasant way of putting it is that I'm taking the place of a dead person.

None of this is quite as weird as it sounds. Mabel Ann Rickdorf had written the advice column for the *Ravensford Chronicle*, located in the town of Ravensford in western Massachusetts, for over thirty years. She had always done so secretly, her identity known only to a handful of newspaper employees who were sworn to keep the matter confidential or be terminated. Since she had gone by the name of Ann in civilian life, her authorship of *Ask Auntie Mabel* had remained one of the great mysteries of regional journalism. Her sudden death by choking at the Big Bun on the eve of her seventieth birthday had both saddened and frightened the manager of the *Chronicle*, Roger St. Claire.

Her column was known to be one of the few reasons why anyone bothered to purchase what might uncharitably be considered an uninspired waste of ink and trees.

In desperation Roger had turned to his old friend, Jessica Hallowell, who later became his live-in girlfriend, if you can say that about a woman well into her seventh decade of life. She's my grandmother and we were sharing the same house at that time. Gran had thoughtfully recommended me for the job based on my slender resume as a writer: four years as a publicist for an art museum in Boston and as an interviewer for *Picture This!* It's sort of an alternative newspaper read only by those unknown artists mentioned in its pages.

So anyway that's how I, Laura Magee, a year and a half ago in my late twenties became the new Auntie Mabel. That's generally my job, although I'm sometimes allowed to do a human-interest story or a bit of investigative journalism.

On my down days I see myself as a pathetic reporter wannabe who gets thrown the occasional story because her grandmother four months ago married the big boss. If you looked up "pathetic" in the dictionary there'd probably be a picture of me sitting at my computer. I was living in a condo owned by my grandmother and boss, working at a job that they arranged for me, and pretending to be a dead woman who knew what a person should do in all of life's difficult situations. What a fraud! I couldn't even get my own life on track, and here I was dispensing nuggets of wisdom to people who were less screwed up than myself. As you can tell, I wasn't having one of my better days.

Roger walked down the hall from his office and across the open newsroom to my desk. He nodded, then coughed slightly, as he always did before he began to speak. I think it was his way of buying time to get his thoughts in order.

"There's something I'd like to talk to you about," he said somberly.

I'm being fired, I thought. It was probably my answer to Overly Maternal in Miller's Falls, the woman whose thirty-five-year-old son had deserted his wife and three children to return to live with his mother because he liked her cooking better. I'd suggested she feed him baby food, which was all he deserved, until he grew up enough to go back to his wife and family. Auntie Mabel had warned me I was coming close to the edge on that one.

Roger sat on the edge of the chair next to my desk, looking extremely uncomfortable. "I have an assignment for you," he said. He took a slip of paper out of his suit-coat pocket and studied it. "Raoul's School of Ballroom Dance is opening up on Elm Street this week. We should do a feature on it with a couple of pictures. I spoke to the owner, and set up an appointment for you at one o'clock today. Is that okay?"

I nodded, suddenly happier. Maybe I wasn't getting fired after all, but I could tell by the look on Roger's face there was more to come so I wasn't out of the woods yet.

"Urm." He cleared his throat again. That could get to really bother me.

"Your grandmother and I seem to be having a bit of a disagreement."

Uh-oh! I could see real trouble coming down the track now. There was no way I was going to end up in the middle of a lover's quarrel, even if the lovers were in their seventies. If I took Roger's side I'd be offending my landlady; if I took Gran's side, I'd be offending my boss. This had lose-lose written all over it in capital letters.

"What about?" I asked.

"Urm."

I wanted to reach across and choke him.

"You know we went to Florida for the winter?"

I nodded. A silly question. Of course, I did. I'd spent most of

December through March envying the two of them while I sat through a typical New England winter.

"Well, I'd like to live there permanently."

"And Gran doesn't want to?" I asked. I figured questions were safe. They didn't commit me to one side or the other.

He looked like he was about to clear his throat again, but the expression on my face stopped him.

"I don't think she'd mind for herself. After all, most of her interests can be pursued anywhere."

Yoga, Japanese flower arranging, meditation, and Eastern religions: yeah, I figured most of those could be practiced in Florida with no problem.

"She thinks I need the *Chronicle* in order to keep my mind active. She believes a steady diet of golf, fishing, reading novels, and sitting around the pool will lead to my steady mental deterioration."

"I see. Well, that is a problem."

We sat and looked everywhere but at each other. Now that I'd admitted that I comprehended the dimensions of the matter, I knew the next thing coming would be a request for help. A plea that Roger didn't want to make, and I didn't want to hear. I decided that it might be in my best interest to be proactive, as they say.

"Why don't I discuss this with Gran and make sure that I really understand what's at issue here?"

Roger glanced at me uncertainly as if only a fool couldn't see the issue.

"Sometimes when two people disagree, it's because the question has just been phrased in an unfortunate way," I explained. In the back of my mind I could see Auntie Mabel smile with approval at my limp response. "Once the matter is put in a different context the conflict may disappear."

I could see Roger wondering how the issue of spending the

year in Florida was open to a wide range of interpretations.

"Very well," he said finally, standing up, apparently deciding that a quarter of a loaf was better than no loaf at all. "I hope you can work something out."

I didn't like the heavy emphasis being placed on my negotiating skills.

He started away, then turned back. "You won't forget about Raoul's?"

I'd already forgotten. "I'll go there this afternoon."

He nodded. "This relationship stuff makes you think," he said cryptically, then headed back to his office.

I wondered how a man who had been unhappily married for over thirty years before being widowed managed to remain such a novice when it came to relationships. Of course, maybe good marriages and bad marriages are alike in one way; neither requires that you spend much time working things out.

CHAPTER 2

I glanced down at the row of Super Save More bags lined up next to my desk. They formed an orderly row, with the bag containing the oldest letters closest to my chair so they would be answered soonest. I never like to have more than three bags lined up. Auntie Mabel constantly reminds me that each letter represents a real human problem that needs to be solved as quickly as possible, so I shouldn't allow myself to fall far behind. Who knew what tragedies might result from such laziness? Taking this to heart I tend to see the row of bags as little tan people staring at me with doleful eyes, asking me how long it will be before I get around to their concerns. Some people accumulate guilt by the thimbleful, I gathered it by the bagful.

I reached in the bag closest to me and was delighted to find only eight letters remained. If I worked diligently I would be down to two bags by the time I stopped for lunch. For the next two hours I rolled right along, dispensing advice with the expeditiousness of a cafeteria worker doling out the shepherd's pie on the middle-school chow line. The cat with a clock in its stomach that sat on top of my desk was showing eleven forty-five when I reached in the bag and found one lonely letter yet remaining. I spread it out on my desk, hoping that I could dispense with it quickly and move on to lunch.

Dear Auntie Mabel,
I've never written a letter like this before, but I don't know

what to do or who to turn to for advice. I met Jack about six weeks ago. Right away I thought that he was the most charming man I'd ever known. But I was reluctant to get involved with him because Jack is a number of years younger than I am. When I mentioned that to him, he said it didn't matter because he preferred more mature women. I can't tell you how happy I've been, Auntie Mabel, since I met Jack. The five years after my divorce have been a long, lonely time, and I was convinced that now things were going to turn around for me. When Jack casually mentioned that he was having some problems getting a bank loan, I was happy to offer him a sizeable sum from my savings to help him. The problem is that since I gave Jack the money, I've noticed a definite cooling in his feelings toward me. Whenever I call to see when we can get together, he gives me the excuse that he has to work, and he'll get back to me. But he never does. I can't tell my family because they don't know about Jack, and they'd just tell me I'd been a fool—an old fool, who's been swindled by a cute, younger man. I'm hurt, but more than that, I'm angry. I want to confront him, but I don't know what I can really do to get my money back.

Desperate in Ravensford

Dear Desperate,

I think you have sized up Jack correctly. He sounds like nothing but a fraud and swindler. I think you should contact a lawyer to find out what your legal rights are. Even if there is no binding contract here that would enable you to get your money back, you can put it down as a gift to him on your income tax. A conversation with the local police might also be advisable since a man like Jack may well be into criminal activities. Even if you can't get your money back, you may exact a measure of revenge.

Auntie Mabel

I could see Auntie Mabel shaking her head reprovingly. She considered revenge to be a base motive, while I thought that sometimes it was the only form of punishment available to the weak. Sometimes the nice guys needed a little encouragement to fight back. I glanced at the postmark on the letter. It had come in to the paper over two weeks ago. Too bad that it had percolated down to the bottom of the bag. I could imagine Desperate checking the *Chronicle* daily, hoping to see Auntie's reply. I hit the key that sent my answer off. At least she'd have a response within the next week. I smiled to myself. Sometimes this job did have its moments of satisfaction.

My eye traveled from the postmark to the left-hand corner of the envelope, and I saw the name "Marion M. Jensen" written boldly above her address. Although most people gave themselves fictitious names in their letters, some slavishly wrote their real names in their return addresses. Maybe they thought advice columnists were bound by the same vow of secrecy as priests in a confessional. That wasn't true. I sincerely hoped that no one ever admitted to committing a serious crime in a letter, but if someone did, there was no doubt in my mind that I'd definitely hand it over to the police in a flash.

I pushed myself away from my desk and rubbed my eyes. All that reading can be a challenging task. I went to the office closet to prepare for my trip to Raoul's. I picked up the necessary photography equipment, which consisted of the small digital camera all of us used, except for the "real photographer" on staff who had his own equipment, and I made sure that I had a fresh notebook. Then I grabbed the empty grocery bag next to my desk and moved the other two up the line. At least I'd be getting out this afternoon, I thought to myself, as I stuffed the empty Super Save More bag into the recycle bin with a feeling of freedom. A bag emptied and an outdoor excursion coming up, life sure was good at the *Ravensford Chronicle*.

I pulled my lunch bag out of the small refrigerator in the back corner of the office and stopped at the coffee maker to pour myself a mug of bitter brew from what remained in the morning pot. I returned to my desk and got out the plastic container of yogurt and peeled off the top. Normally with my lunch I read a novel or the Boston newspaper, if I've bothered to pick one up. But I had just finished all the books I'd borrowed from the library, and I hadn't been out this morning for a paper. So I reached across the desk and flipped over yesterday's *Chronicle*, which I hadn't bothered to look at. The thrill of reading my own anonymous columns had disappeared months ago, and the news of Ravensford tended toward a certain sameness: auto accidents, burglaries, and cuts in the already inadequate school funding. But I still liked to glance through the phone call-in line, so I could be reassured that my neighbors were still as opinionated as usual. As I slid the paper toward me, the first section flipped over and I was faced with the obituaries. Although I didn't know many of the people in town, my eye ran quickly over the page.

"Marion Michelle Jensen, 53, of this city." My eye moved past the line, then returned with a sense of shock that sent my spoon clattering down on the desk. How many Marion M. Jensens could there be in a town the size of Ravensford? I read the article. There was nothing about "dying after a long illness" or "donations should be made to the cancer fund." There was no indication at all as to the cause of death, only the vague statement that she had "died at home," leaving behind a daughter and a mother who lived in town. The article also said that she had worked for the last ten years in the offices at the Stanhope Cement Company. Viewing hours were today at Fegoda's Funeral Home with burial tomorrow. I stared at the small picture next to the obituary. It was rather formal, as if she'd been dressed up for a special occasion, but she looked like a nice woman, someone who just wanted to have a happy life.

I sat back in my chair. A feeling of emptiness came over me as I realized that Desperate in Ravensford would never get to see my response to her letter. She had died in the middle of our conversation. If only I'd gotten to her letter sooner, at least she might have felt a sense of comfort that someone had cared about her problem. A darker thought came into my mind. What if her death was somehow related to her conflict with "Jack"?

Don't jump to conclusions, girl, Auntie Mabel warned. *You've got no reason to think that this is anything other than a natural death.*

"But what if," I insisted. "I can't just let it go. No one else knows about her relationship with 'Jack' other than me. It's my responsibility to find out if he had anything to do with her death."

Auntie Mabel frowned, then she nodded. *But at least do it through official channels. Contact Chief Farantello.*

It was my turn to nod agreement, but I resisted.

Michael Farantello was the chief of the small detective branch in Ravensford. We'd dated on and off for a total of about three months, and I'd thought that maybe, just maybe, it was going to lead to something. However, it all ended when his daughter was diagnosed with diabetes. Farantello and her mother were divorced, but the girl—Andrea is her name—using all the wiles of a thirteen-year-old, said that the one thing she thought would help her recover most was to have her parents return to living together. Pretty clever; I had to hand it to the kid. If you're going to have a serious illness, you should take advantage of it to get the one thing you want out of life, having your family back together again. I'm not really as cold about all this as I sound. It could be that Andrea wasn't really that manipulative, and Michael was a little too quick to feel guilty about having a girlfriend. Who knows? At any rate, he suggested that we stop seeing each other until Andrea showed some definite signs of improvement. We'd gotten together briefly over the winter when Andrea's condition had improved, but it hadn't lasted. I wasn't certain that Andrea's condition would ever be good enough for us to be together permanently.

Well, Auntie Mabel prodded me.

I shook my head. "Not just yet. I'll contact Farantello after I've done some checking on my own. There may be a simple explanation for Marion's death that had nothing to do with 'Jack.' "

You're avoiding Chief Farantello, Auntie Mabel said in an accusatory tone.

"So call me human," I shot back, quickly spooning the remaining yogurt into my mouth and gulping some too hot coffee.

Auntie Mabel remained silent, and before she could come up with any new ideas, I grabbed my camera and headed out the door.

Raoul's School of Ballroom Dance was in a small strip mall just outside the center of town. A double storefront sandwiched between a music store and a liquor store, the mall seemed to provide just about all you would need for a good time. I moved backwards and forwards and fiddled with the zoom lens until I managed to get a picture of the front that didn't show the establishments on either side. Stuffing my notebook in the back pocket of my jeans, I walked up to the glass door of Raoul's, which sported the silhouette of a couple doing an improbably deep dip. I wasn't sure I would trust any man to tip me that far backwards with only a hardwood floor behind my head.

I walked inside. There was a tiny lobby and an unoccupied desk with a pile of brochures on top. I took one. The more information you had, the easier it was to write the story.

18

I went through a curved archway and found myself facing a surprisingly large and empty room. No outdoor light made it into this section and the ceiling lights were set at restaurant dim. Aside from a complicated-looking sound system at the other end of the room, all I could see was a small table off to the side holding several large silver statuettes of people dancing. The table was covered with a white cloth, which made it appear like an altar. I wracked my memory and managed to dredge up the name Terpsichore for the Greek muse of dance. Who said my time in college was wasted?

No one appeared to be around. Maybe the owner was next-door buying some music or at his other neighbors finding a means to drown his sorrows at the absence of business. The long expanse of polished wood floor gleamed seductively. I put down my camera, walked out into the middle of the floor, and did a tentative spin. I was surprised at how smoothly I turned. Childhood memories of spinning around in the middle of fields of wildflowers until I fell to the ground in giddy delight went through my mind. I wasn't sure that I had ever actually done that, but I felt that every little girl should have. I tried another turn, letting more abandon creep into my movements. My arms went out from my sides with hands turned up as I went around and around, the darkened room spinning before me.

It seemed as though I could hear music, a song that reminded me of old movies with Fred and Ginger. An arm came around my waist and a hand took mine. Suddenly I was swept way across the floor, my feet having learned on their own how to dance. I thought there was a man holding me in his arms, but I closed my eyes and didn't dare look up at his face. This was a dream I didn't want to end.

Around the floor we went, his firm lead telling me exactly what to do, so we were together as one. I wasn't certain my feet were even touching the floor. I knew we looked graceful, just like every dazzling couple in every "dance" movie I'd ever seen. I was in a luscious gown and he was in tails, and we had that indefinable something called class. All the other dancers had cleared the floor and stood along the sides of the ballroom staring with a mixture of envy and amazement as we floated past them. But like all dreams, this one ended with the final chord and silence echoing around the room.

My partner released me. I opened my eyes and was half-surprised to see that there was actually a flesh and blood man standing in front of me. Tall and close to handsome, with long, light brown hair and blue eyes, he gave me a boyish grin that made him look even more adorable.

"Sorry for taking that dance without asking."

You can take anything you want without asking, I almost replied, then decided that might be open to misinterpretation.

"What dance was that?" I asked.

"The fox-trot," he replied.

"I've heard of it," I said, vaguely recalling a few dance lessons my friend Vicky had given me when I was going to be her maid of honor.

"Are you Raoul?" I asked, still a bit stunned.

"No."

I tried to compose myself, wondering whether some passerby had just happened into the studio and decided to dance with me.

"Aren't you the owner?"

"Yes, I am." He stuck out his hand. "Chris Bell."

I took his hand. It fit just as smoothly in mine as when we danced. "Then why is—"

"This studio called Raoul's?" He finished the sentence for me.

I nodded.

"I have no idea."

A smile played along his lips.

"I'm a reporter from the *Chronicle,* and I'm trying to do a story on your opening," I said, getting a little testy. I pulled out my notebook and put on my just-the-facts face.

"Sorry," he said, instantly contrite. "But you see, I bought the place from Sidney Baumberger. He'd had it for the last fourteen years, and retired recently due to arthritis. He purchased it from somebody named Tim O'Brien, who started the studio. You know what I think?"

The hint of mystery in his voice sucked me in. "What?" I asked breathlessly.

"I don't think there ever was a Raoul. I think O'Brien was probably one of the dark Irish, and he figured that pretending to be Latin would bring in the women."

"Hmm." I didn't think plain old Chris Bell was going to have much trouble in that regard either. "What's that all about?" I asked, pointing to the trophies.

He blushed. "I know. It's a little ostentatious. I intend to have a more discreet case installed out in the lobby to hold them as soon as I have the money."

"Those are yours?"

"Yeah. I was a competitive ballroom dancer in college and went on to do some amateur competitions after that. I won a few times."

"Quite a few, I'd say."

He smiled. "Well, I have to share the credit. It takes two to tango, as they say."

"Did you always have the same partner?"

He nodded.

"Is she working here with you?" I asked as much for personal as professional information.

"She got married. She's living out in California now."

I asked Chris some questions about what dances he taught,

the rates he charged, and all the other business type of stuff. I also took a couple of pictures of the interior. We worked out some vague but attractive wording that would bring people in to see what the studio was about. I promised to emphasize the fact that he offered a free demonstration lesson.

"You might also tell people that ballroom dancing is really having a resurgence."

I gave him a skeptical glance.

"Really. I know, everyone thinks that only the World War II generation and soon-to-be marrieds care about it, but lot of young people are taking an interest. All that non-touching dancing is getting kind of old. People want to get back in contact again without feeling that it has to lead to something more. Think how nice it is to be in a man's arms without worrying about what's going to come next."

I pondered that and wondered if it was possible.

Chris gave me a long look. "You know you're pretty graceful. Maybe you'd consider taking lessons."

I smiled to myself. Whenever I did a story on a new business, the proprietor always tried to get me to buy some of the product. I recalled the butcher's shop I'd done a story on recently where the guy tried to convince me that I should buy twenty pounds of ground round. "You could always freeze it," he told me. "And you'd be surprised how fast it would disappear."

Yeah, I thought, if I fed a football team.

Compared to that, ballroom dancing seemed like an attractive possibility.

"I'll think about it," I said, turning toward the door. "But I don't have much money right now."

"And I don't have many students," Chris said. "Maybe we could work out a deal for a reduced rate."

I looked up at him, and he gave me a hopeful smile. With his

22

boyish, aw-shucks good looks, I figured that he wouldn't be without students for long—at least not without female ones.

"I'll give it some thought," I said, and hurried out of the studio before I found myself signing a contract for fifty lessons.

I went straight back to the *Chronicle* offices tucked up a narrow lane from Main Street. I pushed through the double glass door and waved to Grissy, who now sat behind the counter, having taken the morning off. She's the receptionist and mistress of all trades who answers the phone, takes the advertisements, and deals with complaints about missed deliveries. A tall blond woman in her early thirties, she was from Germany and, as if to prove the stereotype, extremely efficient. She had recently replaced Mrs. Pear, who had finally found a new husband while on one of her many smoke breaks.

I went past Grissy's desk and into the one large room where the part-time reporters had their desks. These were the folks who handled the special stuff: the local sports, the issues in education, and social events. They rarely used their desks, generally emailing their stories from home. I was full-time staff, but not technically a reporter. There was one full-time reporter at the moment, and he had his own small, private office. I knew Gran was pushing for Roger to add a second full-time reporter's position, so I might have a shot at promotion. But so far the budget wouldn't allow it. My desk was among the part-timers, but it was the best of them, being back in the corner by a window.

I settled gingerly into my temperamental desk chair and typed my password into the terminal. While I waited for the screen to pop up, Derrick Malone, the new full-time reporter, walked into the room. Roger had hired him out of the broadcast media where I'd heard he had been an assistant producer. In his early thirties and rather intense-looking, he had a thick head of hair that always seemed so casually arranged I suspected he spent serious time working on it in the morning. He gave me a brief nod, then immediately disappeared into his office and closed the door. The big advantage of a private office is that no one knows how much work you're doing.

Small talk wasn't his strength. And the few times I'd tried to start up a conversation with him about Ravensford politics, he'd quickly made it clear that he had access to information that made my opinions hopelessly irrelevant. Maybe he did. Did that mean he couldn't throw me a few crumbs of casual chat out of politeness? But I always made a point of reading his articles, and he had a way with words.

I spent the next twenty minutes writing and then refining my little piece on Raoul's. I even included a clever little comment about there being only a virtual Raoul. If Sam Aaronson, the managing editor, didn't like that flash of humor he could always take it out. He'd never been shy in the past about editing my work. I included two photos as an attachment to give him options, then punched the key that sent my story forty feet down the hall to his computer.

I sat back in the chair and checked my watch: three o'clock. I looked out the window at the bright blue September sky, temperature in the high sixties with a nice warm sun. Fall is definitely the best season in New England. It was a nice day to take a stroll. I could easily walk across the town green and a couple of blocks over to Fegoda's Funeral Home. That would give the Jensen family twenty minutes to settle down before I arrived. The newspaper had mentioned a daughter and mother. Even though Marion had said that no one knew about her relationship with "Jack," there was always a chance that one of them knew more than she suspected. Or maybe her best friend would be there, perhaps the one person, other than Auntie Mabel, to whom she had confided her deepest secrets. It was worth a shot.

"Hi."

I spun my chair around so fast that it almost sent me sprawling head over heels onto the institutional green floor. Years of holding Auntie Mabel's bulk had weakened the chair's springs, so it did unexpected and potentially embarrassing things.

"Sorry to startle you," Derrick Malone said.

"Hi," I replied, trying to subtly rebalance myself in the chair.

"Nice day, isn't it," he said looking out the window.

"Yes."

We looked out the window in intense silence for a moment as if we never expected to see another nice day again and really wanted to remember this one.

"I was wondering . . . I've got these tickets to a concert up at the college for Wednesday night. It's a string quartet. I guess they're pretty good; they've played in New York City. Anyway, if you're free, I was wondering if you'd like to go with me."

Gone was the self-confidence bordering on arrogance that was there when I had tried to discuss politics with him, now replaced by the hesitance of a teenage boy asking a girl out on a first date. It was cute; it was endearing. I wondered if he was only going out with me because my Gran was married to the owner of the paper. Then I figured, what the heck, who cares? It certainly wouldn't be the first time that a guy had gone out with me for some ulterior motive.

"I realize that you may already have a boyfriend, but you're the only single woman around my age that I've met so far where I wouldn't have a conflict of interest in going out with her."

I gave him a quizzical look.

"You know, if I'm going to write a story about someone, it doesn't look good if we have a personal relationship. People would question my objectivity. But you're a colleague."

That made me feel so wanted. I truly was the only fish in the sea.

"So this is sort of a way of keeping it all in the family, in a manner of speaking. I'm a safe date."

He thought for a moment. "I guess you could put it that way."

Kind of like going out with your cousin, I was going to say, but decided not to torture him further.

"Sure, I'd be happy to go out with you."

"Great," he said, actually smiling for the first time. "I'll pick you up around seven."

"Do you know where I live?"

"At Roger's and your grandmother's condo, right?"

I nodded. Did everyone know that I was getting free housing?

"Sure, I know where that is."

Nothing is secret in this town, I thought, grabbing my bag and heading out the door to Fegoda's. I certainly hoped the same was true when it came to Marion Jensen.

CHAPTER 3

Fegoda's Funeral Home is a monument to death, a sort of stone mini-castle where you wouldn't be surprised to hear that folks awaiting the plague were doing the danse macabre in the huge front room. Frank Fegoda, the man in the black suit who in some mysterious way knew I had arrived and opened the heavy wood door for me before I could knock, was cadaverous enough to be the leader of the dancing pack. He silently pointed a long thin finger to one of the rooms in the back when I told him the name of the person I'd come to see.

I could understand immediately why Marion had been relegated to a back room. There were only three people sitting off to the side when I came in, making even that small room seem empty. I dutifully went up to stand by the coffin and studied the body. It's hard to judge a person's looks once they're dead. I don't care how much people carry on about the marvels of the undertakers' trade, there's something not quite . . . oh, I guess the word is "lifelike" about the way someone looks once they're gone. Marion had been an attractive middle-aged woman who looked like she stayed in pretty good shape. Beyond that it was anyone's guess what kind of an impression she would have made when alive.

As I turned away from the coffin, there were two people standing next to each other and looking at me expectantly. One was a woman in her seventies, whom I figured to be Marion's mother. The other was a woman in her mid-twenties. Since she looked like a younger version of Marion, I guessed it was her daughter. I froze for an instant, realizing that I hadn't worked out a cover story for myself. I couldn't very well admit to being Auntie Mabel, so who was I supposed to be and what was my excuse for being here? As I walked up to them, their faces arranged in expressions of somber greeting, I decided I had to do what good reporters through the ages have always done; I had to lie.

"Hi," I said, taking the older woman's thin hand. "I'm Laura Magee. I used to work in the office with Marion. I'm very sorry for your loss."

The woman nodded, her eyes filling with tears. "Thank you for coming, dear."

I quickly moved on to the daughter.

"I'm Katie Jensen," the girl said, giving my hand a powerful squeeze that suggested years of field hockey or softball.

She stepped aside for a moment as her grandmother went back to her seat next to a woman of about the same age who might have been her sister. Then she quickly returned to stand directly in front of me.

"I thought my mother worked alone in the office?" she said. "And the folks from Stanhope aren't coming until tonight."

Hmm. The gerbil that passed for my brain raced even faster on its wheel.

"Actually, I worked there as a temp during a busy time a couple of years ago. But I would run into your mother around town off and on."

Katie nodded, not quite convinced, probably wondering why I would come to the wake of such a casual acquaintance.

I looked back over my shoulder at the coffin.

"As a matter of fact, I ran into your mother at the supermarket a while back. She didn't mention anything about being ill."

"She wasn't ill."

"How did she die?"

The girl pulled me a few feet away from the older folks.

"She fell down the cellar stairs."

"I see."

"At least that's what the police say."

"You sound like you don't believe them."

"Her body was found at the foot of the stairs, but Mom was a healthy woman in her early fifties."

"Accidents can happen to anyone," I said gently.

"What are the odds?" she snapped back.

Some people handle grief with tears; others face it with anger. Clearly the latter was Katie's way. Anyway, I told myself, I was on her side, more or less. I was here because I was afraid that Marion's death was no accident.

"So what do you think happened?"

Faced with having to provide an explanation for her mother's death, Katie's face dissolved. She pulled an incongruous red bandana out of her suit-jacket pocket and gave her nose a loud blow.

"I don't know," she said hoarsely.

"Was she on some kind of medication that could have caused her to lose her balance?"

"She took medicine for her blood pressure, but I don't think it bothered her." We stared across the dimly lit room for a moment. "Oh, I don't know what I think," Katie burst out suddenly. "But I can't believe she could have just fallen down the stairs."

"Do you think she was pushed?"

I guess I had expected her to be surprised at the suggestion, but instead her eyes narrowed.

"That's a funny thing to say."

"Not really. If you don't think it was an accident, then what else could it be?"

29

"You mean, murder," she whispered.

As she said the word her mouth took the shape of someone savoring an unusual food for the first time, intrigued but not sure whether she liked the new experience or not.

"Was your mother seeing anyone?" I asked.

"You mean a boyfriend?" The girl shook her head. "In the five years since she divorced Dad, she hasn't gone out much. There was some guy a few years ago that she saw for a while. But I don't know about anyone since then."

"Did she see your father often?"

Katie smiled. "He left Mom for a younger woman and never looked back. He moved out to the Boston area, and I don't think she's actually seen him since the divorce."

"What did she do for fun?"

"She went places with Grandma and me. She liked to read and knit."

The woman had lived like a nun if Katie was to be believed. Of course, daughters probably weren't always reliable judges of their mothers' lives.

"So no boyfriend?"

"Why do you keep harping on that?" the girl said, shoving her face toward mine.

Time for another lie. "Well, it's just that when I saw your mother a few weeks ago, she mentioned something about going out with a new guy."

"Who?"

"She didn't tell me his name."

Katie snorted. "I'm sure that if she was dating someone she'd have told me about it and probably Grandma. You must have misunderstood."

"Sure. Of course, it's possible that she didn't want to tell the two of you until she was sure that it was something serious. Had she been acting any differently lately?"

The girl opened her mouth to give me a quick negative, then stopped.

"She did seem a little more excited for the last couple of months. I even asked her about it, but she just brushed me off. But when I saw her last week, she seemed kind of down. I asked her if anything was wrong, and she told me that things were just really busy at work."

I nodded.

"Do you think she was going out with a violent guy? Why wouldn't she tell me about that?"

"Do you tell your mother about all of your dates?" I asked.

She frowned. "So how are we going to find out what happened?"

The word "we" worried me a bit. I wasn't sure I wanted a partner.

"Let me think about it."

"If you come up with any ideas, get back to me." Katie took one of the memorial cards off the table next to her and jotted down a number on the back. "This is my cell phone. Call me anytime."

I nodded. As I left the room I waved to the grandmother who called out "thank you for coming."

I wondered if I had done anyone any favors.

bucket and a bag full of groceries at the bottom of the stairs. We surmised that she left the bucket on the stairs, planning to carry it downstairs later, then forgot it was there and stepped in it while she was going down with the groceries. She lost her balance and for one fatal moment couldn't get herself to drop the grocery bag and grab the railing. It could happen to anyone."

"I suppose," I said doubtfully.

"Laura, I've answered your question. Now why don't you tell me why you're so interested in Marion's death?"

"You've shown me yours, so I should show you mine," I said. I could have kicked myself for such tasteless teasing. I didn't blame Farantello for not smiling.

Not trusting myself to say anything more, I reached in my bag and got out Marion's letter to Auntie Mabel. Farantello was one of the few people in town who knew my occupation. In fact the original Auntie Mabel had been a sort of unofficial police informant, revealing information to Farantello when she thought it might help prevent a crime, so I was just carrying on a long-standing tradition. I watched Michael read the letter. I saw his eyes go through it once, then return to the top and carefully go through it again. He'd told me once that successful detective work was mostly a matter of being fully present in the moment, so that you really paid attention to the evidence that was around you.

"What do you think?" I asked when his brown eyes focused on mine. "Maybe she didn't just fall down those stairs. She could have had a little help."

He frowned. "It seems that she may have been involved with a less than forthright guy."

"And she was planning to confront him."

"Possibly. But she had already given him the money. I doubt there was any way she was going to get it back. What would he have to gain by killing her?"

34

"Maybe she planned to expose him by telling people what he'd done."

Farantello gave me a long glance. "According to this, she hasn't even told her family and friends about this guy. Even when things were going well she kept it a secret because of the age difference. Now that he's conned her, I doubt that she was going to go around announcing it to strangers."

"But maybe her anger got the better of her embarrassment. If this guy was really going to stay in town, he couldn't risk having her spreading this story about him."

"Okay, I'll check with her family. Maybe they know more about this than Marion realized."

"I already talked to her daughter at the wake today."

Farantello gave a sigh. "It might have been better if you'd discussed it with me first."

I shrugged. "I figured that if they told me she had died in some perfectly normal way, there'd be no point in bothering you." I smiled as if to show that the last thing I'd want to do is waste police time. "Maybe her neighbors saw something. What time of day did she fall?"

He looked up at the ceiling. "She got home from work at six. Her daughter called at nine and didn't get an answer. She didn't get an answer when she called back at eleven. She became alarmed and went over to the house. She's the one who found the body."

Funny she didn't mention finding the body, I thought to myself. But maybe she got too upset talking about it.

"Any idea how long she'd been dead?"

"At least an hour."

"So we're looking at some time between six and ten. Have you asked around the neighborhood to see if anyone saw something?"

"As a matter of fact we did."

I raised an eyebrow.

"The daughter kept saying how she couldn't believe that her mother had just fallen like that. I figured she was just in denial. No one finds it easy to accept that some pointless accident can take the life of someone you love. The senselessness of it all is hard to swallow. You want it to be part of something that at least gives her death some meaning, even if it's a crime."

"So you talked to the neighbors just to humor her?"

Farantello smiled slightly. "Call it family of the victim therapy."

"And nobody saw anything."

"Not exactly. Mrs. Hannity, a woman in her late eighties who lives up the street a bit, said that she'd seen a red car parked in front of the house sometimes. But she doesn't know if it was there that night or even that week. Time is sort of compressed for Mrs. Hannity."

"That's all?"

"I didn't have a motive, so I couldn't go much further. To all appearances it was an accident, and we had no reason to think otherwise." Farantello held the letter up in the air. "I'll dig a level deeper now that I have this, but all we have is a suspicion."

"How about talking to her friends or co-workers?"

He nodded.

"Her co-workers from Stanhope Cement will be at the viewing tonight. If you'd like me to go back . . ."

Farantello held up a hand. "I'll take over from here."

"Just think about it, Farantello," I said. His first name was Michael, but I almost never used it. There was something about the way his last name rolled off the tongue that appealed to me. "If you or one of your people starts asking questions at the funeral home, it will be all around town in a day that something suspicious happened. Your perp might find out about it and there goes the element of surprise."

"And you could do it better?"

"Sure. I'll just ask around until I find Marion's best friend from work, then I'll carefully ask her whether Marion had a new boyfriend. And don't worry, I'll be subtle."

"Okay, but be discreet."

"Of course," I agreed.

Farantello sat back until the springs in the swivel chair squeaked. "I heard through the grapevine that you were involved in a murder investigation while you were down in Jersey. Did the police there treat you as well as I do?"

I paused for a moment, not sure how to answer.

"They didn't give me any breaks on the professional side."

Farantello smiled complacently.

"But on the personal side, it was a lot less painful," I said, making his smile disappear.

He looked like he wanted to say more, maybe to apologize again for the way things turned out between us. But I left the office before he had a chance to begin.

CHAPTER 5

I settled down behind my desk and eyed the two bags standing there like little soldiers demanding attention. I was still keyed up after my conversation with Farantello and knew that an hour spent answering letters would help to calm me down. I reached into the first bag, swirled my hand around in the pile of letters, and randomly pulled one out. I slit the envelope, removed the typed letter, and unfolded it on my desk, feeling a small surge of excitement at the prospect of getting a glimpse into someone else's life.

Dear Auntie Mabel:

I have been reading your column with great interest since it resumed several weeks ago. Unfortunately, I have started to detect the same negative attitude toward men that I found in the responses of your predecessor. Please take note of what happened to her and adjust your answers accordingly.

Dickens

The absurd but flattering thought momentarily ran through my head that somehow Charles Dickens was commenting on my column from the next world. Then the tone of the letter struck me like a slap across the face. I read the short paragraph again, my hands beginning to shake and my stomach twisting. This was clearly a threat made all the more menacing by the pseudo-polite wording of the letter, which suggested that here was someone who didn't get mad but got even. My mind spun and the words began to blur on the page.

Calm down, child, and think, I heard Auntie Mabel say. My mind cleared enough to read the letter one more time, and sequential thoughts slowly formed out of the swirl. How did the writer know that the original Auntie Mabel was no longer writing the column? Were our styles that markedly different, or did Dickens have inside information? Although it was general knowledge around the newspaper that I wrote the column, Roger had given me to believe that employees were strictly warned not to disseminate this information.

A second thought took shape. Dickens clearly implied that something bad had happened to my predecessor because of her responses. Now granted, Auntie Mabel's death by choking at the Big Bun on their all-you-can-eat shrimp and lobster night was a bad thing. If only one of the many people watching her struggles had been capable of performing the Heimlich maneuver on a large person, she would have been saved, and I'd be doing who-knows-what. But this hardly sounded like murder, and Dickens had clearly insinuated that my predecessor's death was punishment for what she had written. Roger St. Claire was gone for the day, but I promised myself that the first thing tomorrow morning I would question him in detail about Auntie Mabel's demise.

Does Dickens know who I am? That was the third and most worrisome thought that occurred to me. Again, my identity was supposed to be kept secret, but when one looked around the world at how much confidential information is routinely leaked from so-called security organizations, I had to wonder how much faith to have in the *Chronicle*'s ability to keep my paltry secret.

Speaking of identities, a thought occurred to me, and I snatched the envelope off the desk. Damn, no return address. Clearly Dickens was not as careless as poor Marion, probably not a mistake to be expected in a potential murderer. I wondered if there was any way to discover the identity of the letter writer. I focused on the name "Dickens." It wasn't just the name of an author. My grandmother occasionally used the phrase "a little dickens" to describe a poorly behaved child. I wondered exactly what the word meant. I reached over and pulled the dictionary off my shelf. In a second I had the right page: "dickens, 'di-kenz, n. (euphemism), the devil." I stared at the definition for a long moment as if English had suddenly turned into a foreign language, then slowly let the book close.

"I've just been threatened by the devil," I said to myself, not sure whether I wanted to laugh or cry.

After a few moments spent absorbing the shock, I pulled my jacket from the back of the chair and walked to the front desk where Grissy was working on tomorrow's classifieds.

"Grissy, I need you to do something."

There must have been a special energy in my voice giving it an air of command because Grissy's Germanic spine straightened, and she snapped to attention as much as one can when seated in a chair. She was fully focused on me, awaiting my orders. A small smile played across her lips as if this was what she lived for.

"If anyone comes into this office attempting to find out the identity of the person who writes the Auntie Mabel column, you are to tell them nothing, and, if possible, you should get their name and address."

She nodded crisply. "I will create a request for information form that will require them to give us that information, and say we will get back to them with an answer within three business days."

"Which of course we will never do."

"Of course."

"And if you see any strangers loitering in the vicinity of our

40

offices, you will notify the police."

"I will demand that they send an officer immediately."

I nodded, wishing I could think of some more orders to give her. I felt a strong desire to say "carry on," but instead I wished her a good evening and left. As I walked out to my car, I found myself glancing around me as if expecting to be attacked any minute. It was good I had two things to do tonight or else I would have been tempted to go home, lock the doors, and hide under the blankets. Not a very mature or proactive response. But as it was, I had to go to Fegoda's Funeral Home to check on Marion Jensen's dating habits, and after that I had promised my friend Corinne that I would drop in at her open house for her new antiques gallery. Trying to convince myself that Dickens couldn't possibly know Auntie Mabel's true identity, I started up my car and headed back to my condo.

My condo wasn't technically mine. My grandmother and Roger St. Claire owned it. They were letting me live there for the first year free. After that I would pay rent. Hopefully my salary at the newspaper would be increased by then, so I could afford it. The condo was in a good location, just down the hill from the town center and across the street from a public golf course. As I got out of my car I could see that there were a number of golfers getting in some tee time on a beautiful fall afternoon. I ambled up the walk to my front door, pretending to myself that I wasn't the least bit worried about someone spying on me. My pretense must not have worked very well because I felt a lot better once I was inside with the door shut and locked behind me. Even then, I went through the place trying to remember if everything was exactly as I'd left it. I didn't really believe anyone had broken in while I was at work, but I intended to play it safe.

Only after assuring myself that everything was secure, did I open the refrigerator and take out a yogurt. I would be eating later at Corinne's open house, so I just wanted something to hold me until then. At five-six with ample curves, I had to watch my diet and gets lots of exercise to avoid becoming zaftig. I settled in on the sofa, and read the *Boston Globe* as I ate. This was my one tie with the city where I had lived for the greater part of the last decade while in college and in my early working career. Deep down I suppose I harbored some hopes of returning there, although I wasn't sure how. Of course, I also wasn't taking any positive steps to bring about my return, like applying for jobs there. I frequently worried that I had settled down in Ravensford out of laziness or inertia and that my real future lay somewhere else. As usual I got drowsy when thinking about my future, and in a couple of minutes I was sound asleep.

When I awakened an hour had passed, and it was time for me to get ready to go to the wake. Since I didn't plan to return home between the wake and Corinne's open house, I had to wear something suitable to both. I had a black dress that was demure enough for the funeral home and, with the addition of a sparkly necklace, would pass muster for a more social occasion. When I was ready I locked the door carefully behind me and headed out to the parking lot, staring deeply into all the shadows along the way. Nothing threatening loomed out at me from the darkness and soon I was safely in my car driving away.

When I pulled into the parking lot behind Fegoda's, it was fuller than I had expected. And when I entered the room for Marion's wake, it was almost a standing-room-only crowd. Given the high level of conversation, I guessed that many of the people here knew each other, so I was willing to bet that the Stanhope Cement contingent had arrived. I sat down on the fringe of a group of four women who were chatting away. The woman right next to me nodded after giving me a slightly puzzled glance, as if trying to recall what I did at Stanhope. I smiled and leaned into the conversation, nodding as if I knew what they were talking about. Stanhope must have a happy work environment because no one accused me of being a company spy trying to find out the employees' real view of management.

When there was a lull in the chatter, I turned to the woman next to me and asked in a low voice, "Who would you say was Marion's best friend at the company?"

She thought for a moment. "Oh, I guess that would be Charlotte Stevens. They worked side by side in order processing before Marion got promoted."

I gazed around the room as if trying to spot Charlotte. I shook my head in pretend frustration.

"Is she here?" I asked.

My new friend gave me an odd look. "She's right there," she said, pointing to a woman sitting two rows in front of me.

"You'd hardly know her with that new hair style, would you," I gushed.

Before the woman next to me could really start to wonder what I did at Stanhope, I walked briskly down the row and went up two, settling into a seat next to Charlotte. She glanced over at me and nodded. From the expression on her face, I surmised that she was truly grieving for Marion.

"It's really a shame," I murmured.

Charlotte glanced over at me. "It certainly is. She was only fifty-three."

I guessed Charlotte was about the same age.

"And to die in a freak accident like that."

"It's hard to believe. Marion was one of the least clumsy people I know. We were on the company bowling team together. She was a great athlete."

"Well, I guess accidents can happen to anybody."

Charlotte eyed me carefully. "Do you work at Stanhope? I don't recognize you."

"No, I'm actually a friend of Marion's daughter, Katie."

I could see her starting to dismiss me as someone who really didn't know the deceased, so I hurried on, "But I ran into Marion in the supermarket a few weeks ago and she was telling me she had a new boyfriend. She seemed so happy. That just makes this all the more tragic."

Charlotte nodded. "She did seem happy a few weeks ago. But when I asked her about him a few days ago, she closed up and didn't want to talk about it."

"Did she ever tell you his name?" I asked.

Charlotte shook her head and smiled. "I would kid her that the guy must be imaginary. But she said, no, he was very real. All I learned is that he wasn't someone who worked at Stanhope."

"I wonder if he's here now," I said, scanning the crowd as if he would be wearing a placard reading "Sleazy Boyfriend."

"I think I recognize all the men here as employees of Stanhope."

"I wonder if there's someone that she would have told his name to?"

"I was her best friend," Charlotte said proudly.

"Can you think of any other way we can find this guy?"

"Why is that so important?"

I froze for a moment because I couldn't very well tell her that I suspected him of being a murderer.

"Well, what if he lives outside of Ravensford? He might not even know that Marion has died."

"I never thought of that," she said with a stricken look on her face.

"So can you think of any way we can find this guy?"

"All I know is that Marion would go to the bar at the Collins Inn, and sometimes she would talk to men there. I told her that seemed awfully risky, but she said that a single woman had to take chances if she wanted to meet a man." Charlotte fingered her wedding ring, "I'm glad I don't have to worry about that."

The Collins Inn was run by Millicent Collins, the last living descendent of Captain Collins, who was the only officer that George Washington had ever publicly threatened to horse whip. Over the years the Collins brand had been buffed up quite a lot by the family, until now only a few historians knew that he wasn't a great hero of the Revolution.

"Yeah, it's a jungle out there," I said, glancing down at my own naked finger. "Well, maybe I'll stop by the Collins Inn and see if anyone knows this guy."

Charlotte nodded. "If you do find him, tell him that Marion was a wonderful woman."

I promised to do that, although I didn't think he would care.

CHAPTER 6

To go from Fegoda's to Corinne's shop, I returned to the town green, which was still the center of Ravensford, as it had been since colonial times. Although the town had expanded outward in recent years, the library, several banks, the city hall, and the main firehouse still clustered around the oval park. A couple of blocks of stores and businesses occupied the nineteenth-century buildings that radiated out from the green like the spokes of a wheel, as they always had, but now they had to compete with an office park and several strip malls that had sprung up on the outskirts of town. Residential developments had also grown outward in concentric circles from the old downtown, serving as bedroom communities for those working in Springfield or even further away in Hartford, Connecticut.

Corinne's new shop, Park Street Antiques, was two blocks out from the green on the western spoke, in a two-story white colonial. Most of the nearby houses were rather elegant homes from the mid- to late-nineteenth century, although most of them had been converted into offices for law firms, insurance companies, and medical practices. Corinne had started by renting space a little further up the street, but success had allowed her to expand. It had cost a ton of money to take this building, which had been a rental and suffered from years of neglect, and upgrade it to the level where it was both safe and elegant. Only by creating a small apartment for herself to live in on the second floor had she been able to make the financing work.

I pulled down the long driveway to the parking lot behind the house. I was relieved to find that strong spotlights illuminated the area, but I was still a bit on edge as I walked up the driveway to the front door. Once inside I was greeted by the aroma of incense, which came from candles burning on the buffet table that filled the room to my right. I knew that a number of antiques had been moved out of the rooms in order to provide plenty of space for the gathering. When Corinne had first mentioned the idea of having a gala opening party, I had expressed concern about possible damage to the merchandise, but Corinne had pooh-poohed the problem.

"Most of this stuff isn't valuable," Corinne had said in her usual frank way. "It's just old. A few more stains and scratches will just make it look more desirable. And if somebody really does break something, they'll feel so guilty, they'll probably insist on buying it. Hey, maybe it would be a good idea to leave a few of the more fragile things in strategic locations where somebody is almost bound to knock them over." Then Corinne had given me a broad wink that left me wondering whether she was serious or not.

I had just hung my coat on an ornate rack that appeared to be made out of deer antlers when a firm hand grabbed my arm. I turned and found Corinne smiling at me. She was wearing a bright red dress that helped accentuate her curves and would draw men to her like flies to honey. But there was more to Corinne's appeal. She also had a way of focusing her attention on whomever she was speaking to as if he or she was the only person in the room. Even though she was in her early forties, Corinne appeared a decade younger.

"Glad you finally got here," Corinne said, "there are some people I'd like you to meet."

The last thing I felt like doing was meeting new people. "Maybe I could just browse around on my own for a while or maybe you need some help upstairs in the kitchen."

"The caterer has got it under control, and I don't want you hiding away. This is a chance for you to meet more folks in Ravensford. You've been here more than a year, but outside of the newspaper and police department you hardly know anyone. I want you circulating around the room tonight."

Resigned to my fate, I allowed myself to be escorted into the room with the buffet table. About twenty people were standing around in small conversational groups.

"Red or white?" Corinne asked, pointing to the wine bottles on the table.

"Is the punch spiked?"

Corinne shook her head and I poured myself a glass.

"But loosen up. You need to make some friends."

"You're my friend," I said with a small smile.

"I mean make some more friends. Maybe even a few of the other gender. How does that sound?"

"Unlikely."

Corinne rolled her eyes. "Don't give up before you even start."

Pulling insistently on my arm, she brought me over to meet a couple in their fifties who were admiring a hope chest under the front window.

"Laura, I'd like you to meet George and Doris Pomfret. George is the principal of Ravensford Middle School and his wife teaches there. This is Laura Magee, she works on the *Chronicle*."

Even Corinne didn't know exactly what I did at the paper, so she couldn't give the game away. But I knew I had to think quickly because the first question I'm usually asked involves the specifics of my job. George Pomfret didn't disappoint.

"What do you do on the paper?" he asked, as his eyes followed Corinne sinuously making her way across the room.

"I write up advertisements, classifieds, and once in a while I get to do a story."

Most of that was actually Grissy's work, but I had to say something. I tried to make it sound as boring as possible, so we could get on to another topic.

"It's nice to find a young woman who knows how to write these days," his wife said, her lips forming a stern line of disapproval. "I teach English, and I often despair for the future of the language. Most young people today are barely literate."

I smiled politely. Although I had known colleagues over the years who came close to proving the point, I was reluctant to get into a trashing contest directed at the younger generation. There would be plenty of time for that when I got older.

"Here comes someone else who barely fits into the literate category," George Pomfret mumbled.

I followed his glance and watched as a beefy man of around forty joined us.

"George, Doris," he said as if checking their names off a mental list.

George nodded, while Doris's lips pressed together even more tightly.

His eyes brightened as he looked at me. "And who might you be?"

George opened his mouth to introduce us, but before he could speak I said, "I'm Laura Magee. And who might you be?"

The smiled disappeared from his face. Clearly he wasn't someone who could take as well as he gave.

"I'm Cliff Moore, the chief of police. And although I don't recognize you, I know the name. You've been involved in several crimes here in Ravensford."

"No, I've been involved in *solving* several crimes."

He glared at me. I wasn't very concerned, because he didn't know about my connection to Auntie Mabel. The real Auntie Mabel had never liked the chief and had only made herself known to Farantello with the understanding that he never tell his boss.

"Her grandmother is Jessica Hallowell," George volunteered, proving that everyone knows everyone in a small town.

"So you're *her* granddaughter. I might have known."

I was about to ask him exactly what he meant by that, when Corinne swept by and pulled him away, saying that she wanted him to check on the quality of the lock she'd had installed on her back door.

"Repulsive man," Doris said when he was out of earshot. "I had him in class when I first started teaching: a poor student, and an even poorer excuse for a man. His being chief of police is an embarrassment to the town."

"Let's not get carried away," George said soothingly.

Doris turned to face him. "You can't deny that he'd have been up on charges for assaulting Abby if he wasn't in charge of the police."

"Now we don't know that's true."

His wife gave a derisive snort.

"Who's Abby?" I asked.

"She was Cliff's wife," Doris answered. "Finally she decided she'd gotten enough beatings. She found a good lawyer, got a divorce, and left town."

"Cliff's never been the same since she got custody of the two boys," George added.

"I'll bet he's hardly noticed they're gone," his wife said.

"What does he have against my grandmother?"

"Jessica was one of the leaders of a citizens' drive to get him replaced a couple of years back, but the chief had the mayor in his pocket and nothing came of it. We have a different mayor now, and there's been some talk of starting up the drive again."

"Let's not bore Laura with all the town's dirty linen," George said, taking her arm and guiding her in the direction of the buffet table. "Why don't we get something to eat?"

"Oh, all right," his wife said, allowing herself to be pulled toward the table.

"I think I'll take a look at this for a moment," I said, moving toward a chest of drawers in one corner. I'd had enough of Ravensford gossip for a while.

I stood in the shadowy corner staring at the mahogany chest without really seeing it. I was thinking about Marion's death. Could she have been involved with the chief of police? He was about ten years younger than she, and he had a penchant for violence. But I wasn't sure I could see him as a romantic con man. He just wasn't that smooth, and I wasn't convinced that even he would stoop to defrauding older women.

"Are you thinking of buying?" a voice asked next to my shoulder.

I must have jumped because the woman immediately apologized for startling me.

"I saw you studying this piece so carefully that I began to wonder if you were in the market. It's a fine, serviceable chest, but only about seventy years old and lots of them were made. It wouldn't be much of an investment."

"I was just daydreaming. I'm not really interested in antiques. I'm here because I'm a friend of Corinne's."

The woman put out a nicely manicured hand. Stylishly dressed and made up, I guessed she was in her early forties.

"I'm Stephanie Fleming. I'm a friend of Corinne's, too. Actually I'm a friend and a competitor. I own The Red Barn."

"I've been past that building lots of times," I said. The Red Barn was literally an old red barn on the north edge of town. The farm it had been part of was long gone, but the barn had survived and been made over into a large antiques store.

"Actually, Corinne and I aren't really competitors most of the time. I sell upscale antiques, many are of museum quality, while Corinne pretty much confines herself to attic finds and what she gets at estate sales. Between us we divide up the market pretty well and don't usually get in each other's way."

"It must be fun dealing with beautiful items all the time."

The woman shrugged. "It was fun when I collected as a hobby, but like anything else, now that it's become my business, I don't get quite the same enjoyment out of it. I almost never purchase anything now just because I like the item, I've got to have a good idea as to whom I can sell the piece."

"Too bad it couldn't have stayed a hobby then," I said.

Stephanie gave me a tight smile. "A house full of antiques is what I got from my divorce settlement, so I decided to make the most of it. Do you live here in town?"

I explained that I lived in a condo by the golf course, but used to live in Jessica Hallowell's house.

"That's a nice old place. Any interesting pieces inside?"

"I wouldn't know one if I saw it."

Stephanie laughed. "Well, I guess I'm not going to do any business talking to you."

"Hi, Stephanie," a man said, joining us. "Did I hear you say you were trying to make a sale?"

"A business owner always has to be on the prowl," Stephanie said, giving his arm a squeeze. "Laura, this is Brian Nash."

Nash was a tall, thin man of around my age. He had the stoop a lot of tall men get who don't want to be noticed. He wore thick glasses with black plastic frames that gave him either a scholarly or nerdy look depending on your point of view.

"Brian works as an English teacher at the high school."

"What do you do, Laura?" Stephanie asked.

"I work on the *Chronicle*. I'm basically a secretary, although occasionally I get to write a story."

"Ah, another writer," Brian said with a bright smile. "We

should get together for coffee some time and discuss the profession."

"I'm afraid that my kind of writing is more cut and dried than creative."

"At least you don't have to grade hundreds of papers. That's truly dreary."

I was tempted to say he should try answering mail all day from people complaining about their lives.

"You'd better not say anything too negative about your job," Stephanie said to me. "It could get back to your boss."

I looked across the room and saw that Roger St. Claire was talking to the Pomfrets.

"And don't get me wrong," Nash said, suddenly nervous. "I know I'm lucky to have a job. I substituted in Ravensford over a year ago. That's why they had me in mind when a tenured position finally opened up."

I nodded vaguely, said, "Excuse me," and quickly headed toward Roger.

Doris was going on about the state of education when I reached their group.

"Sorry," I said, seizing Roger by the arm. "But I have to discuss a matter of some urgency with you regarding work."

Before he could object I had guided him to a dark corner on the other side of the room.

"That was very rude," Roger said. "And what can we possibly have to discuss that won't wait until morning?"

"How did the original Auntie Mabel die?"

"You know how. She choked to death at the Big Bun."

"You want to stick to that story?" I asked.

"Of course, it's the truth."

I reached in my bag and took out the letter. "Then how do you explain this?"

As he read, I watched his Adam's apple bob up and down.

The more it bobbed, the more upset he was. This was a real showstopper.

"You see my point?" I asked when he was finished reading. "He makes her death sound like he brought it about. I'm not sure how anyone could make a person choke to death on her food."

Roger cleared his throat. It was a thorough clearing that went down to the soles of his shoes. Never a good sign.

"There is something that you don't know," he said and paused.

"What don't I know?"

"There was another Auntie Mabel. Someone I hired right after the original one choked to death but before I hired you. Holly Preston worked in the ad department, so I just included the column in her duties. She only had the job for about a month."

"Why did you replace her so soon?"

"She died."

I felt a clenching in my abdomen.

"She died? How?"

"She was struck by a car. It was a hit-and-run. Tragic really, she was only in her forties and a very good worker."

"Did the police ever catch the person who hit her?"

"Not to my knowledge."

"Did Holly receive any threats similar to this?"

"No."

"Maybe she did, and Holly didn't tell you about them."

"Why would Holly conceal this kind of thing from me?"

"Did Holly or the original Auntie Mabel ever get complaints about their columns?"

"Holly didn't have the job long enough to get any. But the original Auntie Mabel occasionally got irate letters disagreeing with her advice or correcting her on some fact or other. But nothing like this," he said waving the letter in front of him. "This is malicious."

"How can I find out more about the way Holly Preston died?"

"You could try the morgue."

"Surely, they don't still have her body there."

"No, no. I meant the morgue at the *Chronicle* where we keep back copies of the paper. We did a front-page story on her death, and followed up on it for a couple of weeks. That would include most of what was in the police report. I'm sure you could also talk with Detective Farantello."

"Is there any way this letter writer could find out that I'm Auntie Mabel? You warn the people at the paper not to tell anyone who she is, don't you?"

"Well, I certainly ask them not to bruit it about."

Not bruiting it about didn't sound strong enough to me.

"I think you should send out an email first thing tomorrow morning to all employees telling them that under no circumstances should they reveal Auntie Mabel's identity, and if anyone tries to find out, they should report it to you."

"I'll do that, of course, but surely this must be some kind of a prank. No one could possibly get angry enough at an advice columnist to try to murder her."

"Tell that to Holly Preston."

"I'll ask your grandmother what she thinks we should do."

"Not just yet. Let's not upset her unless it's absolutely necessary. Okay?"

Reluctantly he nodded his head. I was wondering how long it would take my grandmother to find out that something was wrong.

I turned away and walked over to the buffet table. Not paying attention to what I was doing, I reached out for a plate, then quickly drew my hand back down when I saw how badly it was shaking. Was it from anger or fear? I wondered. And decided that it was a little bit of both.

"Are you okay?"

Corinne appeared at my side with a concerned expression on her face.

"Fine."

"You don't look fine."

"It's the lighting."

"I saw you staring at the food like you were afraid it was going to attack you. You have to relax." She took me by the arm and led me down the buffet table. "Try some of this pâté, and that rum cake over there is to die for. If you like rum, that is. Personally I can't stand the stuff."

"Don't fuss over me. I'll be fine."

"Did Cliff Moore get under your skin? He has a way of doing that with women. I knew I shouldn't have invited him."

"He's a jerk, but that isn't the problem. I've just got things on my mind from work."

"Okay. Well I have to run, but try to enjoy yourself. Have plenty to eat. If there's a lot left over, it'll just test my self-discipline." Corinne patted her hips, "And we know how strong that is."

As Corinne moved away, I grabbed her arm.

"Who's that man?"

"What man?"

I pointed three rooms over to a man standing near the door. He was in the shadows, but something told me that he had been staring at me.

"I don't recognize him. Why? Would you like to meet him?"

Not bothering to answer, I walked rapidly across the room in the direction of the mystery man. He saw me coming. He quickly turned and headed for the back door. I went through the crowd as fast as I dared; however, by the time I reached the door he had disappeared. I kept going until I was out on the side by the porch. I looked both ways up and down the driveway but there was no sign of him. A car started up out on the street in front of the store. I ran off the porch and up the drive, but by the time I got there, all that could be seen were taillights receding into the distance.

"What was that all about?"

I turned. Brian Nash was standing behind me looking up the street. In the glow of the streetlight his expression showed concern for my eccentric behavior.

"Just someone I thought I knew," I answered, walking past him and heading for the front porch. "I guess I was wrong."

Brian shook his head. "From the way he ran, I'd say you were right."

CHAPTER 7

The next morning I went to the Ravensford Public Library. Mrs. Marilyn Hollingsworth stood behind the main desk. A trim woman in her late fifties with stylishly permed gray hair, she glanced up from the book she was leafing through and smiled at me as I walked across the lobby. Marilyn was a friend of my grandmother's, and they both belonged to a book group that met at the library one Wednesday evening a month. I'd been invited to join when I first came to town, but since Marilyn was currently the youngest member, I had politely turned them down. I had no intention of being the sole representative of youth to a bunch of women old enough to be my grandmother.

After exchanging a few pleasantries about the weather, changeable as always in New England, I asked if they carried back issues of the *Chronicle* and the regional newspaper, the *Springfield Republican*. Roger St. Claire had suggested that I consult the back issues of the *Chronicle* housed in the basement of our office building, but I had a feeling that the office manager, Sam Aaronson, who had the key, would want to know what I was looking for. I didn't want to share my concerns with anybody at the paper just yet.

"We carry the *Chronicle* in paper form for the last five years. The *Republican* we carry for the last six months. We have microfiche for earlier years, and you can check the back issues of the *Republican* over the Internet. What dates did you want?"

I did some rapid mental calculations. Holly had been Auntie Mabel shortly before I took over, so I decided that going six weeks back from the start of my employment would probably include the time of her death. I was about to give Marilyn those dates when I remembered that my grandmother had told me several times that Marilyn kept track of everything that happened in town. So much so that she was the town's unofficial historian. I tried a different tack.

"I'm trying to find out some information about the death of Holly Preston. I'm writing a history of the *Chronicle,* and I wanted to give an accurate account of her death. I was going to use what I could find in the paper, but just now I got to thinking that you probably knew her and could tell me more about her personally."

"I wouldn't say she was a friend of mine," Marilyn began, "but I knew her pretty well because she used to come in from time to time to do research for a newspaper article or to borrow books."

"But you weren't friends?"

"We had very different personalities. Holly . . . well . . . I guess that the best word to describe her is diffuse. She never seemed to focus on one thing for very long, and her opinions were usually more a matter of emotion than based on careful reasoning. She tended to shillyshally."

A tightening of Marilyn's mouth indicated this to be a serious moral failing. I started to see why she got on so well with my grandmother.

"But she was very sweet," the librarian added quickly as if trying to take the edge off of her judgment.

"Do you happen to remember when Holly died?"

The librarian nodded. "It was over the Labor Day weekend. I remember because we were closed for the holiday, and when I came back, the story was on the front page of the paper."

"Should I check out the back issues?" I asked.

"No need. I can tell you more than you'll find in the paper."

"I gather it was a hit-and-run."

Marilyn nodded grimly. "The driver was never caught. I don't know how someone can run a person down, then leave her there to die."

"Where did the accident happen?"

"Right in front of her house. She had one of those rural mailboxes at the curb. It was on the other side the street from her house, so she had to cross over to get the mail. The road isn't all that busy; the driver should have seen her. Probably he was drunk."

"What time of day did it happen?"

"Holly had just gotten home from work. She usually went in early and left early, so it was probably around three o'clock."

"A little early for a drunk to be out."

"Some people drink all day long," Marilyn replied, putting the books in front of her together into a neat pile that showed her disapproval of such disorder.

"What sort of work did Holly do on the paper?" I asked, largely to find out if Holly's role as Auntie Mabel was common knowledge.

"Can't they tell you back at the paper?" Marilyn asked, eyeing me suspiciously.

"I've just started my research," I said lamely.

"Well, she was no journalist. I think she handled the classifieds and the occasional obituary or wedding. Probably she was a general secretary."

I nodded. Clearly Holly had done a pretty good job of keeping quiet about her work, but not good enough if Dickens had found out who she was and where she lived. I had a clear picture in my mind of a man waiting by the side of the road for the woman to cross the street and check her mail. Probably she did so at the same time every day, so it would be easy to know when to arrive. Then all he had to do was wait until she was in the middle of the street, step on the gas . . . in my mind I could hear the screech of tires as the car pulled away from the curb and see Holly's expression of surprise and disbelief just before impact.

"I can easily pull out the newspaper article on Holly's accident, although I've told you more than was in it. People were coming in here and talking about what happened for a week after her death, so I got a lot of details."

"I guess that won't be necessary, then. Thanks for your help."

As I walked across the parking lot to my car, I tried to piece together what I knew so far. Dickens clearly had discovered Auntie Mabel's identity or else he could not have made a sly reference to Holly's death in his note. That didn't necessarily mean he was responsible. He could just be taking advantage of circumstances in order to frighten me. Or he could be a cold-blooded murderer. The only way he could have found out about Holly's job was if he was a close friend of hers or had contacts on the *Chronicle* who revealed the information to him. Checking out the columns that Holly had written might give some indication of how she had angered someone enough to be killed. Not that an advice column, no matter how hostile, could ever be a justification for murder. It would take a crazy person to think that way.

The thought that Dickens was most likely a lunatic and currently sizing me up as the next victim caused me to drop my keys as I fumbled to unlock the car. As I straightened from picking them up, I happened to glance toward the bank parking lot on the other side of a chain-link fence from the library. A man was sitting in a car staring at me. Our eyes met and in that instant I knew he was the same man who had been watching me at the party last night. He immediately hit the gas and sped out of the parking lot, but not before I saw his license plate and wrote the number down on the palm of my left hand.

CHAPTER 8

I drove back to the newspaper office with my hands shaking on the wheel. I had a license plate number, now I had to decide what to do with it. As much as I didn't like going to Farantello for help, I couldn't think of any other way to find out the identity of my shadow. Unlike television private investigators, I didn't have a friend in the DMV who could give me that type of information. Also, if this guy following me was Dickens, which seemed likely, he was a murderer and this was clearly a police matter. I'd have to swallow my pride and drop the case in Farantello's generally capable hands.

When I walked into the newspaper office, Grissy immediately looked up from what she was reading and snapped to attention.

"No one has, as of yet, attempted to ascertain Auntie Mabel's identity," she reported.

I couldn't resist smiling. "Thanks, Grissy, stay on the alert."

She nodded as if that went without saying.

I went through the gate into the newsroom area and carefully settled into my chair, which gave a low wheeze of protest. After years of holding Auntie Mabel's formidable body, I wasn't surprised. I wondered if I had been with the paper long enough to put in for one of those ergonomic chairs. They probably sold for more than a month of my salary, but maybe I could get Roger to go along with it, especially right now when he needed my help with Grandma.

As if on cue, Roger St. Claire came down the hall from his

office. He stood in the doorway and began jerking his head in an alarming fashion. Either his collar was exceptionally tight or he was having some kind of a fit. My grandmother would never forgive me if I failed to apply CPR to Roger in his time of need. So I rushed across the open space between us ready to tear open the collar of his shirt. When I reached up for his neck, he jumped backward in surprise.

"What are you doing?" he said in a stage whisper.

"I thought something was wrong. You were acting oddly."

"I just wanted to call you into my office in a subtle way."

"Okay," I said, wondering how dancing around like a choking chicken would fail to attract attention.

I followed him down the hall to his office. He slipped in behind his desk, leaving me the wooden chair that hit me right across the shoulder blades when I settled back. I sat on the edge of the seat, and watched as he did his preliminary hemming and hawing. When that got to be too much, I focused on the picture of a covered bridge on the calendar behind his desk.

"Have you found out what happened to Holly Preston?" he asked.

I nodded.

"It could have been an accident," Roger said tentatively, sending up a trial balloon to see if I'd let it fly.

"Not likely," I replied, shooting it down. "Dickens pretty clearly took responsibility for her death in his letter."

"He may have been bluffing."

"How did he know that Holly was Auntie Mabel?"

"People talk. Maybe someone on the staff let it slip." Roger's face became stern. "But that won't happen again. I sent out a very clear email message to everyone who works here that they are not to divulge Auntie Mabel's true identity."

I was tempted to say something about closing barn doors after the cow has hit the road, but I decided that would be unkind. He was doing his best.

"You said last night that Holly never mentioned receiving a threatening letter."

He shook his head. "But she may have received one and not taken it seriously. I mean how seriously would you have taken your letter if it hadn't mentioned Holly's death?"

He had a point. A handful of nasty, occasionally even obscene, letters had come across my desk since I started this job. Although unsettling, I usually dropped them in the circular file without a second thought. Dickens had stood out because of the implied threat.

"Do you have a file of Holly's columns?"

"Yes. I'll have Sam send you the file electronically. She was only on the job for about three weeks, so there aren't very many."

"How come no one in the office mentioned Holly to me when I first took over the job?"

Roger went through his neck-stretching routine.

"I asked them not to. I thought you would settle in better if you didn't know that your immediate predecessor had died violently. After all, the original Auntie Mabel's death was quite disturbing enough. I was afraid that knowing of a second death might put you off."

"Thanks," I said.

Roger nodded, missing the hint of sarcasm in my voice.

"We have one other problem," he said slowly.

"What's that?"

"Well, your grandmother got me to tell her about this matter."

"I thought we agreed to keep it to ourselves."

He gave a helpless shrug. "She knows me too well. She immediately realized that something was wrong and wouldn't give me any peace until I told her about it."

"What did she say?"

"Nothing. Well, that's not exactly true. She threw out one of those pearls of eastern wisdom that I can never follow. Something about the wise man solving his problems by letting them mature."

"What does that mean?"

"I have no clue."

I couldn't blame Roger. When she was in her oriental wisdom moods, conversation often boiled down to interpreting cryptic remarks. Since she had been going out with Roger, her eastern phases were punctuated by periods when she sounded like a hard-driving reporter from the nineteen-forties. It made for a real roller-coaster ride.

"She wants to see you," Roger said.

I nodded, accepting the inevitable. She'd be sure to have a plan.

"Perhaps when you see her you could mention what we talked about."

"About your moving to Florida?"

He nodded. "She might be more willing to consider it while she has other things on her mind."

The fact that Roger thought that to be true proved to me that he had a lot to learn about my grandmother. She could definitely keep track of a dozen things at once.

"I'll mention it to her, but I'm still trying to come up with an angle that will win her over."

"Please do what you can."

I got to my feet. "Remember to have Sam send me Holly's columns."

Roger, who had probably already forgotten about it, nodded. "You'll have them by the end of the day."

I worked on answering Auntie Mabel letters for the rest of the morning. I found that concentrating on my answers helped me forget about the fact that my life had been threatened. I also felt relatively safe in the office surrounded by people. And when Derrick stopped by my desk to remind me of our date tomorrow tonight, I sounded more enthusiastic than normal because it would get me out in a crowd. The last thing I wanted to do was be by myself.

After lunch, I decided that it was time to focus on Marion Jensen's case, rather than worrying about my own. I decided to question the one witness the police had. I looked up Hannity in the phone book and found an Ester Hannity living on the same street as Marion. Farantello thought she had sounded confused, but in my experience a lot of people are nervous talking to the police, and if they have a chance to talk with a personable female reporter, they are much more coherent. I had to work up my nerve to walk out into the parking lot and get into my car. My head was on a swivel as I tried to check out all the parked cars in every direction. When I didn't see anything suspicious, I got into my car and headed to the eastern edge of town where Marion Jensen had lived.

I slowed down as I drove past Marion's small bungalow. Mrs. Hannity's house was two doors up on the opposite side of the street. That would give her a pretty good view of the front of Marion's place, including the driveway. The Hannity house was a small Victorian, recently painted, with a nicely kept garden along the front of the house. I walked up on the porch and rang the bell. I heard a melodious pealing somewhere deep inside. A few minutes later the front door opened and a thin, older woman with a head of gray curls appeared behind the storm door. She appeared friendly and welcoming enough, but I could see she wasn't going to open the outside door until I'd announced my business.

"Hi, I'm Laura Magee. I work for the *Ravensford Chronicle*."

"I already get the paper, my dear, if you're selling subscriptions."

"No, I'm a reporter for the paper." That wasn't completely a lie. Occasionally I got to play the part of a reporter. "I'm here to talk to you about Marion Jensen."

Mrs. Hannity paused. I saw her hand hover over the handle to the storm door.

"I don't know what I can tell you. The police didn't seem to take me very seriously."

"Well, I will," I promised.

She opened the door. "Follow me," she said and spryly led the way down the short hall. We turned left and went into the living room. I would have expected the room to be filled with fifty-year-old furniture, but instead it was sparsely furnished with contemporary pieces.

"What a nice room," I commented.

"Thank you. I just redid it last year. I try to redecorate a room a year. That means that every six years or so the whole house is new and up to date. Home decoration is one of my passions."

I nodded. Not being of the nesting persuasion myself, I could still appreciate someone who was.

When we were seated and I had turned down her offer of coffee or tea, I took out my notebook, which makes me look and feel more like a reporter.

"Did you know Marion Jensen well?" I began.

"I wouldn't say well. We've been neighbors for more than twenty years. Once in a while when we happened to be outside at the same time, we'd get together for a chat."

"Was she a nice person?"

"Oh, very nice. Do you remember that big snowstorm we had two years ago? Well, I couldn't get anyone to shovel me out, and I was willing to pay. Marion saw me over here struggling to clear my walk, and she and her daughter dug me out. She wouldn't take anything for it except for a couple of pieces of my

Boston cream pie."

"She sounds like a real good neighbor."

Mrs. Hannity nodded. "Are you sure you wouldn't like a cup of tea? I have some homemade cookies."

It was partly the temptation of the cookies and partly the woman's obvious desire for company that made me agree. While she was busy in the kitchen, I surveyed the room. On a table next to the fireplace there were photographs. There was a picture of a much younger version of Mrs. Hannity standing beside a young man that I took to be her husband. Other pictures indicated that she had two sons and a daughter and a number of grandchildren. I walked out into the kitchen, which proved to be something out of a magazine.

"Your kitchen is lovely."

"Thank you. That was last year's project. I don't think I'll redo this in six years, it was far too expensive."

"Can I help with anything?"

She nodded to a tray on the table that held an assortment of cookies, cups, and cream and sugar.

"If you would put that on the coffee table, I'll be right out with the teapot."

I carried the tray out to the living room. Mrs. Hannity came along in a minute and poured our tea.

"I see that you have several children," I said, taking a bit of a delicious macaroon.

"Yes," she said, smiling, but then the smile disappeared. "They all live quite a distance away. I only get to see them a couple of times a year. I've thought of relocating to live closer to one of them, but I've lived my whole life in Ravensford, and I know it so well. I'm not sure if I'd be able to adjust to a new place at my time in life. Plus whichever one I moved near would have more responsibility to take care of me as I grow older and that doesn't seem quite fair."

I thought about my grandmother. I was the only family she had nearby, except for Roger, who's older than she is. I could easily end up spending some time as a caregiver. If they moved to Florida who would take care of her?

"But you aren't here to listen to my problems, you wanted to know more about poor Marion," Mrs. Hannity said.

"You told the police something about a red car that you saw by her house on the night she died."

"I think it was that night. But I can't be sure. It might have been the night before. The days sort of blend together once you stop working."

"What kind of work did you do?"

"I was a legal secretary for Attorney Hoffmeyer here in town. I worked there for over forty years. I only retired when he closed up his practice."

"About this red car," I said, returning to the subject. "Had you ever seen it before?"

"That's what the police never asked me. And to be honest they were in such a hurry, I got flustered and forgot to tell them."

"You had seen the car before."

"I think so, but not for several weeks. I think that car used to be in front of her house a lot for a couple of months, then a few weeks ago, I suddenly stopped seeing it."

"Until the night Marion died."

"I think it was the same car. To be honest I'm not very good at telling one car from another, but it was a red sedan and the same color as the one that was there weeks earlier."

"Did you ever see the driver?"

"Only enough to know that it was a man. He would come by and pick Marion up in the early evening and then they'd come back late at night." She gave me a level look. "Sometimes it would still be there in the morning."

"I see," I said, feeling slightly embarrassed.

"I don't blame Marion. She was a relatively young woman, after all. She might have been thinking about marrying again."

"Would you know the man if you saw him?"

Mrs. Hannity took a sip of tea. "I only ever saw him from the back. He was quite tall, but I never saw his face."

"Do you know what time he left on the night Marion died?"

"Assuming it was the night she died, I saw the car there at nine, but it was gone when I went to bed at eleven."

"You didn't hear anything that night? Any sounds of people arguing?"

"No. But I'm pretty far away from Marion's house, and I play the television rather loud."

I finished my tea and tried to think of another question to ask.

"The newspaper said that Marion's death was an accident. That she fell down the cellar stairs," Mrs. Hannity said, giving me a shrewd look. "Do you think something different happened?"

I shook my head as I got to my feet. "I don't know."

"Marion was a nice woman," Mrs. Hannity said, as we walked down the hall to the front door. "Do you think she was too nice to the wrong man?"

"That's what I'm trying to find out," I said. "Could you keep it kind of a secret that we had this conversation? This is sort of an undercover investigation."

Mrs. Hannity's eyes twinkled. "I'll do it under one condition."

"What's that?"

"You have to promise to come back and tell me what happened once your investigation is over."

"It's a deal," I said.

As I walked back to the car, I reviewed what I knew of that

night. Katie, Marion's daughter, had called at nine and eleven and gotten no response. According to Mrs. Hannity, Marion's friend was there by nine, so maybe she didn't bother to answer the phone, and when he left before eleven, she could already have been dead. The timing made murder a possibility, but I was still no closer to knowing the identity of Marion's boyfriend. Marion's best friend, Charlotte, had told me that Marion liked to go to the Collins Inn bar. Maybe she met him there. I decided that it was time for me to have a talk with a friendly bartender.

CHAPTER 9

Before I got in the car, I carefully looked up and down the street to see if I was being followed. I didn't see any suspicious vehicles, although there was one car parked about two blocks away. As I pulled away from Mrs. Hannity's house, I decided I should take the bull by the horns and visit my grandmother. She had good reason to be concerned about me. Not that Gran was the type to force you to do something; that was more my mother's approach. Whenever I hit a bump on the road of life, she would suggest that I go back to college and get a teaching certificate. My mother was a fine teacher, and she seemed convinced it was the right career for everybody, and most especially for someone like me, who seemed unable to find a husband.

Knowing that my life had been threatened, however, I expected that even my easygoing Gran might have some suggestions. I was also a bit apprehensive about suggesting that Roger and she move to Florida. Gran didn't interfere in my relationships, no matter how tangled, so I didn't think it appropriate to interfere in hers. But on the way over to her house, I actually had an inspiration that I thought might solve the problem, enabling everyone to get more or less what he or she wanted.

I parked in front of the garage around the back of the house, and went up to the kitchen door. Only strangers or the family on formal occasions went to the front door. I knocked and waited, then knocked again. I might have given up and left, but

Gran's little blue subcompact was parked in the driveway, so I figured she must be home. I tried the door and it opened. I went inside, a little apprehensive at what I might find. Perhaps she had fallen and become incapacitated. Various images of a body lying on the floor went through my mind. When I got to the living room, I found Gran on the floor all right, but not helpless. She was sitting in a half-lotus, meditating. She used to sit in the full-lotus until last year when her knees began to give her some problems. She was either completely oblivious to my presence or putting on a very good act because there was no expression on her face.

I sat in a chair and quietly waited, knowing that eventually she would return from wherever she was. After about ten minutes she opened her eyes. She gently smiled as she saw me sitting in the chair.

"Hello, Laura."

"Hi, Gran, how are you?"

"I'm fine," she said, looking peaceful. Then her face clouded, "But more importantly, how are you? Roger told me about the threatening note you received."

I nodded. "It's upsetting, but I'm trying to deal with it."

"How?"

"By attempting to discover the identity of the person threatening me. I'm going to look back over Holly's letters and see if I can find anything that might give me a clue as to whom he might be."

"Do you have any clue to this person's identity?"

Reluctantly I told her about my being followed.

"You didn't recognize this man?"

"I only saw him from a distance, but I don't think I've seen him before."

My grandmother looked into the distance, a pensive expression on her face.

"I think, my dear, that this has gone beyond being a situation that you can handle yourself. I think it's time for you to take Michael Farantello into your confidence."

Even though deep down I agreed, a spontaneous "no" began to form on my lips.

"A wise person delays answering until the emotions have calmed," Gran said, no doubt quoting the *Tao Te Ching* or something of the sort. So I followed her advice and took a couple of deep breaths before responding. Surprisingly it did make a difference.

"Maybe I should talk to Farantello, although I hate to ask him for help."

"Most understandable, after all, he has hurt you deeply."

"Not that deeply," I said. "After all we've only gone out for maybe the total of a few months, working around all his decisions to get back with his ex-wife."

"It has still been painful."

I nodded my head, not trusting myself to speak without showing emotion.

"I am sure he will help you."

"Out of a sense of guilt, if nothing else," I said.

Gran gave me an admonishing glance. "Farantello is a good man. He will help you because he is conscientious about doing his job."

"That's true," I admitted.

"Remember, there comes a time when you must seek help even from those who have hurt you."

"Right, I've got it." There was only so much of the wisdom of the orient that I could take in one session.

Gran nodded and started to get to her feet.

"Roger asked me to speak with you about his plan to move to Florida."

She collapsed back down into the half-lotus. The tight lips

and narrowed eyes told me she wasn't happy.

"Roger should not have involved you in our personal disagreement."

"He was just seeking help wherever he could. Isn't that what the wise man does?"

A small smile passed over Gran's lips and she nodded.

I went on. "Roger knows I care about the two of you, and he was hoping I might have some ideas that would help solve this dilemma."

"But first you have to know the problem. You weren't with us in Florida. By the end of a week, all Roger would do is spend the morning reading the newspaper, then in the afternoon he would nap or, heaven help us, watch the soaps. In the evening we'd go out for the early bird special in some local restaurant, and we'd be in bed by ten. That was his routine, day after day."

"But surely you didn't have to follow it."

Gran sighed. "At first I took yoga lessons at a nearby studio and joined an evening meditation group. But Roger seemed to resent any time I spent away from him. He wanted me there at home, even though we weren't doing anything. I had to fight for my own freedom, and I found myself slipping more and more into his schedule. Back here in Ravensford, he's got the paper, and we can lead independent lives. When we meet at night we have plenty to talk about because we've both been active during the day."

"Wouldn't it be possible to find more for Roger to do in Florida?" I asked.

Gran shifted her position to face me.

"What did you have in mind?"

I took a deep breath. My idea didn't seem as strong now as when I'd thought of it while riding in the car. But it was the only idea I had, so I decided to express it.

"Couldn't Roger find a part-time position teaching journalism at some college near where you stay? Or something like that . . . something . . . productive and time-consuming?"

Gran paused for a moment, no doubt examining the suggestion from all sides.

"Actually, I know of a couple of colleges within a half-hour of where we are, and probably a little research would turn up several more."

"I'm not sure Roger would have the academic credentials to teach but surely his background would more than make up for that."

"Actually, Roger went to journalism school when he was a young man. His father insisted that he have the proper preparation for running the *Chronicle*. He has a master's degree in journalism."

"Better yet. And think of the benefits, it will keep him busy and force him to get out of the house on a regular schedule."

Gran chewed on her lower lip doubtfully.

"But I'm not sure I can see Roger as a teacher. I'm not sure whether he would relate well to young people."

I wasn't sure of that myself, but I wasn't going to tell Gran that.

"Well, he raised a son, so he has some experience with young people." I didn't dwell on the fact that until recently they'd been estranged and even now their relationship was a cautious one. "And he works with fairly young employees at the paper all the time."

"Yes, I guess we will have to see."

"He might turn out to be a natural."

Gran gave a decisive nod of her head.

"I'm going to get right on this. I'm going to search Roger's computer to see if he has a resume already developed. If not, I'll put one together. Then I'll do a search to find colleges in our area and where to send application letters. I'll blanket the whole region, surely something will turn up."

I smiled to myself. This was the side of Gran you didn't see while she was dreamily quoting Chinese aphorisms. This was the woman who in less than a year had gotten Roger to update the *Chronicle* in many ways. Most particularly we now actually reported the news, whereas when I first came on board we were so afraid of offending people that we often offered only a watered-down account of what had happened. We might not be investigative journalism at its best, but we were definitely more hard-hitting than a year ago.

"Sounds like a great plan, Gran."

She nodded. "I can't leave the groundwork to Roger, he'd hem and haw and never get around to it. But if I do the preliminary stuff and actually get him a position, he'll do his best to get the job done. One thing about Roger, he's conscientious."

I agreed and stood up. Gran gracefully rose to her feet and faced me.

"Where are you going now?" she asked.

I laughed. "I'm taking your advice and going to see Farantello."

"A wise young woman takes the advice of her elders," Gran said, then paused. "And a wise older woman takes the advice of youth."

She bowed to me, and I bowed in return.

CHAPTER 10

The next morning, after a restless night, I sat on the other side of the desk from Farantello. I had filled him in on what I had learned from Mrs. Hannity, and at Marion's wake. Then I gave him the note I'd received from Dickens. Being careful to only touch it on the edges, he had placed it in the center of his blotter and was reading it carefully. When he looked up at me at last, his normally sad expression was even more forlorn than usual. I wanted to take him in my arms and comfort him. It gave me a sense of physical pain to realize that we didn't have that kind of relationship anymore.

"Who has seen this note other than yourself?"

"I showed it to Roger. He told my grandmother about it."

"So as far as you know only you and Roger have handled it?"

I nodded, and watched while he carefully put it in a plastic evidence bag.

"That note implies that Dickens killed Holly Preston. Was there anything to indicate that her death was anything other than a hit-and-run?" I asked.

Farantello sat quietly at his desk for a moment as if reviewing the file in his head.

"There were two things. First of all it happened in the daytime, with good visibility. It should have been very easy to see Holly walking across the street from her mailbox. Secondly, there were no signs of skid marks."

"The driver didn't even try to stop?"

"Apparently not. We assumed that the driver was under the influence of alcohol or a drug of some kind."

"The car must have had serious damage to its front end after an impact like that."

"We went around to all the auto body shops to put them on the lookout for a car with that kind of damage, but came up with nothing."

"The neighbors didn't see or hear anything?"

"Most of them were at work. Holly was done at the *Chronicle* by three o'clock, so she got home before most of the working people in the neighborhood. A couple of people reported hearing a loud noise out in the street, but by the time they got to their windows to look out all they could see was Holly lying there."

"So you never had any suspects?"

Farantello shook his head. "Did Holly get a threatening letter like this one?" he asked.

"If she did, she never told Roger St. Claire about it. He had no inkling of Holly having any problems. I'm going to go over her old columns to see if there's anything there."

"I don't imagine you have the original correspondence she received."

"No. That's all been thrown away."

Farantello shrugged as if to say that police work was never easy.

"I've got another problem," I said.

"Aside from being threatened by a possible killer?"

"A related problem, I think. Someone has been following me. I spotted him several times in different parts of town." I took a slip of paper out of my pants pocket and slid it across the desk to Farantello. "The last time I managed to get a license plate number. He shouldn't be too hard to find."

Farantello took the piece of paper and stared at it for a moment. His lips tightened in a thin line of disapproval. I wondered what I had done wrong now. Before I could ask, Farantello stood up, excused himself, and left the room. I sat there studying the light beige walls before moving on to scan the personal items on Farantello's desk. From the back I saw a picture on his desk. I was tempted to turn it around and see if it was his wife and daughter, but then I decided that maybe I really didn't want to know. I debated it back and forth until I heard footsteps coming down the hall. I plastered a bland expression on my face and tried to ignore the pain deep behind my breastbone.

Farantello came through the door first, followed by another man.

"That's the guy who's been following me," I blurted out, pointing an accusatory finger.

The guy blushed but didn't say anything. He stood at attention while Farantello went back to his seat behind the desk.

"This is Officer Keeler," Farantello said. "He's the man who has been following you."

"Why was he following me?"

Farantello twisted uncomfortably in his chair. "Because I ordered him to."

"Why would you do a thing like that?" I could hear my voice getting louder.

"I was concerned when you came to me about the Marion Jensen case. I knew I couldn't stop you from poking around in the matter, so I decided that I could at least try to keep you safe by assigning Keeler to follow you."

"Like I needed any protection."

Farantello sighed. "If Marion Jensen was pushed down those cellar stairs, there's a killer out there who would probably be willing to kill again to avoid discovery. I was just trying to keep you safe."

"If you were only interested in my safety, why didn't you tell me I was being followed? Do you know how nervous it's made me seeing *him* everywhere I went?" I said, pointing at Keeler.

"I didn't tell you because I was trying to kill two birds with one stone. Officer Keeler is a probationary detective, so this was also a test to see how good he is at following someone." Farantello stared sternly at Keeler. "I'm afraid he's fallen short of my expectations."

The younger officer got red in the face but remained at attention.

"Does he know about Auntie Mabel?"

Farantello nodded.

"Does he know enough to keep quiet about it? That even the chief of police doesn't know?"

Farantello looked at Keeler, who nodded.

"He and I are the only ones who know. And we'll keep it that way."

"So you turned protecting me into a training lesson?" I asked.

"It was the only way I could justify it financially."

"Well now you can assign him to follow someone else around."

Farantello shook his head. "Now, more than ever, you need protection. Whoever wrote this note might mean business. It's possible that you have two killers who are less than happy with you."

I hated being followed. The sense of being under scrutiny sent a creepy feeling down my spine. I'd constantly be asking myself whether I wanted the police to know I'd made this stop. On the other hand, Farantello was right, I had possibly gotten myself on the wrong side of two killers. Right this minute a guy could be out there planning to run me over on my way across the street, while another was scheming how he could push me down a flight of stairs.

"Okay. Let's keep the officer following me," I said.

"Thanks for making the prudent choice," Farantello said, looking relieved. He turned his attention to the officer. "Follow Ms. Magee at a safe distance, and when she's out of the car make sure you are close enough to offer assistance and protection."

"Yes, sir."

"You obviously no longer have to worry about whether Ms. Magee sees you, but you should stay alert to the possibility that somebody else is following her. If you see the same car in her vicinity or a suspicious person, follow up on it."

"Yes, sir."

"Wait outside."

He saluted, then stiffly turned around and went out into the hall.

"I wouldn't tell Keeler, but trailing someone who is already nervous isn't easy. You probably would never have spotted him if you weren't already afraid of being followed."

I thought of how my attention was drawn to him while at Corinne's open house and decided that Farantello was probably right.

"I appreciate your assigning me personal protection," I said.

"Wouldn't be able to do it normally, but having a training budget partially funded by the state makes all things possible."

I left Farantello's office. Officer Keeler was standing in the hallway facing the door as if afraid that I might slip past him.

"I'm going back to the *Chronicle* now, in case you lose me," I teased.

"I won't lose you, ma'am," he said without cracking a smile.

I felt badly about teasing him. Obviously he was taking all of this very seriously.

"Don't call me 'ma'am.' If you're going to be following me around all day, at least you can call me Laura." He couldn't have been more than a year or two younger than myself.

"Okay, Laura," he said, and I thought that I saw the hint of a smile.

"How about giving me your cell phone number in case I need to contact you for help?"

He nodded and we exchanged numbers.

"Good, now we're in this together," I said.

"Absolutely," he replied, and again I saw the quick smile.

CHAPTER 11

I ate lunch at my desk and spent the rest of the afternoon getting caught up on Auntie Mabel letters. Most of them were similar to ones I'd answered in the past, so I was only half paying attention and letting the other half of my mind worry about the murders of Marion Jensen and Holly Preston.

Remember, Laura, each letter deserves a thoughtful and considered reply. No two problems are exactly alike, and they must be treated with careful respect.

"Yes, Auntie Mabel," I muttered to myself. She obviously wasn't going to cut me any slack even when I was under stress. I reviewed the last three letters I had answered and made some appropriate changes.

Derrick came out of his office, rushing to go somewhere or other for a story.

"See you at seven?" he asked, making a gun out of his hand and firing at me.

"Right," I said, managing to give him a happy smile.

I wasn't sure whether I'd actually be safer in a crowd or at home in my condo. But I was determined not to change my life in any significant way just because I'd been threatened. Who knew whether Dickens would even make good on his threat? He might just be messing with my mind, although Holly's death indicated the opposite. That thought got me nervous again, and I tried to immerse myself in answering letters. That more or less worked until five, when I headed home.

I left the front door to my condo open and walked through every room, just in case someone was hiding there waiting for me. I figured that I could run out the open door and be in my car in a matter of seconds if an intruder appeared. No one came charging out, and the windows seemed to be locked just as I had left them. I returned to close the door, then went out into the kitchen and fixed myself a light dinner of cold chicken left over from yesterday. I didn't want to eat very much in case Derrick wanted to go out to get something later. After eating I took a shower. Then I selected a knit dress that hugged my curves but at the same time was very comfortable to wear. I put on my good black shoes with three-inch heels. They were a bit too large and had a tendency to slip off my feet, but they did wonderful things for my legs. I grabbed a sweater because although the September days were warm, the nights could have a chill in them.

Derrick arrived promptly at seven. He prowled around my living room for a few minutes, while I got my sweater and double- and triple-checked that the back door was locked. As we went out to the car I looked around to see if I could spot Officer Keeler. He had followed me home, keeping about half a block behind me, but when I parked in front of my condo, he had disappeared. I thought I saw him parked in front of the building next to mine, but I couldn't be sure. I didn't want him to lose me, but I couldn't very well ask Derrick to hang on for a minute while I checked in with my bodyguard. That would be too good a story for Derrick to leave alone.

"So how did you get involved in writing for a newspaper?" Derrick asked, once we were out on the street.

"I did some writing on the fine arts when I lived in Boston, so when I moved out here, Roger thought I had the skills to work on the paper." That was the short and proper answer that didn't give anything away about why I left Boston (a cheating boyfriend) or how Roger heard of me (through my grandmother.)

"Of course, I guess what you do isn't exactly journalism," Derrick said.

"It has its own challenges," I said, biting my tongue.

Derrick must have detected that he had put a foot wrong because he said, "Not that what you do doesn't have a place in a newspaper, but it isn't quite the same as getting the news to people. Digging for the truth and all that."

"How did you start in journalism?" I asked, deciding my career was a topic best left alone.

"Actually I started in television in Boston. I had an internship in college and that turned into a job as a writer and assistant producer. I even got to do some spots on air. Then I thought that getting experience in the print media might help me return to television with better credentials and more of a chance to get ahead."

"That sounds like a good plan," I said as we went around the town green and headed out toward the college.

I wondered whether anyone would willingly leave Boston for Ravensford. I suspected that for some reason he had lost his job in Boston and working on the *Chronicle* was all he could get. He was handsome enough to be a television personality, but I'd heard from my friends in Boston that only a special handful made the grade. Probably Derrick was getting some experience and licking his wounds until he decided what to do next.

"Why is the boss so insistent all of a sudden that we keep Auntie Mabel's identity a secret?" he asked.

I couldn't very well tell the truth that it was to keep a killer from finding me, so instead I said, "It's been part of the *Chronicle*'s tradition to have Auntie Mabel be anonymous. That way her advice can be frank and truthful, and she doesn't have to worry about offending anyone."

"Do you always talk about yourself in the third person?"

I laughed. "Only when I'm discussing Auntie Mabel. In a way she does seem like a different personality from my own. I always try to answer letters the way the original Auntie Mabel would have wanted them to be done."

"I see," Derrick said, but puzzlement was written all over his face.

Fortunately, by now we had reached the college campus. Derrick turned in and made his way to the parking lot nearest the auditorium. That still left us with a sizeable stroll on the winding paths that crisscrossed the campus.

"This is a lovely time of year, don't you think?"

Derrick nodded curtly, clearly discouraging small talk, and set a pace that had me rushing to keep up with him. By the time we got to the front door, I felt like I had run a sprint, not easy to do in my ill-fitting shoes. Derrick handed our tickets to the man at the door and took a seat at the back, even though it was open seating and there were lots of seats available toward the front.

"Don't you want to sit closer to the quartet?" I asked.

"This is better in case of an emergency," he answered mysteriously.

Was he expecting a fire, flood, or hurricane? I wondered.

I was studying the program to see if I was familiar with any of the pieces to be played when Derrick nudged me.

"Isn't that the president of the college up in the front?"

I said it was and also pointed out the provost. Almost a year ago I'd been involved in a story that took place partially on the campus, so I knew some members of the administration and faculty.

Derrick was out of his seat like a shot. He marched up the center aisle, and from what I could make out watching from a distance, he introduced himself to the president and the provost.

88

After talking with them for a few minutes, he walked along the front row saying hello to various people, a couple of whom I recognized as members of the Ravensford City Council. Over the next ten minutes he worked his way across the room until he settled down next to me. Now I knew why he had been in such a hurry to get here, he wanted time to work the room.

"Do you always do that?"

"Do what?"

"Just go up and introduce yourself to people."

"Sure, it's part of the job. The more people who know me, the more contacts I have. The next time there's a good story on campus, I'll call the president or provost, remind them where we met, and get a quote. I've already got several faculty members who are experts in different fields, so when an issue comes up, say the economy takes a dip, I can get this guy in economics to give me a few quotes for my story. It lends weight to a piece."

I nodded. It made sense, but it wasn't the kind of thing I'd be comfortable doing. If I had a story to write about something, I had no trouble doing an interview, but to just impose on people so they'd know my name was outside my comfort zone; one more reason why I'd probably never make a really good investigative reporter. I wasn't exactly shy, but I didn't have the self-confidence bordering on arrogance that every good reporter I'd met seemed to possess.

The lights in the auditorium dimmed, and the performers came out to general applause. As the quartet began to play I found myself drifting along on the melody and listening as it changed and developed. I didn't know a lot about classical music, but a boyfriend of mine in Boston had been training as a pianist. Learning to listen to music was one of the happier memories he'd left me with. I was completely focused on the sounds surrounding me when Derrick began twitching beside me. I saw the screen of his phone light up, and he left his seat and went out the back door into the hallway. He returned in three minutes.

"There's a fire in the paper warehouse on Fourth Street. We have to go," he whispered in my ear.

"Can't somebody else cover it?" I asked, already knowing the answer. There was no one else who covered hard news, except for a part-timer who probably wouldn't be available on such short notice. I was really asking Derrick to stay for our date and to get the story later, secondhand.

"A friend of mine in the fire department just gave me a call. I can't pass this up. You can stay if you want. Maybe you could get a ride home with someone or you could always take a taxi."

I shook my head and followed him out of the auditorium. If I thought that our walk in from the parking lot was fast, it was a crawl by comparison to the pace Derrick set on the way back. When I lagged behind, hampered by my shoes, he grabbed my arm and began pulling me along. His grip became tighter and tighter until it started to hurt. I was going to have bruises in the morning. Finally I stopped in my tracks and jerked my arm out of his grasp.

"That's enough, Derrick! That fire will still be there if you arrive five minutes later."

"Sorry," he mumbled unconvincingly.

The pace slowed a bit, and he no longer had his hand on my arm. I could have taken my shoes off and walked in my bare feet. That would have been faster, but I wasn't about to risk a cut foot so Derrick could get his story a little sooner. Also, I was still fuming at being dragged out of the concert. Now I knew why he sat in the back.

Did I really think he should miss a story in order to attend a concert with me? Maybe not, but it would have been nice if he'd seemed a bit sorrier about the whole thing. I was starting to suspect that I was along just to prove that he could get a date, and I was a safe date because I worked on the paper as well and would understand if he left for a story.

"I have to stop at the office to pick up the camera," he said as we got in the car.

He left the implied question hanging. I knew the office was much closer to the fire than my condo, and he was really wondering if he could leave me at the office and go to the fire.

"Why don't you leave me at the office?" I said.

"I'll come back and get you after I'm done covering the fire."

"No, I can get home myself from there."

"Are you sure?"

I nodded.

"Thanks, you're a sport."

I hadn't been called that since I was a kid and agreed to play football with the neighborhood boys.

We didn't say anything to each other during the drive back. Once we were at the *Chronicle* and while Derrick was rooting around in his office getting his stuff together, I punched Office Keeler's number into my phone.

"My date is going to be leaving alone in about five minutes," I said softly. "A couple of minutes later I'm coming out. Can you pick me up and give me a ride home?"

"Will do," he replied.

It was a short answer, but one that I found comforting.

Derrick came out from the back room with the camera around his neck and a reporter's pad clutched in his hand.

"Sorry we didn't get to have our date tonight. I'll make it up to you some other time."

"Don't mention it," I said, and meant it.

Once I was sure his car had driven away. I locked up the newspaper office and walked out to the sidewalk. I began walking up the street to the parking lot.

"Over here," I heard a voice say softly.

I looked over and saw Keeler standing next to a car parked by the curb. He held the door open for me, and I slid inside. He started the engine and pulled away from the curb. I don't think he would have asked why my date went wrong, but I felt a need to explain.

"My date was a reporter, and he had to go cover a fire."

"The one on Fourth."

"That's right."

"It's already under control. It wasn't much of a blaze."

I was sure Derrick would blame me for keeping him from catching the fire during its full glory.

"That's okay," I said. "It wasn't much of a date."

By the light of the dashboard I saw a smile pass over his lips, but he didn't say anything.

"Will you get in trouble for giving me a lift?"

"Only if you tell the boss."

"Why would he get angry?"

"By picking you up I'm revealing that I'm following you. If the bad guy is around watching, he'll be on to me."

"Oh."

"But I'm pretty sure no one else was following you tonight, so I don't think we have to worry."

"Good. Following me around must put a real crimp in your social life."

"Police hours, especially when you're a detective, can be unpredictable."

I could tell he was happy to use the word "detective."

When we got back to my place, he got out of the car and opened the door of the condo for me. I realized that I could become accustomed to being treated like a princess.

"Well, thank you," I said.

"Why don't I come inside and check around just to make

sure everything is secure?"

I agreed. We went inside. I stayed in the living room while he checked out the rest of the place.

"Everything looks fine," he said, coming back to stand next to me.

"Do you get to go off duty now?" I asked.

He nodded. "Once you're secure at home, I can leave. But if anything happens, just give me a call."

"I will."

"Goodnight."

"Goodnight, and thanks."

He gave me a casual two-fingered salute, and walked back to his car. I watched him pull away, then locked the door.

CHAPTER 12

No sooner had Keeler driven away than I looked at the clock and realized it was only eight-forty-five. So much had happened that I had thought the hour was much later. It also occurred to me this would be the ideal time to drop in at the Collins Inn to see if anyone there remembered Marion Jensen meeting up with a guy there. I wished I hadn't sent Keeler home because going out after dark on my own wasn't an appealing idea. At the same time, I couldn't bring myself to call him back on duty just to satisfy some investigative whim of mine.

And what are the chances of my having a problem? I asked myself. After all, Keeler hadn't seen anyone following me. And the odds are pretty good that Dickens doesn't have any idea of my real identity. I also didn't like the idea of being so dependent on Farantello's help. I'd solved other cases without any assistance from him, and I didn't want to give him control over my professional life. Still, this was the first time I'd been involved in something where there had been a direct threat against me.

I went back and forth arguing each side of the issue, until finally Auntie Mabel intervened.

Whatever you're going to do, child, do it. This constant stewing and fretting isn't going to accomplish anything.

I went into the kitchen and pulled my car keys from the hook. With a burst of determination I put on my sweater, slipped into my ill-fitting shoes, and went out the door. I walked down the sidewalk to my car. I stood there for a moment just looking around to see if I could spot anyone suspicious waiting out there for me. Every car in the lot that I could see appeared empty, so I got in my car and headed out to the Collins Inn.

It was about nine o'clock when I arrived at the Inn. The bar is at one end of the building, and was clearly the place to be because all the cars were clustered at that end of the parking lot. Although Millicent Collins, the prim owner of the Inn and protector of the family name, liked to emphasize the rental of rooms and the elegant dining room, I was willing to bet that the take from the bar was what kept the place in the black.

As I walked inside I was reminded once again that it is the oldest part of the building, even predating the captain, and going back to 1750. Captain Ashcroft Collins, who, according to Millicent, the last surviving member of the Collins clan, was a Revolutionary War hero, may have founded the Inn, but the truth as I heard it was that the captain did little to keep the business afloat. It was his hard-working wife and battalion of daughters who did all the chores. The low ceiling and wide floorboards once again impressed me. A huge walk-in fireplace in which a suitable fire was merrily blazing filled one wall, taking the chill and dampness out of the room. Less impressive were the cheap bunting and decorative rifles and drums that were scattered around. Millicent always knew how to ruin the genuine with the tacky.

I found an empty seat at the bar, and was pleased to find that one of the bartenders was an older gentleman who had helped me once before. I didn't expect him to recognize me, but when he came down to my end of the bar, he gave me a lingering glance.

"Haven't see you for a while," he said, wiping the bar.

"It's been a few months. I'm surprised you recognized me."

"Not many people come in here and ask me about a

murdered man. You tend to remember that."

I nodded. "I guess it is attention-grabbing."

"I saw in the paper that they caught the guy who killed him."

"That's right."

He stopped wiping the bar and leaned over closer to me. "Did you have anything to do with that?"

"A little."

He nodded. "I know you don't come in here to drink. Did you have a question?"

I took the obituary of Marion Jensen out of my pocket and opened it on the bar. Fortunately her picture was pretty much up-to-date. Some people have photos in their obituaries from when they were in their twenties, even though they died in their eighties. But Marion's picture looked very much like the body I'd seen in the funeral home.

The bartender read the piece and stared at the picture for a while.

"Yeah, I've seen her in here quite a few times. She looked a little younger in real life. We chatted once in a while. She seemed like a nice lady. Was she murdered, too?"

"I don't know."

The bartender shook his head sadly, then got called away to the other end of the bar. I folded up the obituary, put it in my pocket, and looked around the room. There was a pretty good crowd for a weeknight. A group of guys were together near the television, and there was a table of women sitting back in the corner. There was one couple talking at the bar. I wondered how often Marion had come here looking for companionship. The crowd looked a little young for her. I commented on that to the bartender when he returned.

He shrugged. "It all depends on the night. On some nights you get a lot of the divorced singles in here. That runs to an older crowd."

"Did Marion ever meet anyone here?"

"She'd come in by herself and sit at the bar. Sometimes a guy would come in and buy her a drink, and they'd talk."

"Did she leave with them?"

"A few times, I guess, I don't always notice. It depends on how busy we are."

"Going back a few months, did you ever see her with a particular man more than once? Maybe someone quite a bit younger than Marion?"

He frowned, then nodded. "There was one guy. She came in with him a couple of times about two months ago. They would sit at a table and talk with a lot of touching and looking into each other's eyes. I was happy for her at first because I thought she had found someone."

"What happened to change your mind?"

"I saw him in here others nights with different women." The bartender shook his head. "He must be pretty smooth because I never saw him in here alone."

"Do you know his name?"

He shook his head.

"What does he look like?"

"About average. A little on the tall side, looks to be in his late twenties or early thirties." He smiled, "Bring the guy in here, and I'll identify him for you."

"If I find a likely suspect, I might just do that."

"You know if this guy is a murderer, maybe you shouldn't be wandering around by yourself looking for him. It could be dangerous."

"Don't worry. The police are already involved. If there's any rough stuff, I'll leave it to them."

"See that you do," he warned.

After thanking him again for his help, I slid off the stool and made my way out the door. Once I got to the parking lot I headed directly to my car. There was no way I was going to stand outside alone more than I had to. I left the parking lot thinking to myself that if I could just get some idea of who Marion's boyfriend might be, I could easily take him to the bar to get scoped out by my eyewitness. But finding a likely suspect was the hard part. All I knew so far was that he drove a red car and was a smooth talker. Even in a small, unsophisticated place like Ravensford there were probably a lot of guys who fit that description.

I glanced in the rearview mirror and saw a car was following close behind me. I turned on the road that headed into the center of town. The car continued to stay with me. I only had a couple of more turns before I'd be home, but I'd read somewhere that if you were followed the last thing you wanted to do was bring the person to where you lived. Maybe he already knew that, but I couldn't be sure.

I swung a sharp left at the next traffic light, then made a sharp right into the parking lot of the police station. I turned around in my seat and watched as the car passed right on by. I sat for a moment taking a few deep breaths and letting my pulse settle down. When I was calmer, I thought about exactly what had taken place. A car had tailgated me. That happens. Some drivers follow too close as their normal way of driving. It didn't prove that someone was following me. I was pretty sure no one had tailed me from my condo, so how could anyone have picked me up at the Inn? Dickens might be good, but he didn't have supernatural powers.

I pulled out of the police parking lot and made sure there was no other car in sight. From there I cautiously made my way home, spending more time looking at the rearview mirror than through the windshield. I parked right in front on my condo and quickly made my way inside. I breathed easier when I had checked out the place, and put the chain on the front door.

I collapsed on the sofa. I knew I'd feel better in the morning when Keeler was back on the job, but I also knew that police surveillance couldn't go on indefinitely. I had to find some way to discover the identity of Dickens before my fear forced me to leave town.

CHAPTER 13

I arrived at work the next morning feeling much happier and more confident. Part of that was due to the weather. A lovely early fall morning is always better than the darkness of night when it comes to lifting the spirits. I'd also had my own personal police escort all the way from my condo to the parking lot of the paper, so I was feeling much safer and more at ease. Furthermore, I had decided during my restless night that I would find some time in the morning to go through Holly Preston's columns to see if I could discover whether any of her answers could have provoked the attack.

When I walked through the door of the newspaper, I was surprised to see that Grissy wasn't seated at her desk. Instead she was circling the newsroom in the arms of Chris Bell, who was loudly humming a tune. Around the room they went, Chris smiling and leading a blushing Grissy through turns and spins until they finally came to a halt in front of me.

I applauded. "I never knew you could dance like that," I said to Grissy.

"Every German girl learns to dance the waltz," she said. Then she smiled at Chris. "But it helps to have such a skilled partner."

Chris gave a small bow and thanked Grissy for the dance.

"Are you here to take out an ad for your dance studio?" I asked.

He shook his head. "I came to talk with you."

"Okay," I said and led him to my desk. He settled into the chair across from me.

I looked at him expectantly, half-dreading he was going to make another pitch for me to take dance classes.

He cleared his throat, reminding me momentarily of Roger doing the same thing when he was nervous.

"I came by to ask if you would like to go out with me, maybe to dinner and a movie."

He sat there with his longish hair and boyish smile, and I wondered if any woman was able to resist him. But I called upon the reserves of common sense I'd built up over years of dating.

"I won't go to dinner with you, but I will go to a movie."

He gave me a hurt look. "I'll admit that the studio isn't bringing in tons of money, but I can afford dinner."

I smiled. "I didn't mean to cast any aspersions on your resources, but I don't go out to dinner on a first date."

"Why not?"

"Because dinners take at least an hour, and probably more. During that time you have to make conversation. I want to be sure that I have that much to say to a guy before I go out to dinner with him."

"And with a movie if you get bored . . ."

"You can always watch the movie."

Chris grinned. "That makes a lot of sense. But how about if we aren't bored with each other after the movie, we go out for a drink?"

"You've got a deal."

After Chris had left, I walked up to Grissy's desk to see if I had any messages.

"I couldn't help hearing. I think you made a wise decision."

"Why's that?"

"Because someone who is that skilled at dancing is probably

good at doing other things as well," she said, giving me a lewd wink.

"That's not going to happen on a first date."

Grissy nodded. "You should always wait until the second," she said firmly.

I returned to my desk hoping that I hadn't made a serious mistake that would result in a dreadful evening, when, who should rush in but Derrick, reporter's notebook in hand. I saw him look at me out of the corner of his eye as if he couldn't decide whether to talk to me or go hide in his office. Finally his guilty conscience won out and he walked over to my desk looking everywhere except at me.

"I'm sorry we had to rush away from that concert last night."

"So am I." So was the bruised arm I had from being dragged halfway across the college campus.

"It turned out not to be much of a story after all. The fire department got the blaze put out before it really got going."

"Too bad."

He nodded, missing my sarcasm. "You never know with those things."

He stood there for a moment as if not sure what to say next.

"Well, I'd really like to make it up to you. Maybe we could go out on a real date some time."

"I don't think so," I said.

He frowned and finally looked directly at me.

"Why not?"

"I don't think it's a good idea to go out with people from work. If it develops into something serious, then being around the other person is a distraction. If it doesn't work out, all sorts of bad feelings can be introduced into the workplace."

Derrick stood there, apparently confused, as if the thought of emotions being involved in dating was an alien concept.

"Do you follow me?" I asked.

"Yeah, I guess so. All right."

Looking at the ground as if he might find an answer there for what had just happened, he slowly made his way back to his office. Once the door closed, Grissy spun her chair around.

"And then there are some who just aren't good at any of the important things," she whispered.

I spent the rest of the morning working on Auntie Mabel replies. Just as I was opening my sandwich for lunch, one of the guys from the printing shed, really a Quonset attached to the back of the building, came in with several copies of today's paper literally hot off the press. I turned to my column because I'd been checking daily to see when my response to Marion would be printed. There it was. Whoever killed Marion wasn't going to be very happy to see my reply. But what were the chances that he'd even read my column?

What if Marion told him about writing the letter to me? Auntie Mabel said.

I paused. A further thought came to me: what if he thought that Marion had revealed his identity to me in that letter? Then there would be another person out there, aside from Dickens, who would be happy to see me dead. I pushed down the fear that was growing in my gut. I had to remain rational and calm. The important thing, the only thing that would save me, was to discover the identity of the killers of Holly Preston and Marion Jenkins.

I turned to my computer and opened the file of Holly's Auntie Mabel replies that Roger had sent me. Even though Holly had only held the job for a month, she'd answered sixty-five letters, so it took me over an hour to scroll through them all looking for a clue as to whom she might have offended. Her replies generally seemed to be a bit milder in tone than my own, and didn't seem intended to be particularly offensive to men, which was what had bothered Dickens. I was almost at the end of the file when the following letter caught my attention.

Dear Auntie Mabel,

I feel very foolish writing this letter. As a woman of a "certain age" I should have been more prudent in my behavior. But the long and short of it is, I became involved with a much younger man. I don't know why I did. Probably it was vanity, I flattered myself into believing that I could still be attractive to younger men, and part of it was loneliness, it had been a long time since my divorce and I'd not been in a serious relationship. But all excuses aside, I never saw him for what he was, even after he borrowed considerable amounts of money and didn't repay me. In spite of all that, I am still torn as to whether I should break things off with him. I do like him, and a lot of the things he's done are just because he's young.

Uncertain in Ravensford

Dear Uncertain,

It sounds to me like you've been conned by an operator, a younger man who preys on lonely older women. I think you should contact a lawyer to see about whether you can legally recover some of the money you have given him. Although the police will probably be reluctant to get officially involved in this matter, they may be willing to have an informal conversation with your friend, which will prevent him from defrauding other women in the future.

Auntie Mabel

I sat back in my chair and rubbed my eyes. Holly had gotten a letter almost identical to mine from Marion Jensen and had responded even more forcibly than I had. Was this what had provoked Dickens into killing Holly? But that seemed to indicate

Dickens and the phony lover were one and the same person, which meant that the killer of Holly and Marion was the same man. I liked the idea that there was only one killer after me rather than two, but there was one problem. Why would Dickens have written to me before he saw my answer to Marion Jensen's letter in the paper?

Because Marion told him she had written to you, Auntie Mabel answered.

I thought about that for a long moment. Here was a man who liked to manipulate women into doing what he wanted. He preyed on their fear of aging, their loneliness, and their vanity to virtually steal money from them. He very likely had a low opinion of women and got angry when he thought they were going against his wishes. A strongly written letter by Auntie Mabel would infuriate him because it represented the type of independent woman he couldn't abide, and it also threatened his control over the woman he was exploiting. So when Holly wrote her strong response she became his enemy, and he was determined to destroy her.

When Marion told him that she had written to Auntie Mabel, he decided to threaten me into not writing a strong letter in response. Probably he hoped I wouldn't answer at all, and that I might give up the Auntie Mabel job altogether. Unfortunately for his plan, I had answered Marion's letter before receiving his threat. Had I softened any of my replies as a result of his letter? I thought about it. Maybe I had been a shade more circumspect, but I didn't think it had substantially changed the nature of my answers.

I looked over at the copy of the *Chronicle* sitting on my desk containing my rather strong response to Marion's letter. Dickens would either think that I was ignoring his threat or hadn't received his warning in time. But either way, what would be the point in his harming me now that the answer had been printed?

I could think of two reasons: one rational; the other not so much. The rational reason was that he might expect me to do what I had done. Go to the police and suggest that Marion's death was no accident. Killing me would prevent that. This reason didn't hold much water. If I was going to go to the police it had probably already happened, so why try to kill me now when it would only serve to reinforce police suspicions? The second, less rational, reason was that he simply hated Auntie Mabel because she represented the kind of strong woman of whom he had an obsessional fear. I checked the date of Holly's reply. It had been printed four days before her death. So Dickens had been so furious at Holly's response that he had killed her out of vengeance.

The newspaper on my desk loomed up at me. Was he planning to kill me now that my reply had been printed? If Dickens was running true to form, I had a bad feeling that was the case. I leaned back in my chair, making the springs squeal in protest and stopping just short of toppling over. If I could discover who had killed Marion or Holly, I'd have my man because he was one and the same. But how close was I to achieving that? All I had so far was a bartender who had seen the man who was probably Marion's killer, and Mrs. Hannity's statement that he drove a red car and was there the night of Marion's death.

I wondered if Farantello could get a police sketch artist to draw a picture based on the bartender's description of Marion's boyfriend. That would give us at least some idea of who we were looking for. I sat there for a moment mildly elated at the idea of having a face to put with the spooky name. But what were the chances of finding this guy before he attacked me? That thought got my stomach churning all over again.

You know what you need? Auntie Mabel said. *You need some exercise.*

"Do not!" I said out loud, causing Grissy to turn and look at me.

"Did you say something?" she asked.

"Just talking to myself." Suddenly I felt too restless to remain sitting in the office. I stood up and pulled on my sweater. Maybe Auntie Mabel was right. I walked up to Grissy's desk. "I'm all caught up on stuff, so I think I'll go to the gym."

"It is a good thing to keep the body sound," she replied.

"By the way, has anyone asked about the identity of Auntie Mabel since, you know, we talked about it?"

She shook her head firmly. "I would have reported such an inquiry to you." She looked slightly hurt that I could have doubted her efficiency.

"Of course you would," I said, soothingly. "Well, I'll see you tomorrow."

I walked across the parking lot, making sure I was in full view of where Keeler was sitting in his car. I was tempted to wave, but figured that went against regulations. But I made a point of pulling out of the lot slowly, so he wouldn't have any trouble keeping me in sight.

CHAPTER 14

Big Billy's Gym occupies part of an old furniture warehouse, and used to be owned, as one might expect, by Big Billy, a man known for his great girth. Never known to actually exercise himself, he was found one morning lying on a weight bench, dead of a coronary. The next owner kept Big Billy's name on the door, but he was called York—one name, just like a celebrity. I always suspected it was an alias that he got from the name on the weight plates. He wasn't one of the large muscled types that Big Billy's catered to, but he had the lean, hard look of the Special Forces. Rumor had it that he knew fifty ways to kill a man with his bare hands, and none of them involved breaking a sweat. I'd had a little problem at first with men striking up unwanted conversations with me during my routine, until York put out the word that I was to be left alone. The situation had instantly changed.

I nodded to York in his claustrophobic little office, which afforded him a view over the entire gym floor. He may have nodded back or just been stretching his neck, sometimes it was hard to tell. I got onto an elliptical trainer and started the first part of my aerobics routine. I was staring at the television set, which was hanging from the ceiling and tuned to the news, when a head bobbed up on my right side.

"Hi," a man's voice said. "Sorry if I'm disturbing you."

I glanced down, and there was the fellow I'd met the other night at Corinne's open house. I struggled to recall his name.

"Brian Nash," he said, seeing by the confusion on my face that I'd forgotten his name. He smiled faintly as if he was accustomed to not being remembered.

"Sorry," I said, sticking out my hand. "Hi, again."

"I'm surprised to see you here. There aren't many women members."

I was surprised to see him here, too. With his scholar's stoop and thick glasses, he hardly looked like a gym rat.

"There are a few, but most of them are much more dedicated to bodybuilding than I am."

He made a face. "Women bodybuilders are so lean and muscled that they don't look very feminine to me."

"Well, I'm not sure how I feel about men's bodybuilding. I'm impressed by their dedication and what they're able to do with their bodies, but sometimes I think guys with less muscle look more fit and natural."

"I agree with you. Of course there's not much chance of my packing a lot of muscle on my long, skinny frame," he said with a self-deprecating smile.

"Being lean is probably healthier," I said.

There was a short silence as we both tried to think of more to say. I glanced up at York's office, and saw him looking down at us. In a few minutes he'd be over suggesting that Brian move on with his workout. I was never going to get a date by going to the gym.

"Did you ever find that guy you were following that other night?"

For a moment my mind was blank, then I realized that he was talking about Keeler. I didn't know quite how to answer. There was no way I was going to tell him that it turned out to be a cop assigned to follow me.

"Nope. Never did. He just looked like somebody I knew. I guess I was wrong."

"Funny how that can happen."

"Sure is." I glanced at the clock. It read one-thirty. "Didn't you say you were an English teacher in the high school?"

"Yep. At good old Ravensford High."

"Isn't it a little early for your day to be over?"

He blushed. "You caught me. I called in sick today because I felt I had a cold coming on. I decided that getting a little exercise in the afternoon might prevent my getting sick."

"I hope that works for you."

"I'm starting to feel better already," he said with a smile.

I didn't know whether to interpret that as flirting or a statement of fact. I saw York get out of his chair and come down the stairs to the gym floor.

"I know this is going to sound weird, but we probably shouldn't talk any longer. The guy who owns this place doesn't let anyone talk to me for more than a few minutes."

Brian blushed. "Who does he think he is? He can't tell you how long to talk to people."

York had reached the gym floor and was heading slowly in our direction.

"Please don't make an issue out of this. We'll talk some other time."

"Is that a promise?"

"Sure."

"How about giving me your phone number?"

York was getting closer. I quickly recited my phone number. Brian nodded. I wondered if he would remember it.

"Bye," I said firmly to move him on his way.

He started walking away just as York arrived.

"Everything okay, Magee?"

"Yeah, it is. Thanks, York."

He nodded. He made a tour of the gym floor, taking a particularly close look at Brian, who was now on the other side of the room, before returning to his office. I pedaled away on the trainer thinking to myself about how much things had changed. A few days ago no one wanted to go out with me, now I had Derrick, Chris, and Brian all asking me out. I wondered if being in fear for my life had in some way made me more attractive, maybe bringing a rosy bloom to my cheek. I doubted that, but I could easily imagine that it made me appear more needy. Maybe that attracted the men. On that sobering thought I decided to focus on the exercise instead of daydreaming.

When I returned to the office I worked on a few more Auntie Mabel letters, but after an hour or so I found myself staring into space and thinking about poor Holly Preston, my predecessor. I knew that Holly had answered a letter from someone who was dating a younger guy who was exploiting her, but what I didn't know was whether she had ever received a threatening letter like I had. Roger had told me that she had never mentioned such a letter to him, but I could easily imagine Holly being reluctant to talk with the owner of the paper about such a threat. If she were going to talk to anyone, I guessed it would probably be Sam Aaronson, the managing editor.

With that thought in mind, I made my way down the hall to Sam's office, which was just before you got to Roger's. But whereas Roger was out of the office as much as he was in, Sam came in early in the morning and stayed in his office until evening, every day, six days a week. He was sitting in there now with the blinds closed, wearing a gambler's eyeshade and staring at the computer screen on which he put the paper together. He looked like some small-time crook trying to find a way to game the system in Vegas. Keeping a small-town paper afloat gave you about the same odds.

"What can I do for you, Magee?" he asked, after I stood silently in the doorway for several seconds. I never knocked because it seemed to disturb him.

"I wanted to ask you a question about Holly Preston. You remember her?"

"She worked here up until about a year ago. I'm not so senile that I can't remember that far back. What about her?" His eyes never left the computer screen and his fingers were whizzing over the keys.

"I know she was doing the same job that I'm doing now."

"Not exactly," Sam corrected. "She was mostly doing what Grissy is doing. She added the Auntie Mabel column to her other duties."

I nodded: that description made me feel really lazy. Holly had done the work of the two of us.

"Okay. Did Holly ever mention receiving any threatening letters in relation to the column?"

His fingers stopped and Sam turned from the screen to look at me.

"She came to me one day and said she didn't want to be Auntie Mabel anymore."

"Did she say why?"

"Only that she didn't feel comfortable giving people advice about their personal lives."

"Is that all?"

"She also said something about not wanting to make people angry. I asked her what she meant, but she wouldn't say anything more. Holly was a thin-skinned person, and I could easily believe that she didn't feel comfortable being Auntie Mabel."

As opposed to me with my armadillo-like skin, I supposed.

"Have you received a threatening letter?" Sam asked me, his watery blue eye fixed on mine.

"Oh, you know, the usual letters from people who think you got an answer wrong. Nothing disturbing." I ended with a casual

112

laugh, but Sam kept staring at me, unconvinced.

"You should tell me if you get any," Sam said. "There are all kinds of crazy people out there, and you never know what will set them off."

"How long before she died did Holly come to talk with you?"

"A couple of days. After she died we started running old Auntie Mabel columns. We kept that up until we hired you a few weeks later."

"It was a shame that she died that way," I said.

Sam's eyes went back to the computer screen.

"Get back to work, Magee," he said gruffly, but I didn't think his heart was really in it.

I returned to my desk and worked diligently until quitting time. I knew I should have gone to see Farantello today to tell him that whoever had killed Marion Jensen was probably the same person who killed Holly Preston. I was also going to suggest that he get the bartender in to do a police sketch. But it always took me awhile to gear myself up for a meeting with him, so I decided to delay until the morning. I went out into the parking lot and looked around carefully. There was no one in sight except for Keeler sitting in his car in the back corner reading the newspaper. To give him credit, he was alert and glanced up as I walked across the parking lot and leaned in his driver's side window.

"How was your day?" I asked.

"Probably a lot like yours but even more boring."

"You should have come into the gym with me to have a workout."

"Against policy."

"Okay. Well, I'm going home now, and I won't be out again until the morning. So you can have an early night."

"I appreciate your telling me."

"In the morning I'm going down to the police station."

A look of concern passed over his face.

"Nothing to do with you," I reassured him. "But I have to talk to Farantello about something."

"Okay. Are you leaving at the usual time?"

I nodded.

"Well, I'll be there," he said.

After saying goodnight I headed back to my car and drove home. I waved goodbye to Keeler as he pulled out of my parking lot, then went inside and locked the door. I flipped through my mail for the day, which was a couple of bills mixed in with a slug of advertisements. I quickly changed out of my work clothes into jeans and a sweatshirt. I could easily have worn super casual clothes to work. Writing the Auntie Mabel column didn't put me in much direct contact with the public. But I thought it was important to dress professionally because, as Auntie Mabel always said, the clothes you wear set the tone for the way you do the job. I also figured that Roger St. Claire preferred to see his staff in more formal attire.

Next I went through the refrigerator to see what I could find, and discovered some leftover stew that I had made three days ago. I heated it up in a pot, and ate it along with a small salad as I read a newsmagazine. I didn't care much one way or the other about cooking. I liked to prepare food for friends when I was having a party, not something I had done yet in Ravensford, but cooking for one is hard to get excited about. But I certainly couldn't afford to eat out every day, and most prepared foods were downright unhealthy. I didn't intend to end up tipping the scale at a high number like Auntie Mabel.

After supper I did a load of wash and thought about calling my mother. But she had the uncanny ability to detect from my tone of voice when something was wrong. She didn't seem to hear the words but only the inflection behind them, and I figured my tone would somehow give away the fact that a crazed killer was after me. Then, no matter what I said, she and my dad would come driving out from the eastern part of the state to rescue me. Unfortunately such a rescue would involve taking me back to the parental home and urging me to become a teacher like my mom. I knew a lot of folks in their twenties who had returned to live with their parents out of financial necessity, but I wasn't in their shoes. Not quite, not yet. And I enjoyed having my freedom, even if that meant facing danger on my own. After all, I had my grandmother, and I had Farantello, more or less.

So instead of calling my mother, I read a biography of Thomas Jefferson that I had started a couple of days ago. Then for the last hour before going to sleep I watched television. I had just turned out the lights and started to relax when I heard what sounded like hail hitting my bedroom window. Hail in September seemed pretty unlikely, but then I heard a second barrage. I turned on the light and got out of bed. I raised the shade and looked outside. By the glow of the lights in the parking lot there was no sign of hail or rain.

But then I heard the same sound rattling my front living room window. Not turning the living room lights on, I went to the front window and peeked out around the side of the shade. Security lights, which are kept on all night by the management, illuminated the plantings in front of my house and the pea-sized white gravel that was used to keep down weeds. Suddenly I had a bad feeling that I knew where my hail was coming from. I went to the other side of the window and peeked out at an angle from which I could see my front porch. Something white was sitting in the middle of my doormat, but I couldn't make out exactly what it was. I went to my hall closet and got out my softball bat, which went back to the days when I worked for the museum in Boston. We were in a league composed of the folks involved with cultural institutions: the library, the museums, the symphony orchestra, and the staffs of several Boston colleges. We on the museum team always beat the librarians because they were even more sedentary than us, and we trounced the folks in the orchestra who were too afraid of hurting their precious hands, but usually the colleges had lots of former athletes on their staffs, and one of them invariably took the trophy.

All of this went through my mind as I tried to remain calm. Thinking about small irrelevancies somehow seemed to help. Bat in hand I opened my front door. Now I could see what was on my doormat. It was a piece of paper held in place by a medium-sized rock. I paused, trying to determine if there was anyone nearby about to jump out at me. I cautiously opened the storm door and stepped forward. I bent down, all the while looking up in case someone was out there. I grabbed the slip of paper, took a long step backwards, and shut the door in one smooth movement. I immediately locked it.

The piece of paper was folder in half. I opened it up and read the typed message.

I know where you live.
Dickens

CHAPTER 15

The next morning I got up feeling like I'd only had a couple of hours of sleep because that's all I'd had. After spending over an hour processing the note, as people say, I decided that any way you looked at it this was bad news. Somehow Dickens had learned my identity just as he had learned Holly Preston's. There were only two ways I could see this happening: somebody on the paper leaked the information or somebody on the paper was Dickens. The first possibility opened the door to the entire population of the town and ultimately the world. The second narrowed the list of suspects down too much. I went through a mental checklist of all the employees. Sam and Roger were too old, so were the two men in the printing division. We had four reporters. Derrick did hard news and a part-timer handled the society page. The society reporter was a young woman. There was also an older man who worked part-time covering sports, and another older man who worked part-time handling stories about the schools and education. That left Derrick as the only male employee under forty. Now Derrick was far from my notion of an ideal date, but I couldn't picture him as a murderous lothario who seduces women for money, then kills them.

I showered with the bathroom door open, so I could more or less hear what was going on in all parts of the condo. As the hot water sluiced over me I tried to get over the creepiness I felt at the idea that Dickens had been out there somewhere in the darkness watching me read his note. He could easily follow me around town, waiting for the ideal moment to stage my "accidental" death. Keeler could give me some protection but not enough. If a cop had followed Holly Preston, he might have arrested the man who killed her, but he would probably not have been able to prevent the attack. The killer would always have the advantage of selecting his own time and place. My best chance was to go on the offensive and discover his identity before he put his plan into action. Since I didn't know how much time that left me, I figured I had better get started as soon as possible.

After a quick breakfast of toast, juice, and a cup of coffee, I got dressed and hurried out the front door. I tried not to be too obvious in looking around for Keeler. Fortunately he was parked a few cars down from the front of my house. I didn't let on that I saw him. From now on I was going to be careful, just in case Dickens had me under observation.

I drove to the police department, checking my rearview mirror frequently to see if someone other than Keeler was following me. I didn't spot anyone, but that gave me little comfort. Dickens had been a step ahead of me so far and might be watching me in some way I couldn't imagine.

The desk sergeant said he would see if Farantello was available in response to my request. I breathed a sigh of relief when he returned a minute later to say that Farantello would see me.

"Nice to have you come by again so soon," Farantello said cheerfully as he directed me to a plastic chair. After I sat down, he took one look at my solemn face and his own smile disappeared.

"What's wrong?" he asked, frowning.

I started by giving him my theory about how the killer of Holly Preston and Marion Jensen were one and the same man. I then told him about the bartender at the Collins Inn who had seen Marion's boyfriend.

"We'll have him sit down with our police sketch artist as soon as possible," Farantello said. "Finding him was a good piece of police work."

I nodded.

"You don't seem very happy about it."

I took the note out of my pocket, leaned over, and placed it in the middle of the desk.

"This is what's making me a shade troubled," I said, downplaying my fears like a storybook heroine.

Farantello read the note without touching it. Then he used a pair of tweezers to place it in a plastic evidence bag. When he looked up at me his usually sorrowful brown eyes were even sadder.

"I've always wanted men to follow me around, but this is getting ridiculous," I said, trying to smile but finding that my teeth stuck to my lips.

"This isn't funny."

"I use humor to keep me sane."

Farantello nodded. "I know."

"So what should we do now?" I asked.

"*You* should get out of town until we can apprehend this guy. Couldn't you go visit your parents for a week or two? I'm sure Roger would give you the time off."

The idea seemed tempting, it certainly did. But then all the problems it would cause jumped into my mind.

"How would I explain to my parents why I was suddenly coming home?"

"Wouldn't they believe you just missed them and wanted to visit?"

"My mother would know there was more to it than that, and she'd keep after me until I told her. Then she'd be so worried about me that she'd never let me return to Ravensford. My grandmother would worry as well, and she'd blame herself

119

because she got me the job as Auntie Mabel." I shook my head. "The only way this is going to work out is if I stay right here and help catch the killer."

"Is that the way it has to be?" he asked, giving me a bleak look.

"It's the only way I can see it working."

"Then I think we should bring Keeler up to speed." He picked up the phone and asked for Keeler to join us. In a few seconds my shadow was standing at attention in front of Farantello's desk.

"At ease, detective," Farantello said, then he succinctly explained what had happened so far in the investigation. When he got to the part about the note on my doorstep, Keeler frowned.

"Sorry, sir, I should have stayed at the condo longer."

"Not your fault," Farantello said. "You can't be on duty both day and night. The problem is I don't have anyone I can spare for night duty. I could have a patrol car drive by several times during the night to make sure everything is secure, but that doesn't seem to me to be enough."

"I have a guest room," I said.

"What are you suggesting?" Farantello eyed me narrowly.

"Detective Keeler could spend the night in my guest room. He'd be there to protect me, plus get his rest."

I kept the smile off my face. Surely Farantello could see the merit of my suggestion even if it did put a handsome detective in my home for the night. Farantello knew if he hadn't run back home to his wife, he would be spending the night and it wouldn't be in the guest room. I glanced up at Keeler and was surprised to see that he was blushing.

Farantello cleared his throat.

"You have a good idea there, Laura. Is it all right with you, Detective?"

"Yes, sir."

"Good. Get your things together while Laura's at work. She'll be safe there. Then pick up your tail again."

"How will I avoid being spotted if I go into her house?" asked Keeler. "This Dickens guy could have the house under observation."

"Do you have a back door?" Farantello asked me.

"I do. Officer Keeler could walk around behind the row of condos and come to the back door. That way he probably wouldn't be seen."

Keeler nodded.

"Anything else?" Farantello asked, sliding his chair back from his desk and starting to stand.

"Do you have a wife, Officer Keeler?" I asked.

"No."

"A companion, a steady girlfriend?"

"No."

"Good. I wouldn't want things to get awkward."

"There's nothing to make it awkward," he said with the shadow of a smile.

"Good," I said. "I appreciate your help."

Farantello nodded. "Don't worry, we'll catch this guy before he can hurt anyone else."

Keeler stood back and let me go through the door ahead of him, but we walked down the hall side by side.

"Are you going directly to work?" he asked.

I nodded.

"I'll follow you there, then run back to my apartment and throw some things together for tonight."

"Fine."

"Don't leave work for at least an hour."

"I won't. I appreciate your doing this," I said.

I think he was about to say, "that's all part of the job," but that probably sounded awfully pompous even to him. Instead he just smiled and gave me a nod.

Grissy gave me a theatrical wink.

"What's that for?" I asked.

"Isn't tonight the night when you're going out with Chris Bell?"

"You're right." I had forgotten all about it, what with everything that had been happening. Keeler would have a late night tailing me. I'd have to give him a call.

"You don't seem very enthusiastic about it."

I shrugged. "I've just got some things on my mind. Not a big deal."

"If you'd like me to stand in for you, I can go home and get my dancing shoes."

"We're going to a movie. I don't have any intention of doing any dancing."

Grissy shook her head. "With your attitude, it's surprising that he made such an effort to get a date with you."

I was about to say that lots of guys wanted to go out with me when the truth of what she said hit me. Chris Bell, who I'd only met once at his dance studio, had come to the paper to invite me out on a date. That did show an unusually high level of effort. Now it could all be innocent and maybe Chris did find something about me that was appealing, but what if Dickens had decided to get close to me? I could easily imagine him being like a cat and wanting to play with his prey before finishing it off.

"Are you okay?"

Grissy was looking at me with concern.

"You just seemed to be in your own little world there for a minute."

I gave a weak laugh. "Like I said, I've just got things on my mind. Nothing to worry about."

I walked over to my desk and sank down in the chair. I pictured Chris's boyish face. I remembered the smooth way he had swept me off my feet and spun me around his studio. He certainly was charming enough to have been Marion Jensen's mysterious boyfriend. He was also the right age. I had him pegged at his late twenties or early thirties. Could he be planning to seduce me in order to make his victory even more complete? You get someone to fall in love with you, then you kill them. Said like that it sounded laughably melodramatic, but the idea didn't strike me as being outside the realm of possibility.

So what should I do? Play it safe and cancel my date or go ahead with it, and hope that it would give me new evidence as to Dickens's identity?

You won't solve your problems by running away from them.

As always, Auntie Mabel had somewhat trite but solid advice. I had given Farantello a big pitch about how I had to stay in town and help solve this case. That wasn't going to happen if I ran away from an opportunity to gather information. How could I best use this opportunity to my advantage? I watched the sunlight stream through the old wooden blinds as I thought about it. Suddenly it came to me. Chris and I were going out for drinks after the movie. Why not take him to the Collins Inn? Maybe my friendly bartender would be there and could make identification.

Smiling to myself at my own cleverness, I jumped slightly when the phone on my desk rang. I hoped it wasn't Chris canceling.

"Hi, this is Corinne. How're you doing?"

"Pretty good."

"I haven't talked to you since the night of my open house. You didn't quite seem yourself and left so suddenly I was a little concerned about you."

"I had a few things on my mind that night. Nothing important. I was just trying to absorb some new information."

Yeah, like just learning that my predecessor had been murdered and that I was being followed around town. At least the following part had turned out to be Keeler, but the dead predecessor still weighed heavily on my mind.

"I understand. I thought that since we haven't had a good chat for a while, maybe you'd like to get together for lunch. I can't leave because my assistant is out sick today, but I figured I'd throw together a salad and we could eat right here."

"That sounds wonderful." Even though I couldn't tell Corinne my problems because it would give away my identity as Auntie Mabel, I figured it would help me get my mind off myself.

"Good. See you around twelve-thirty. I'll be ravenous by then because I only had a piece of toast for breakfast."

"On another one of your diets?"

"Not really. I had to come in early to see a client who's been flirting with buying a chest of drawers I'd like to unload."

"Any luck?"

"We're still doing the old negotiations dance. We're only fifty dollars apart, so I may cave and let her have it for less. Sometimes letting a customer think she's getting a steal will bring her back for more."

"Sounds like good psychology. I'll see you at twelve-thirty."

After hanging up, I reached into the Super Save More bag nearest my desk and pulled out another letter.

Dear Auntie Mabel,

I am an attractive (if I do say so myself) woman in my twenties working as a nurse in a small medical practice. The doctor I work most closely with is a man. Yesterday he told me that he has to let me go because his wife came in and saw me.

She thinks I am too much of a temptation to her husband and that he is likely to be unfaithful if I remain in the workplace. The doctor has never acted inappropriately to me, and our relationship is purely professional. I don't think I should lose my job just because of my looks. What can I do?

Pretty in Ravensford

Dear Pretty,

You could sue, but that would probably be expensive and you can't be sure you'd win. There is also the possibility that this doctor has a history of harassing female employees and that is the cause of his wife's concern. Even if that isn't true, her suspicions would probably make the working environment difficult. Demand that he allow you to quit and give you a glowing letter of recommendation, then get your pretty face out of there.

Auntie Mabel

I wondered for a moment before I hit the key to send my response over to Sam whether this answer would make Dickens angrier with me than he was already.

Don't self-censor because of that man or it will never end. You have to be true to your own views or else your advice will be worth nothing.

As usual Auntie Mabel was right, and I firmly hit the button sending my answer out. I had to maintain my personal integrity, plus, even if I wanted to, there was no way I could tailor my answers to satisfy someone as unhinged as Dickens. Having reassured myself, I settled down and worked steadily until it was time to visit Corinne. Just before I was ready to leave, I called Keeler and told him where I was going, since I planned to walk. Corinne's gallery was only six blocks or so away from the newspaper's offices.

"Do you have to walk?" he asked.

"No. But I need the exercise after a morning behind the computer. And I don't think I'll be in any danger walking on downtown streets in the middle of the day." What I didn't tell him was that this was my little act of defiance, my way of showing Dickens I wasn't afraid of him. I knew all this courage was only temporary, and tonight would be a different matter.

I heard him sigh. "Okay. I'll drive around the block a couple of times, so I'll have you in sight part of the way. But be diligent, and don't go wandering off the sidewalk."

I promised him I wouldn't. As I left I told Grissy where I was going.

"Don't overexert yourself by walking too far," she warned. "You want to save your energy for the date this evening."

"A date that obviously means a lot more to you than it does to me. Too bad you're not going out with Chris," I snapped, then realized how conceited that sounded. "Sorry," I said belatedly.

Grissy shrugged. "We Teutonic princesses realize that many men are intimidated by us. It takes a special man to be our mate."

I looked hard to see if she was joking, but her expression was serious.

"Well," I said, "I suppose you have a point."

Grissy nodded firmly. "But I am certain that the right man will come along some day. And I will know him when I see him."

"Good, good," I said, moving toward the front door before she could expand on her mating practices.

As I walked up the street away from the newspaper, I saw Keeler drive by. He went to the corner and turned left. I expected he would go around the corner and keep circling my location. Even though it was the middle of the day, I was surprised that there were so few people walking on the street. I saw a few figures three or four blocks away, but aside from a fellow who seemed homeless and was pushing a grocery cart with what appeared to be all his possessions in it there was no one else nearby. Since I'd always heard that a woman alone should walk with a sense of purpose and determination, I held my head high and stepped out at a sprightly clip. My walk may have turned into something of a trot, because by the time I reached Corinne's front door I was slightly out of breath.

I walked inside and immediately appreciated the relief from the bright sunlight. I saw Corinne in the back of the shop by the cash register. She was leaning against the counter talking to a man. As I walked toward them, I noticed that he had a full head of dark wavy hair and the kind of looks that would get you noticed. He and Corinne were leaning toward each other as they talked in a way that suggested some level of intimacy.

Corinne and the man laughed, and she stepped away from him as I approached. I felt slightly uncomfortable, as if I were intruding on a personal moment.

"Hi, Laura. This is my friend Jeffrey Ralston."

He said hello and we shook hands. On closer inspection he looked to be around my age, late twenties to early thirties. He had a hundred-watt smile, and I found myself automatically smiling back.

"Laura works on the *Ravensford Chronicle*," Corinne said.

"What do you do there?" he asked.

I told my usual lie about working in classifieds and advertising.

"Then I may be getting in touch with you to take out an advertisement."

"Jeffrey is a lawyer who's rather new in town," Corinne explained. "He left a large practice in Springfield to hang out his own shingle here in Ravensford."

There were a number of lawyers with practices in the center

of town because we had a small district courthouse.

"Well, I'm sure we'd be happy to have your business," I replied.

"I'd better get back to work and let you folks get on with your lunch," Jeffrey said. He smiled at me. "Very nice meeting you."

"You, too."

"I'll be talking to you later," he said to Corinne.

"He seems nice," I said after he left the shop.

Corinne nodded. "I'll go upstairs and bring down the salad. I sliced some cold chicken on top to give us some protein, and it has a nice honey sesame dressing."

"Can I help?"

"Sure. You can bring down the plates and napkins; we'll eat off of that old door I've got set up as a table."

I followed Corinne up the stairs in the rear of the shop that led to her living quarters. It was the attic of the house and had been made over into an apartment by some previous tenant. You entered into a living room at the back of the house, which seemed larger than it was because the ceiling went up to the peak of the roof. There was a short hallway with a bathroom and a galley kitchen off of it. In the front of the house was a pretty good-sized bedroom. Corinne had remodeled the apartment extensively before moving in. She always seemed to have money. I didn't know how much was from her divorce of ten years ago, and how much she had made from the store.

In the kitchen I got the plates down from where she indicated. I also took the silverware and a couple of napkins with me while Corinne sliced some homemade bread and put the finishing touches on the salad. I went back downstairs and over to the old door that was set on two barrels with four mismatched chairs around it. I had once commented to Corinne that this setup had a rather primitive look for a furniture store. She had smiled and said I would never believe how rustic and eclectic some people wanted their furnishings to look, especially the people who gravitated to antiques. I set the table and a minute later Corinne arrived with the salad.

For the first few minutes we both focused on the food, enjoying the salad and wonderful homemade bread. Once we had taken the edge off our hunger, I looked over at Corinne and said, "Jeffrey seems nice. Are the two of you going out?"

She grinned. "Was it that obvious?"

"Not really. You just seemed very relaxed together, more than if you were only acquaintances."

Corinne pushed her thick blond hair back over her shoulder. "I don't really know him that well. We've only been dating for about three weeks, but what I know so far I like."

"He is a bit younger than you," I said cautiously.

"Well, you know me, sometimes they're younger; sometimes they're older. I'm an equal opportunity dater."

I nodded and smiled. "Do you ever wonder why younger men go out with older women?"

Corinne paused, then slowly took another forkful of salad.

"Maybe because they want to be with someone more experienced, maybe because they have mommy issues. Who can tell? If I like the person and we get along, I don't bother to analyze it. Over-thinking can kill a relationship."

"I suppose that's true."

I had the feeling that my line of inquiry was pushing into territory Corinne didn't want to enter, but I felt I had to at least warn her based on what I knew.

"Do you ever think that some younger men at least are in it for the money?"

Corinne gave me a puzzled look, then her expression turned to one of annoyance.

"Are you suggesting that Jeffrey is only going out with me

because he plans to ask me for money, and that I'll be so thankful to have a younger lover that I'll give it to him?"

The food formed a lump in my throat. "I've heard of it happening," I mumbled.

"Well, it won't happen to me. I never give men money, that's a sure way to damage a relationship. And if asked, I take it as a definite sign that it's time to check out. I also don't feel beholden to any man who goes out with me, whatever their age. They're getting as much as they're giving, and neither of us has a reason to feel shortchanged."

"I guess you're right. You just hear about it happening."

"I can imagine a different type of woman might get involved in that kind of a situation, but not me. Anyway, why are people so critical of relationships where the woman is older? You're about twelve years younger than Farantello, but probably no one criticizes you."

She stared hard, as if daring me to disagree. I just nodded. I figured I'd pushed the issue as far as I could without provoking a quarrel, so I changed the subject back to the shop and in a few minutes we were having a congenial conversation. But I was only half-listening because I was wondering how Dickens would react to a woman strong enough to refuse his request for money. After all, he had killed Marion Jenkins because she demanded repayment and was threatening to make their relationship public. Wouldn't he fear the same kind of public exposure from someone like Corinne? Didn't that put her in danger if Jeff turned out to be Dickens?

On the other hand, Dickens had been doing this for a long time. Wouldn't he be able to recognize which women he could talk into giving him money and which would tell him to take a hike? Corinne certainly fell into the second category and any man who knew her at all well would realize that. This would seem to indicate that her relationship with Jeffrey Ralston was a safe one. Plus it was hard to imagine that a successful lawyer, assuming Ralston was one, would need to augment his income by swindling older women.

Dickens doesn't do it for the money. He does it for the power and the love of the game, Auntie Mabel said sternly. I knew she was right. For Dickens the money was only a sort of token that he took away as a sign of his conquest. Sure, he probably used the money to make his life easier, but its psychological importance was more significant. So I couldn't discount Ralston because he might not need the money. The more I thought about it, the less good I felt about Corinne's relationship. Maybe Dickens would see her as a challenge. A strong woman who was hard to manipulate would be a more valuable conquest than a lonely, insecure Marion Jensen.

But how could I warn Corinne without telling her the whole story and revealing that I was Auntie Mabel? And even if I did tell her everything, wouldn't she still insist that Ralston was an upright guy and that she could look out for herself? As I left Corinne, who surely must have wondered why I had been so abstracted for the last fifteen minutes, and walked back to the office, I realized that until I could find the man who went out with Jenkins, I wouldn't be able to break open the case. Many men went out with older women. I had to find the right one.

CHAPTER 16

I sat at my desk staring at the letter I had just taken out of a Super Save More bag, but not really seeing it. My mind was still searching for a way to warn Corinne about the predator who was in Ravensford without giving away the whole story. So far I hadn't arrived at any solution.

"Laura, can I see you for a minute?"

I looked up and saw Roger standing in the hallway that led to his office. I gingerly climbed out of my broken chair and followed him down the hall. As usual I ended up sitting in the hard wooden chair across from his desk, the one with the slats that pressed sharply against my shoulder blades, while Roger sat behind his large cluttered desk in an office that hadn't changed in forty years.

"Your grandmother has given me this list," Roger began, and thrust a sheet of paper across the desk in my direction.

It was a list of educational institutions in Florida.

"She wants me to write to each of these, sending along a copy of my resume in the hope that one of them will offer me a part-time teaching position."

I nodded.

"She said that the idea was yours," he said accusingly.

I flinched. "Well, Gran will only go to Florida full-time if she feels that you have enough to do. I thought this was a good compromise. It would keep you moderately busy, but still leave you with lots of free time."

He gave a grunt of dismay. "But a teacher . . . can you imagine me as a teacher?"

I'd never really thought about it, but I didn't think it would be helpful to tell him that.

"Most people with your level of experience in a particular field would want to share it with the younger generation."

"But does the younger generation want to hear it? That's the point."

I had to admit that Roger was being more persuasive on this topic than on most.

"Maybe not generally, but once you're a teacher in front of a class, they'll listen to you. They have to if they want to graduate."

"And another thing," Roger went on as if he hadn't heard me, "I don't possess a great deal of practical day-to-day experience in running a paper. Sam has always done that for me. He should be the one teaching a class. He runs the operation, I just happen to own a newspaper."

I tried shifting around to find a comfortable position in the chair. My right shoulder blade was numb, so I twisted to put more pressure on my left.

"I'm sure you'll find that you know a lot more than you think you do. Probably you've learned a great deal by just being in the newsroom and making the upper-management decisions. You've probably taken in tons of valuable information by osmosis."

He gave me a highly skeptical look.

"And maybe you could get Sam to help you out with preparing the course," I added.

Roger was about to reply but he stopped himself and sat there quietly. Slowly the angry red flush left his cheeks, and when he spoke it was with a soft, resigned voice.

"This is the best deal you could get for me with your

grandmother?"

I nodded. "I don't think you're going to do any better than this."

He sighed. "Okay, I'll start sending out my inquiry letters right away. At least that will show I'm making an effort. If anything comes of them, I'll worry about that in the future."

"Good idea. Like I said, we'll find a way to make it work."

Somewhat reassured, he gave me a small smile. "Thanks for your help. By the way, how are you getting on with looking into that threatening letter?"

There was no point in worrying Roger. He would just pass on the concern to my grandmother.

"The police are checking it out. They're following up on a few leads."

I stood up and left the office, trying to stretch the kinks out of my back and wishing all I had to worry about was how to get to live full-time in Florida.

Back at my desk, I decided I had better notify Keeler of my date tonight since he would have to follow me.

I punched his number on my cell phone. When I got through I kept my voice low, so Grissy, who was working at the front desk, couldn't hear me. I told Keeler about my date with Chris Bell.

"Have you known him long?" he asked.

"Less than a week."

"How did you meet him?"

"He owns Raoul's School of Ballroom Dance. I met him when I did an article on the place."

"But his name isn't Raoul?"

"It's a long story."

"Do you know what kind of vehicle he'll be driving?"

"No."

"And you're going to a movie?"

"That's right. And after that we're going to the Collins Inn for a drink."

"How do you know?"

"What do you mean?"

"Doesn't the man usually decide where you go?"

I smiled. "Don't be so old-fashioned. I'll get him to take me there."

"Okay. Well, I'll follow you at a discreet distance."

"Do you want to move your stuff into my spare room before I go out with Chris?"

"Better if I do it after dark. You weren't planning on having this fellow . . . um . . . spend the night, were you?"

"No." I almost went on to say that this was a first date, then decided I really didn't have to provide an explanation.

"Okay. As soon as this guy leaves, I'll come around to the back door and bring my stuff in."

"Sounds like a plan."

After we hung up, I sat for a moment gathering my thoughts before returning to my Auntie Mabel letters.

"Laura."

I glanced up. Roger St. Claire was standing over me.

"You seem lost in thought."

That's what happens when a killer is hunting you, I thought but didn't say.

"Just trying to come up with an answer to a tough letter," I lied.

Roger handed me a business card.

"You did such a good job on Raoul's School of Ballroom Dance that I would like you to be the person to handle our Spotlight on Business column. It will give you a chance to do more real journalism."

More like Chamber of Commerce puffery than journalism, I thought. I looked at the card, which said "THE RED BARN:

Antiques and Collectibles" and gave the name of Stephanie Fleming. I remembered meeting her at Corinne's open house.

"I'd like you to do the usual. Talk to the owner and get the relevant facts, take a few pictures, and promote the place a little. Okay?"

I nodded.

"There's no rush. Do it in the next few days."

"Okay."

"I'm going home to have your grandmother advise me while I write my letters applying for a job. Imagine being a job applicant at my age. I've never applied for a position before."

"I guess the job on the *Chronicle* was just here waiting for you."

"Yes. My father expected me to take over from him."

"Well, you're never too old to start something new," I chirped, sounding perky even to me.

"I suppose," Roger said doubtfully, then he turned and trudged toward the door like a man without hope.

I returned to being Auntie Mabel.

I was putting the finishing touches on my makeup when the doorbell rang. I checked the clock in the kitchen as I walked by and saw that Chris was right on time. I kept the chain on the door when I opened it, so I could peek out and make sure it was really Chris. He shifted over and stared into the space in the doorway.

"Hi," he said, giving me a sort of puzzled look.

I closed the door and took off the chain.

"Sorry about that. There have been several break-ins in the area, so you can't be too careful."

"No, I guess not."

Chris came into the living room. He looked good, if a little preppy, with dark blue trousers, a sweater out of some material

I wanted to touch, and a shirt with a subtle maroon stripe. I felt almost too casual in my washed oxford shirt and black pants. I should have guessed a dancer would pay a lot of attention to how he dressed. I grabbed my sweater and assured Chris I was ready to go. I closed and locked the door behind me, then stood on the porch for a moment to give Keeler lots of time to see me leaving.

"Is there anything wrong?" Chris asked. He was already on the last step of the porch and looking back at me.

"Nope," I said, bounding down the steps to join him.

"That car is mine," he said, directing me to a red car parked in the spot next to mine.

"That red car is yours?" I asked, startled, remembering Mrs. Hannity saying that Marion Jensen's boyfriend had driven a red car.

"Is there anything wrong with that?" Chris asked, sounding worried.

Don't be silly, there are lots of red cars in town, Auntie Mabel said.

"Not a thing," I replied.

We walked down to the car, and he opened the door for me. As we drove out of the parking lot, I glanced over my shoulder to see if Keeler was following.

"Anything wrong?" Chris asked.

"Nope," I replied. "Just stretching my neck." I thought I had seen a car pull out several spaces down. That was probably Keeler.

As we drove to the multiplex, Chris gave me the rundown on the movies playing. Since neither of us was much into action or horror flicks, we settled on a romantic comedy.

"Have you lived in Ravensford long?" Chris asked as we pulled into the parking lot.

"A little over a year."

"How do you like it?"

Now there was a question. There were times when I was bored out of my mind, and other times when the excitement threatened to send me into cardiac arrest. But that sounded a little too strange to tell Chris.

"It's nice if you don't mind living in a small city. There isn't always a lot to do here."

"I originally came from a small town in the Midwest. If you want to talk about nothing to do, that was the place."

"How did you end up here?"

"I went to the University of Massachusetts. That's where I got interested in dancing. After I graduated I taught dancing at a couple of studios, then decided it was time to go out on my own."

"That must have been a tough call."

"Yeah. Well, I had a little money saved up, and I figured this was the time in my life to take a chance. Once I got older and had a family and responsibilities, I wouldn't be willing to take the risk."

I couldn't be sure by looking at him, but from what he had just told me I figured he must be a few years younger than myself. So now I was dating younger men just like Marion and Corinne, although not to the same degree. That would probably come over time, I told myself cheerlessly.

"I hope the dance studio works out for you," I said, as we got out of the car.

"Yeah, so do I."

The movie turned out to be pretty good. Chris seemed to enjoy it even more than I did. He had an infectious laugh, and I was starting to relax into the date. But I knew that the difficult part was next to come. I had to get us into the Collins Inn.

"Why don't we get a drink at the Collins Inn?" I said with forced casualness as we walked toward the car.

"The Collins Inn, isn't that for middle-aged people?"

"They get a mixed crowd. Plus the bar is about the oldest structure in Ravensford. Don't you have any interest in history?"

"Yeah, I guess."

As we drove to the Inn I regaled him with stories about why Captain Collins was one of the great cowards of the American Revolution. I had to take it on faith that Keeler was keeping up because I didn't want to keep glancing over my shoulder as if I were paranoid. When we got to the Inn, I directed Chris to park in the area by the bar.

"So this is going to be an historical experience," he said as we headed into the bar.

"Oh, yeah."

It was some kind of experience. The place was relatively crowded and the low ceilings made it seem claustrophobic. I wondered what it had been like before smoking bans went into effect. I imagined in colonial times the clay pipes must have made the place pretty smoky as well. All the tables were taken, but we found a couple of seats at the bar on the end by the door.

I ordered a white wine and Chris ordered a martini. There appeared to be two bartenders and neither was the guy who could identify Dickens, so it looked like this whole date was going to prove a waste of time. A jukebox started up and the room was filled with the sounds of the early sixties. Chris said something to me, but I couldn't quite hear him over the music and the conversations round me. I figured he was probably trying to tell me that this place had a clientele as old as he had figured. I leaned closer to him, and he repeated what he had said.

"Let's dance."

There was a postage-stamp-sized dance floor in one corner of the room, and before I could say that this was a bad idea, he had half-led and half-carried me across the room.

"You can do the swing, can't you? Everybody learns that somewhere along the way."

Actually I had done some swing dancing when I'd first moved to Boston, where swing clubs were popular, and with Chris giving me a firm lead I found the steps coming back. He twirled me around, did double turns, and one time even lifted me over his head, proving he was a lot stronger than he looked. When we were done, there was even a smattering of applause from the crowd.

"That was fun," I said.

Chris gave me an I-told-you-so look.

I took a big gulp of my wine, and looked down the bar. Suddenly I spotted my friendly bartender. He was at the far end of the room from me, talking to a couple of women.

"I have to go to the restroom," I said to Chris.

I quickly slid off my chair and headed toward my friend. The bartender was still chatting with the two women, so I insinuated myself between them and said in a loud voice, "Hi, how are you tonight?"

The women gave me annoyed looks. The bartender smiled when he recognized me.

"I need you to do your little identification trick for me."

He looked puzzled for a moment, then he smiled and nodded.

"Whom do you want me to check out?" he asked.

"The guy in the navy blue sweater sitting at the end of the bar," I said, motioning with my thumb as if I were hitching a ride.

He wandered down in the direction of Chris, gave him a sort of sidelong glance, then came back to me.

"You know, when I saw the guy he was wearing a baseball

cap. Without the hat I'm not sure."

I surveyed the bar. Right on the other side was a guy wearing a baseball cap. He was wearing a black t-shirt with crossed M-16s and leaning over a woman whose arms were covered with dark purple tattoos.

"Stick with me for a moment," I told the bartender.

I walked around the bar and right up to Mr. M-16. He was now nuzzling the woman's ear, but he stopped when I stood in front of him. He got his nose out of her ear and smiled at me.

"Hi," I said. "Can I borrow your cap for a moment?"

Not waiting for an answer, I snatched it off his head and kept walking to where Chris was sitting.

"Hey, how come you said you were going to the ladies' room and I see you talking with that bartender?" Chris said only half in jest. "Is he why you wanted to come here?"

"Yes," I said, "but not for the reason you think."

"He's old enough to be your father."

Before Chris could say any more, I plopped the hat down on his head, just as the bartender made his way to our end of the bar. He took a long look at Chris and shook his head.

"Are you sure?" I asked.

"There's a resemblance, but he's not hard enough looking."

Speaking of hard looking, the guy whose hat I'd taken was suddenly behind me. He snatched his cap off of Chris's head and gave him a challenging poke in the chest.

"You trying to steal my hat."

"No," Chris protested.

"How about I give you a shot to the head?"

"I wouldn't like that at all," Chris said, licking his lips nervously. He pointed at me. "It was all her idea, don't blame me."

"What kind of a game are you playing?" the man asked, turning to me.

I smiled. "I just wanted to see how my friend looks in a cap. Sorry, I was going to bring it right back to you."

He stared hard at me as if not sure what to do, then he turned and walked away. I heard him mumble something that I preferred to think was "Crazy witch."

"Let's go," Chris said, getting to his feet. "Suddenly I'm not having much fun here."

He looked stern, and I could tell he was angry. We walked out to the car without speaking. In fact we didn't speak at all for the ride home.

When we were parked in front of my condo, I said, "Well, I had a really good time, Chris. Maybe we could do it again."

He shook his head. "I had a good time, too, up until the last ten minutes in the bar. I think you like to do risky things, things that are way too dangerous for me. I'm a dancer, not a fighter. I think you need a tough guy to cover your back, and I'm not that guy."

"I apologize for putting you on the spot back there. Would it matter if I said that it wouldn't happen again?"

He looked at me, his face sad. "You'd mean it right now while you're saying it, but I have a feeling that something similar to this would happen again and again."

I knew in my heart there was a kernel of truth in what he was saying, so I didn't bother arguing with him. I reached over and squeezed his arm.

"Sorry, Chris, I enjoyed dancing with you," I said and got out of the car.

I walked up to the door regretting what I had done to Chris, but how else was I going to discover whether he was a bad guy or not? I was sorry he wouldn't go out with me again. We may never have gotten into a serious relationship, but he was a lot of fun and I would have liked to have him as a friend. So I had lost a possible friend and was no nearer to discovering the identity of Dickens. It hadn't been a very successful night.

Chapter 17

I sat on the sofa for fifteen minutes wondering if there was some way that I could have avoided offending Chris and still gotten the information I needed. I hadn't come up with any bright ideas when there was a knock on my back door. I went out into the kitchen, turned on the outdoor light, and peered through the window in the door. Keeler was standing on the small porch holding a suitcase. I unlocked the door and let him inside.

"Hi," I said. "Follow me and I'll show you where to put your things."

I led him out into a short hallway and into the spare bedroom in the back of the condo. My grandmother had furnished the condo over the summer while I was away. She knew I didn't have much interest in home decoration nor did I have the money to do it. I was pleased to come back to Ravensford and find the condo move-in ready. Gran had purchased a sleeper sofa for the back room, so it doubled as a study and a place to put overnight guests. Keeler would be my first guest, if you could call him that.

"You can put your things in the closet or in there," I said, pointing to a small dresser. "You can use the bathroom in the hall, I have one off the bedroom. When you're settled in come out in the living room. There's something I'd like to tell you."

I went back out and sat on the sofa and in about ten minutes' time Keeler came out. He settled in the occasional chair by the window.

"Would you like something to drink: coffee or tea?"

"No thanks. It's a little late for me to get a shot of caffeine."

"I hope following me around on my date wasn't too boring."

He shrugged and gave me a small smile. "Tailing people is never much fun. Either you're afraid of losing them or waiting forever until they decide to go somewhere."

"Did you spot anyone else following me?"

"Not that I could see." He cleared his throat. "Why did you go to the Collins Inn?"

"That's where the bartender works who can recognize Dickens."

"I know. He's scheduled to meet with a police sketch artist tomorrow."

"Well, I wanted to see if he recognized Chris."

"You thought your date could be a killer?" he asked, looking worried.

"I thought it was a possibility. Since Dickens knows my identity, I thought he might try to get close to me like he's done with his other victims."

"You should have told us your suspicions. We could have investigated this guy without your going on a date with him."

"It seemed like a good plan at the time."

"If he was Dickens, wouldn't he have gotten a little suspicious when you said you wanted to go to the Collins Inn? It isn't really a hangout for young people."

I shrugged.

"Don't underestimate this guy," Keeler said. "He's got to be pretty smart to be pulling off these scams."

"Okay," I said, smiling to show my acquiescence.

"What did you find out?"

I told him about my little adventure in the bar.

"So you found out that your date isn't Dickens. And at the same time, you embarrassed the guy by getting into a confrontation with some thug."

"I'll admit it wasn't a particularly productive night," I said.

"Leave the investigation to the police."

I was a little tired of being criticized. "And what have the police accomplished so far? I found the connection between the deaths of Marion Jenkins and Holly Preston, and I found the bartender who can recognize Dickens. And I found out that Chris Bell isn't Dickens. What have you people done aside from following me around?"

Keeler pursed his lips. I figured he was struggling to keep a hold on his temper, but he could have been trying to prevent a smile. Finally he sighed.

"I admit that we haven't achieved much, but once we have that police sketch we can circulate it and get some leads."

"Let's hope so," I snapped.

I glared at the carpet, knowing that if I looked at him it might lead to a fight.

"Well, I'd better be getting to bed," Keeler said. "I'll check the locks on the doors and windows."

While he was doing that I opened up the sofa bed and went in the linen closet to get sheets and a pillow. I began to make up the bed.

"I'll take care of that," he said, entering the room.

"It's easier if we do it together."

Standing on either side of the bed we put on the sheets and a blanket. Then I stuffed the pillow into a case and put it at the head of the bed. Working together like that seemed to be an intimate thing to do, and I felt myself thawing toward Keeler.

"Well, I'll say goodnight. But there's just one thing," I said

"What's that?"

"If you're going to be staying here, I can't very well be calling you Officer Keeler all the time. What's your first name?"

"John."

"Okay, John it is then. Goodnight, John."

"Goodnight, Laura."

It took me a few seconds after I woke up in the morning to remember there was someone else staying in the condo. It had been several months since I'd had a man around the house even for a visit. The good thing about it was I had enjoyed the best night's sleep I'd had in days. I guess having Keeler on the premises had given me a sense of safety. The downside was that I couldn't just leap out of bed in my shorty pajamas and parade off to make coffee. Instead I put on a very demure bathrobe. I could hear noises in the hall bathroom that sounded like a shower running, so I went back to my own bathroom and began to get ready for the day.

When I was finally dressed and looking as good as I was going to look, I walked out into the hall. Keeler was sitting in the living room with a cup of coffee. I knew his name was John, but for some reason I kept thinking of him by his last name, just as I did with Farantello. Maybe it was a cop thing because they often called each other by their last names.

"I didn't know whether you wanted me to do anything for breakfast, so I just helped myself to a cup of coffee," he said.

"I guess we'll have cereal this morning. What sorts of things can you do for breakfast?"

"I make a pretty fair omelet."

"I'll keep that in mind. Did you sleep well?"

"Very well. That sleeper sofa is good. It doesn't have the usual bar in the middle of your back."

"My grandmother picked it out, and I'm sure she was careful to test it before buying."

I went out into the kitchen and poured some orange juice

and got out the two kinds of cereal I had on hand. I set the table, then called to Keeler that we were ready. I directed him where to sit, then settled down across from him.

He looked around the kitchen, which was very modern with stainless appliances.

"This is a really nice condo. It makes mine look hopelessly tired and out of date."

"This development is brand-new. Again, I can't take any credit, it was my grandmother who picked it out."

"She's married to Roger St. Claire, right?"

I nodded.

"So I guess money wasn't a real problem."

"No, but both of them are pretty thrifty. They're old-fashioned New Englanders, frugal to a fault. I'm sure they got a good deal on this place."

I poured Keeler some more coffee. We served ourselves some cereal and began to eat.

"What's on your agenda for today?"

"I plan to spend the morning writing Auntie Mabel letters. I need to have a backlog in case something else comes up."

"Do you like being an advice columnist?" he asked.

The way he kept his eyes focused on my face made me think that he really cared and wasn't just asking a polite question. But at the same time I wondered if it wasn't a trick cops learned in Interrogation Techniques 101—gaining the confidence of suspects.

"It has its pros and cons. On the one hand you get to read about all the various problems that people have. And even though a lot of them are the same, they're each unique in their own way."

"It's the same way with policing. Lots of people go through red lights, but each of them has an individual excuse for why."

"The bad part about the job is that you have a lot of

responsibility. When you're giving people advice, you have to try to be balanced and tell folks what you think is really the best for them. What's the worst part about being a cop?"

Keeler sipped his coffee and smiled. "Well, like you might expect, you aren't usually seeing people at their best. They've often done something wrong or stupid, and they're stressed or angry. I think the longer you're on the job, the more effort you have to make to remind yourself that people aren't always this way. That sometimes they can be pretty decent."

I nodded. "In my job you start to think that people are always doing stupid things. But you have to remember that even the smartest person will sometimes make a mistake and need advice."

"Even you?" Keeler said with a smile.

"Especially me. I'm always getting into things way over my head and needing help."

"That's what I'm here to provide."

"Well, then, you've got your job cut out for you."

He sipped his coffee and took a glance through the sliders that lead out onto my deck. I studied his profile. He was a handsome, confident guy who was single. I could feel myself starting to be attracted to him, and warned myself not to mix business and pleasure. Maybe after all this aggravation with Dickens was over . . . maybe then.

We cleared the table and made our final preparations to leave.

"I guess I'd better go out the way I came in," Keeler said, reaching for the slider door. "Lock this after I go."

"What if the neighbors see you walking around the back of the building? Won't that seem suspicious?"

"They'll probably think I'm the meter reader. The worst they can do is call the police, and Chief Farantello will take care of it."

He slid the door open and stepped outside. I closed the door behind him and locked it. Then I put a broom handle I use for security in the track. I waited a couple of minutes, and then went out the front door myself. I visually checked my car as I approached it. Nothing seemed out of order. I got in and headed out of the parking lot, checking to see that Keeler was behind me.

When I got to work I pulled in the parking lot and took a space where I could see my car from my desk, just in case anyone planned to tamper with it.

"So how did it go?" Grissy asked me as soon as I entered.

"How did what go?"

She rolled her eyes. "Your date with Chris, of course."

"Not so good. We've pretty much decided that we're incompatible."

"Really?"

I nodded.

"There's nothing weird about him, is there?"

"No. He seems like a very nice guy, just not my type."

"Did he feel the same way about you?"

"Definitely." I was getting a little tired of being cross-examined, and started to head to my desk.

"Would you mind, then, if I asked him out?"

"You?" Although Chris and I clearly had no future together, I still felt a little possessive of him. Maybe if he never met another woman, he'd give me a second shot.

She nodded her head eagerly. "I love men who can dance, and he's not hard on the eyes either."

"I guess I wouldn't have any problem with that." I just hoped Chris wouldn't recount my little episode with the hat. Probably he wouldn't, because it didn't exactly put him in a good light.

I had been working on my Auntie Mabel letters for about an hour when I felt someone was staring at me. I looked up and there was Roger St. Claire. He was wearing a suit, as always, but had a gaily colored scarf draped nonchalantly around his neck. Tall and thin with gray hair, he looked distinguished and just a little bit risqué. For a moment I could understand what Gran found in him.

"New scarf?" I asked.

He nodded. "Your grandmother knitted it for me." He coughed slightly. "She said it brings out my inner boy."

"I see," I said, barely keeping a straight face.

"She also wanted me to let you know that I've sent out my letters of inquiry for a job in Florida," he said glumly.

"Don't you think you'll get one?"

"I'm not sure I want one."

"You'll do fine as a teacher."

Roger shook his head and started to slowly make his way down the hall to his office. He stopped halfway down the hall.

"Have you done that story on The Red Barn yet?"

I shook my head. "I haven't had time." Actually I'd forgotten all about it.

"Get on it, please. I'd like us to have at least one article per week on local businesses."

"Okay."

I finished up the letter I was working on, then called The Red Barn. Stephanie answered and said she'd be delighted to have us do a piece on her store, so I packed a camera and a notebook in my bag. I told Grissy where I was headed.

"Is that one of those places where they sell junk?" she asked, wrinkling her nose up as if she could smell the rot and mildew.

"I think she sells rather high-end antiques."

"Antique is just another name for heavily used. I always like to have things that are new, where no one else has already possessed them."

"Then this wouldn't be the place for you."

She shook her head as if it wasn't the place for anybody with any self-respect.

I made a rather dramatic show of getting in my car, standing by the door longer than necessary so Keeler would know I was leaving. When I heard the engine of his car start, I got in mine and headed down to Main Street. I made a left on Main and headed north. The Red Barn was on the extreme north end of town where there were still some farms and pastures with livestock. Traffic got lighter the further I went from the downtown green, and I could easily see Keeler hanging back about a quarter of a mile behind me. I took a left off of Main onto an east-west intersecting road. I drove about a mile and The Red Barn was on my right. I could see that Keeler was going to have a problem remaining inconspicuous. There were only two vehicles in the lot. As I pulled in and parked, I looked in my rearview mirror and saw him go past the entrance. I figured he was going to park somewhere further down the road where he could be relatively invisible and at the same time keep his eyes on the parking lot.

The Red Barn was indeed a barn and painted red. There were barn doors in the front, but the entrance was a normal-sized door off to the side. On my left as I went in I saw Stephanie Fleming and a man struggling to wrestle a large fireplace mantel into an upright position. They finally got it where they wanted it and clapped their hands to get rid of the dust. The man walked away just as Stephanie saw me. She was wearing jeans and a red blouse that set off her light blond hair nicely.

"That's from some large fireplace," I said.

"Yes, it's from a mansion up in Northampton that a couple is renovating. They decided to put in a more contemporary fireplace, so I purchased this mantel from them. You should have seen my boyfriend and I hoisting it into the back of my pickup truck."

Stephanie was no taller than me and very slender, and the

man who had been helping her wasn't much bigger. So I imagined it had been quite a chore for them.

"Do you have a lot of large pieces?"

She nodded. "Sometimes we move them ourselves. If it's a very heavy piece, I have a couple of movers that I hire."

The space was open just as when it had been a barn with the items arranged in rows with narrow spaces to walk between them. She seemed to have a large inventory.

"What's the focus of your story?" she asked.

"I want to write about the kinds of things you have here. Something that will bring people into your shop."

Stephanie looked thoughtful for a moment.

"Why don't I take you on a quick survey of some of the highlights of my inventory?"

"Sounds fine."

For the next half-hour we marched up and down the aisles. Stephanie would select a particular piece, tell me whether it was Queen Anne, Federal, or Victorian, and discuss the period. We looked at highboys, refectory tables, rocking chairs, and Davenport desks. I took pictures, and I kept scribbling frantically in my notebook, hoping that I'd be able to put all these facts together into a coherent story. Finally when we had reached the end of the last aisle, she turned to me.

"I think one point you should make in your story is that we are not the place for folks looking to buy cut-rate antiques. We are the place for genuine collectors who have educated themselves and know what they want. We have very good pieces and sell them at a fair price. And if we don't have what you want, we have connections that will enable us to get it for you."

"And you said that you got some of this inventory from your divorce."

"You're not going to put that in the story, are you?" she asked, looking alarmed.

"No, of course not. But you mentioned to me when we last met that you did get a lot of antiques as a result of your divorce."

"But that was a relatively small, personal collection. Over the years business has been good, enabling me to expand. I don't know if I still have any of those early pieces. Probably all of them have sold."

"You must be very proud of what you've achieved."

The woman smiled. "I went from being a mother and a housewife, which was all I had done when I was married, to being an entrepreneur with a grown family of successful children. Yes, I am very proud of what I've accomplished."

As we walked back to the front door, she gestured to various other pieces, told me their names, and gave me a brief idea of where they fit into the history of furniture.

"This is going to be a very challenging piece to write because you've given me so much information," I said as we stopped by the door. "Once I have the article done, I'd like to show it to you to make sure I haven't made any egregious mistakes."

"Good idea. I'm here from ten to five every day except for Monday when we're closed. And I want to thank you and Roger for giving me this free publicity."

I went back to the car and stood by the door for a moment. I couldn't see where Keeler was parked, but I trusted that he would see me leave the lot. Putting my bag on the back seat, I started the car and headed back to the office. As I pulled out onto the street, I saw in my rearview mirror a car that looked like Keeler's pull out from the side of the road. Since there was almost no traffic, he kept his distance. I made a right on Main and headed south toward town.

I don't know when I became aware of the car traveling in the opposite direction. Probably not until it was a few blocks away. That was when it swerved onto my side of the road and started coming directly toward me. I looked in my rearview mirror and saw Keeler speeding to catch up with me, but I knew he'd never get here before I met the other car head-on. I kept waiting for the other driver to veer off, but he kept coming. I was vaguely aware that to my right was a steep drop to the meadow below, so if I tried pulling off the road in that direction I'd probably turn over. I stared at the car coming at me. It was close enough now that I could clearly see it was red. Was Dickens playing a game of chicken with me? Would he swerve off at the last minute to save his own life? Or was he suicidal, determined to end this once and for all?

I slowed my speed, not that it did any good at the rate he was coming. He was less than half a block away and coming fast when I hit the gas and swerved to my left and drove on the opposite side of the road. He was past me in a flash. We couldn't have been more than a few inches apart. He almost front-ended Keeler, but managed to abruptly swing around him and head up the road at a high speed. I slowly coasted back to the right side of the road and stopped on the shoulder. My heart was racing and my hands were shaking so badly that I could hardly hold the wheel. The next thing I was aware of was Keeler tapping on my window causing me to jump. He motioned I should roll it down.

"Are you okay?"

"I guess so. Shouldn't you be chasing him or something?" I asked, but relieved that he was standing there beside me.

"He's got too much of a head start. I called it in, but there are lots of ways off this road. He'll probably be long gone before any patrol cars are in the area. Did you get a look at his face?"

I shook my head. "He was wearing a hoodie of some kind. I couldn't make out his face."

"Yeah, neither could I."

"He must have been following me and just waited for his chance to catch me on the return trip."

"I didn't see anyone behind me as we were coming up here, but he could have been following us from a distance." He gave me an appraising look. "Are you okay to drive back to the office?"

My hands had stopped shaking and my heart rate had slowed to almost normal.

"I'll be fine."

"Are you sure?"

"Yeah, yeah, I'm fine."

He reached in and patted my shoulder.

"Don't worry, I'll be right behind you."

I nodded. I didn't find that quite as reassuring as he might think.

CHAPTER 18

"How did it go?" Grissy asked me as I walked into the office.

"What do you mean?" I snapped.

Grissy looked startled at my harsh tone and said tentatively, "How did things go at The Red Barn?"

"Oh, fine. It's quite a place."

I wasn't about to tell her about my near miss. I wanted to keep my problems to myself and to those who absolutely needed to know.

Not encouraging any more small talk, I walked across the room to my desk. I took out my notebook, downloaded the pictures from the camera onto my computer, and began composing the story. Slowly I got into it and my nerves began to calm. Nothing like work to make you forget that someone has tried to kill you. I looked out the window at my car and imagined what it would look like after a head-on collision. I had an image of a windshield shattered from the inside out. It wasn't a pretty picture. I wondered if Dickens really was suicidal or if he figured I'd lose my nerve and go off the side of the road down the embankment. I pulled my mind back to my computer screen and began putting the final touches on the story.

Derrick charged into the office, acting as if he were late for a deadline. He saw me, stopped, and came over to perch on the edge of the chair next to my desk. He didn't say anything at first. He seemed to be trying to decide how to begin.

"I know we pretty much agreed not to go out together," he

said hesitantly.

"That's right."

"But I was just wondering . . ."

"Wondering what?"

"Well, Roger asked me to cover the Chamber of Commerce Dance."

"Doesn't our social reporter usually do that type of thing?"

We have a young, extroverted woman who works part-time handling weddings and social events.

"She can't make it. Her father died and the dance is the day of the funeral."

"What day is it?" I'd seen flyers around town for the event, but paid no attention.

"Tonight."

"Tonight?"

"I just got the assignment. Roger forgot to tell Sam about the death in her family. I was kind of hoping that you'd do me a one-time favor and be my date for the dance."

I stared at my desktop, trying hard to decide what to do.

"You wouldn't have to spend the whole night with me. I'll be working the floor, talking to the movers and shakers. You can dance with whomever you want."

I've had more gracious offers.

"Why don't you go alone?"

He frowned. "It would be embarrassing. It would look like I couldn't find a date."

Well apparently you can't, I thought.

He must have read my mind because he said huffily, "I could get a date, no trouble at all, but not on one day's notice."

I was tempted to ask him who that lucky girl would be, but instead I nodded.

"Under the circumstances, I'll go with you."

His face brightened. "Thanks, Laura, thanks a lot."

He was still thanking me as he backed up and headed toward his office.

"Chris and I are going to the dance, too," Grissy said. "I asked him. I was surprised he didn't already have a date given he's a dancer and all. But I guess he doesn't know anyone in town but his students."

"It's probably tricky going out with your students," I said, "if things don't work out you lose money."

"And maybe she tells people what a lousy teacher you are."

"Well, I hope you'll have a good time," I said.

"You, too."

I shrugged. "I'm doing my duty to help the *Chronicle*. Having a good time has nothing to do with it."

"You never know. You might meet someone there who'll be just perfect for you. You never know when you'll come across Mr. Right."

I was about to express my doubts when the phone rang. It was my former Mr. Right, Farantello.

"We had the bartender come in, and we've got a sketch for you to take a look at. Do you have any time to stop by the station?" he asked.

"Sure. How about at one o'clock."

"Sounds fine. The bartender mentioned that a woman was in the bar the other night who asked him to ID someone. Would that have been you?"

"Yeah. You can scratch Chris Bell of the Raoul dance studio off your list."

"Why did you suspect him?"

"Because he asked to go out with me. And I was figuring that this guy Dickens might try to get close to me in order to find out how much I know."

"I suppose it's possible. Who else is asking you out these days?"

I thought he was asking for personal as well as professional reasons, but I couldn't really refuse to answer.

"Derrick Malone, who works on the paper, has asked me to the dance tonight."

"He knows you're Auntie Mabel. That makes him a suspect."

"I suppose, but I can't imagine Derrick making a living by seducing older women."

"He's been in to interview me. I think I see what you mean."

"Anyone else?"

"Nope."

"Okay. See you at one."

After I hung up the phone I took out the bag with my lunch. I'd read somewhere that eating at your desk is a bad practice. You don't relax enough for good digestion and are likely to get interrupted. But I had no choice. There was no lounge at the paper, and going out to eat meant consuming more calories and more of my income than I cared to do. I was in the middle of my sandwich when a guy from back in the printing shed brought in today's copy of the *Chronicle*. I pulled the paper over in front of me, and began to read the front page. I found myself actually becoming engrossed in an account of last night's school board meeting. The writer added just enough humor to his facts to make the meeting come alive and be amusing.

"Hey, Grissy, who is this David Oliver who writes the school news? I thought we had that professor of education from Ravensford College, Dr. Wiley."

"He retired and moved south somewhere. This is a new guy. I've never met him. I guess he submits his pieces from home."

"He's good."

After finishing my lunch, I dug out my cell phone and let Keeler know that I was heading for the police station to check out the suspect's sketch. He said that he would join me there. I made the half-mile drive over to the police station, hoping what

I'd find there would bring my search to an end. If we recognized Dickens, we'd be a good part of the way to arresting him.

I told the desk sergeant that I was there to see Chief of Detectives Farantello. He said I was expected and ushered me directly into his office. Farantello glanced up at me with his brown eyes the color of just-brewed coffee, looking even more morose than usual. He motioned for me to sit down.

"I hear you had a close call earlier today."

I nodded.

"I gather you didn't get a good look at the guy."

"He was wearing a hood, and I had other things on my mind at the time."

Keeler appeared in the doorway, and Farantello motioned for him to take the other chair.

"Did you get a good look at the person who tried to run Laura off the road?" he asked the officer.

Keeler shook his head. "He went by me doing seventy. I didn't see his face at all."

"How about a license plate number?"

"I only saw the one in the front, and it was covered with mud."

"Too bad." Farantello took two sheets of paper off his desk and handed one to each of us. "This is what the sketch artist was able to make out of the bartender's description."

I stared at the sketch. He was wearing a baseball cap that hid his hair. The face was a bit long with regular features. He looked like a thousand other guys, but there was something about the face that seemed vaguely familiar to me. I tried as hard as I could, but the association just wouldn't come.

"Does he look familiar to either one of you?"

Keeler shook his head.

"There's something about him that looks familiar, but I can't quite place him," I said.

"Keep thinking about it. Sometimes it will click over time."

"I'll give it my best shot. We could run the picture in the *Chronicle* and see if anyone recognizes him."

Farantello shook his head. "Then we'd have to make it public that we think Marion Jensen's death was a murder, which might cause the perpetrator to run. So let's keep quiet on that for a while longer."

"Okay."

"About your episode with Chris Bell, where you brought him into the bar for a possible ID," Farantello said.

I shrugged. "It turned out to be a waste of time."

"What if he had been Dickens, can you imagine how dangerous the situation could have become? If you think this guy really might try to get close to you, I would suggest that you not go on any dates until the case is solved."

"Starting tomorrow. I have to go to the Chamber of Commerce Dance tonight."

Farantello sighed. "Keeler, you're going to that dance tonight as well."

"I am?"

"That's an order."

"Yes, sir. But it's too late for me to get a date."

"Then go alone and be a wallflower, this isn't a social occasion. I want you to keep an eye on Laura."

"Yes, sir."

"I doubt that Dickens will try anything in a crowd of people," I said.

"Better safe than sorry," Farantello said. "How are you and Keeler doing with the nighttime living arrangements? Any problems?"

We both indicated that everything was going along just peachy.

"Okay, then. Take those pictures with you and study them. I want you both able to pick that face out of a crowd. I'm going to distribute these to the patrol units, so they can be on the lookout for this guy."

When we'd all agreed that we knew what to do, Farantello said I should leave first and Keeler would follow in a few minutes. I said that I was going back to work, so there was no reason to worry. Keeler and Farantello exchanged glances that made me wonder if I should be worrying more. As I was walking down the main hall of the police station who should come out of a room but Cliff Moore, the chief of police. At first he gave me one of those smarmy smiles he probably inflicts automatically on young women, but then he recognized me, and the smile disappeared.

"What are you doing here, Ms. Magee?" he asked sharply.

"I had an appointment with Detective Farantello."

"Are you involved in a police investigation again?"

"Not exactly." I mentally scrambled for a way to explain my being here without telling him that I was Auntie Mabel. "I received a threatening letter at the paper. I was reporting it to Detective Farantello."

"I can't imagine why anyone would threaten *you*." He went heavy on the sarcasm to show that he thought people were lined up wanting to get a shot at me.

"I can't either," I said, ignoring his tone.

"I'll go have a talk with Detective Farantello right now to make sure we're doing enough to keep you safe. After all, I wouldn't want to get on the wrong side of your grandmother."

"No, you certainly wouldn't," I said, remaining calm.

Giving me a curt nod, he turned and headed in the direction of Farantello's office to make good on his promise. Keeler slipped out of a nearby men's room once the chief had gone past.

"That can't be good," he said.

"Did you hear that jerk?"

Keeler motioned for me to keep my voice down.

"He may be a jerk, but he's the jerk in charge. If he gets involved in this, it automatically becomes a lot more complicated."

"Let's get out of here," I said, heading down the hall. Keeler stopped at the doorway, motioning that I should go ahead.

I went out to my car. About fifteen seconds later I saw Keeler walk over to his. I started the engine and sat there for a moment calming down and reviewing all the cutting retorts I could have made to Moore. But there was no point in dwelling on would haves, could haves, and should haves. Plus nothing I said to the chief would change his mind about my grandmother or me.

When I got back to the paper, Grissy was virtually bouncing up and down in her chair. She shoved a plastic box across the desk at me.

"Chris just bought me this."

It was an orchid corsage.

Won't that make you the queen of the prom, I almost said, but that sounded too catty.

"That's very nice," I mumbled.

"It was very sweet of him."

Yes, he was the sweet guy that I had so badly embarrassed that he never wanted to see me again. I didn't think Derrick would bring me a corsage. I figured I'd be lucky if he remembered to pick me up. I walked to the back of the room and settled into my chair. I wasn't in the mood to answer any more Auntie Mabel letters largely because I felt I had enough problems of my own. As if to punctuate it, Derrick breezed into the office and gave me a big thumbs-up.

"I'll pick you up at seven. Be ready to go because I want to get there early to talk to some people before the band starts."

"Sure thing," I said, attempting a smile. Out of the corner of my eye I could see Grissy with a sad smile on her face, probably feeling sorry for me.

My phone rang. It was Farantello.

"What did you say to the chief?"

"Nothing."

"He *really* doesn't like you."

"Or the family tree from which I grew."

Suddenly it clicked with Farantello.

"That's right, your grandmother was active in that campaign to get him replaced. No wonder he hates you. Cliff has never been very good at making fine distinctions."

"So what happened?"

"Well, I managed to tell him about the threatening letter without giving away the fact that you're Auntie Mabel."

"That's good."

"The not so good part is that he doesn't think the threat warrants having Keeler following you around all day."

"Even after that creep tried to run me off the road?"

"He thinks that was someone engaging in normal bad driving, and it was not an attempt on your life."

"He should have been there."

"At any rate, I have to reassign Keeler. I can have a patrol car cruise by the paper every so often to look out for suspicious characters."

"What about at night?"

"The news is better there. The chief can't tell Keeler where to spend his evenings, and he's volunteered to spend them with you."

"That's very generous of him," I said, and meant it.

"Be nice to him. Following you around has gotten him on the chief's wrong side, which could be a career stopper, so he deserves to be appreciated."

"I'm sure you came in for your share of grief, too."

"But for me there's no promotion to worry about. As chief of detectives the only spot left is Moore's."

"Maybe you'll have that someday."

"I'm not even sure I want it. You spend more time with budgets and city politics than you do with solving crimes."

"Well, I appreciate what both of you have done."

"Good. But keep in mind that now you're alone wherever you go during the day, so be careful."

I promised him I would. As I looked out the window, I saw Keeler's car pull out of the lot and head up the street. I felt a sudden shock of loneliness. Now I was on my own and not much closer to finding the man who wanted to kill me.

CHAPTER 19

The Ravensford Public Library is a late-nineteenth-century building. Built out of granite blocks, it has the solidity of a time when people were more certain of how the world worked. There was none of this timid use of glass walls, phony stone facades, or plastic moldings. People in those days built things to last. And although the library, which was right off the green, had inadequate parking and high ceilings that made it expensive to heat, no one quite had the nerve to suggest that it be torn down or the library relocated to a more efficient, modern building.

I had never been in the library when it was used for a party, and I was surprised at how easily it adapted to such a purpose. The tables in the main reading room had been pushed back to the walls, revealing the hardwood, which made a fine dance floor. Bunting had been hung from the balcony and draperies strategically placed over the bookshelves to soften their appearance. A refreshment table had been set up near the main desk, and there was already a line of people making their way to the food and drink. Others balancing paper plates in their hands were standing around the edge of the dance floor talking. At the far end of the room I could see the band starting to set up.

Derrick, who at least had walked me in from the bank parking lot, which was already holding the overflow from the library, immediately made his move.

"I see Bill Dempsey, the city councilor, over by the food. I want to talk with him about that zoning variance. Will you be okay on your own?" he asked, hardly bothering to glance at me to receive my consent.

"No, without you by my side I'll turn into a pumpkin and roll out the door," I replied.

"Huh?" He actually turned to look at me.

"Just kidding. Go knock yourself out, Derrick."

Giving me a quick nod, he made a beeline across the room to annoy the councilor.

"Is that your date?"

I turned to my left and there was Keeler looking very good in a dark blue suit.

"I guess you could call him that. He's more my transportation. He got me here, and hopefully he'll take me home. In between I have nothing to do with him."

"If he disappears during the evening, I can always take you home. After all, we're going to the same place."

I smiled. "Should we even be seen together?"

"Now that I'm no longer tailing you, it should be all right. People will think we're just a couple of friends."

"And is that what we are?" I knew I was hopelessly flirting, but standing next to Keeler in the middle of a crowd, I felt safe and relaxed. And I guess that was bringing out the playful side of me.

"I'd like to think so," he said.

"What about after all of this is over, assuming it someday will be, can we still be friends then?"

"That depends."

"On what?"

Keeler paused. "It's pretty much common knowledge around the station that you and Chief Farantello were an item. I'd want to know if that was really in the past tense before we got to be better friends."

"We're not seeing each other now. He's back with his wife."

"And we both know that changes with the seasons. I wouldn't want us to become good friends and then have you waltz off to be with Farantello because he's left his wife again."

Keeler gave me a level stare that kept me from saying anything funny or cute.

"So you want to know if it's really over between Farantello and me?"

He nodded.

"I wish I could give you a simple 'yes' or 'no' answer to that, but the truth is that I'm just not sure myself."

He cleared his throat and looked disappointed.

"When do you think you will know?"

I gave a harsh laugh. "I don't even know the answer to that."

"Okay. Well I'm going to circulate around the room to see if I can spot anyone who looks like this," he said, slipping the artist's sketch of Dickens out of his pocket.

He gave me a nod that wasn't much friendlier than Derrick's and strolled off. I was a real hit with the men tonight. The room was starting to fill up, and the crowd had spread to the dance floor where many small groups were standing and talking. I saw Farantello on the other side of the room, and began to make my way through the intervening throng to reach him. I was halfway there when the crowd cleared for a moment, and I saw that a woman was holding his arm. I stood stock-still, feeling like an idiot. Of course, he would bring his ex-wife to a dance since he was back living with her.

I almost turned and ran back to my corner to hide. But curiosity won out. I had never seen his ex-wife. I wasn't sure I wanted to. But whether I wanted to or not, I stood in the middle of the room waiting for the crowd to shift again so I could get a look at her. I was about to give up when a foursome next to Farantello moved aside and the woman on his arm came into full view.

She wasn't pretty; she was beautiful. She was a tall and slender blonde with the long graceful neck and the high cheekbones of a fashion model. Next to her beauty my looks were laughable. She was a swan, and I was the funny little duckling that everyone thought was so cute and cuddly. The crowd parted some more and on the other side of Farantello was a younger version of his wife. That had to be his daughter, Andrea. She had a grip on her father's other arm. With two such women holding on to him, what chance was there that I would ever pry him loose? Divorced he might be, but he was firmly attached to his family.

Afraid that Farantello would spot me staring at him, I spun around and blindly made my way back to the other side of the room. I stood there for a moment hyperventilating. The major question on my mind wasn't why he had gone back to his wife. The big question was why he had ever taken up with me in the first place. If you have caviar at home, why go out to a pizza joint?

"Hello," Grissy said, coming to stand beside me.

Chris was on the other side of her, holding her arm. I wondered how you got a man to hang around and do that. Probably, I figured, by avoiding dates with boy reporters. Chris nodded, looking vaguely embarrassed at seeing me again. He refused to meet my eye. I figured he'd get over it—someday.

"Isn't the library just perfect for this kind of event? You know in Germany they often use public buildings for social occasions. It adds a certain dignity to the event."

"The band is very good. They have something of a local reputation," Chris added.

There was the sound of static over a public address system. People began moving out of the center of the room as the mayor came forward with a microphone in his hand. He thanked the Chamber of Commerce for sponsoring the dance, and expressed further thanks that the Chamber was going to give the proceeds to the campaign to build a new senior citizen center. He went through a laundry list of names of those who had made the event possible, each name was followed by hearty applause. Then he introduced the band and announced that it was time to dance. As soon as the music started, Grissy waved goodbye to me, and she and Chris swirled off across the floor. I stood there like the flotsam and jetsam the waves leave behind. I looked around the rim of the room, hoping to find someone I could talk to, so I wouldn't feel like such a wallflower. At twelve o'clock from my nine o'clock location I spotted Stephanie Fleming standing alone and slowly made my way over to her.

"Are you by yourself, too?" she asked.

"Not exactly. My date just has better things to do." I pointed to Derrick. He had buttonholed the mayor, who was desperately looking around for someone to relieve him of this barnacle.

Stephanie smiled. "One of the benefits of getting older is that you have a wider range of men to choose from. You can find ones who are more mature. Of course, some would say that maturity is overrated."

"Why isn't your boyfriend with you tonight?"

"He was supposed to be. He begged off at the last minute with an upset stomach." She shook her head. "I think he just doesn't like to dance. Unlike that man over there," she said, indicating Chris.

"I think he has an unfair advantage. He's a dance teacher."

"Well, his date is certainly lucky."

I grunted.

"Oh, I see someone who was looking at a highboy in the shop last week," she said, nodding toward the other side of the room. "I think I'll find out if he's given it any more consideration. I may as well get something out of my being here. See you."

I saw Katie Jensen standing nearby. She saw me at the same time. She said something to the man standing next to her, then headed toward me.

"Have you found out anything about my mother's death?" she whispered, putting her head close to mine.

"Don't spread it around, but it definitely is a suspicious death. The police have some idea of what your mother's boyfriend looked like, and they're searching for him."

I pulled the police sketch out of my pocket and showed it to her.

"Do you recognize him?"

She studied it for a moment, and then shook her head.

"Do the police have any idea who he is?"

"No. Apparently your mother kept very quiet about him."

"Like I told you, she never mentioned him to me. I've been racking my brain trying to remember if she gave any indication of having a boyfriend. The only odd thing about her behavior is that in the last couple of months she started reading the classics. She'd always read a lot, but before it was romances and romantic suspense. She'd go through three or four of them a week, but her taste suddenly changed. She even boxed up all the romances she had around the house and took them to be recycled."

"What did she say when you asked her about the change?"

"She just shrugged. She said something about being at a new point in her life and needing to learn new things."

I looked across the room, trying to figure out what significance that remark might have.

"I wish I could tell you more. Suddenly I feel like I didn't know my mother at all."

"We none of us know our parents as well as we think."

"Please don't give up on this."

"Don't worry, I'm going to keep on it until we get answers."

She reached over and squeezed my hand. "Thanks for doing this for my mother."

I didn't tell her that I was also doing it for myself.

A few minutes later Corinne came by holding Jeff Ralston by the hand. She was wearing a silver-sequined sheath that hugged closely to her lush curves. I saw the eyes of several men drift in our direction as she walked past.

"This is quite an event for Ravensford," she said. "Who are you here with?"

I was getting tired of being asked that question. I was tempted to say I was here by myself, but that sounded even worse.

"Derrick Malone, a reporter on the paper. He's around here somewhere trying to get a scoop."

Corinne looked meaningfully at Jeff, and I thought for a moment she was going to prod him to dance with me. But then she must have come to her senses, realizing there's hardly anything worse than a pity dance. I'd rather be a wallflower.

"I'm sure Derrick will be back once he gets enough information for his story. He's covering the dance for the paper," I said, as if to excuse him for his inattentiveness. Corinne nodded and said goodbye. She and Jeff eased out on the floor and began to dance.

As I watched the dancers moving around the room, I saw Roger and my grandmother go floating past. She saw me and waved. The next dance was a fast one, and they left the floor and headed over to me.

"I didn't know you were going to be here tonight," Gran said.

"Neither did I until the last minute."

"Are you here with someone?"

"In a manner of speaking. He's a reporter from the paper, Derrick Malone. He's spending most of his time talking to the bigwigs."

"I asked him to cover this event," said Roger. "But I didn't expect him to turn it into one long interview session. I think I'll have a chat with the boy." He headed quickly across the room before I could stop him.

"This young man isn't somebody you're serious about, is he?" Gran asked.

"Not in the least. I'm just doing him a favor because he didn't want to come without a date."

"Good. Rudeness in a young man is usually an indication of worse things."

Gran's comment resonated with me. Could Derrick be Dickens? He knew I was Auntie Mabel. Still, I couldn't imagine him seducing Marion Jensen, and was he even in town over a year ago when Holly Preston died? But Dickens must be a good actor, and maybe the Derrick I knew wasn't the real one. Roger rejoined us.

"I told Derrick that he should be dancing with Laura rather than harassing public officials. That boy is certainly keen, but he doesn't know when enough is enough."

Derrick came over and stood in front of me as the band struck up a slow dance.

"I think we should dance," he announced, as if it were a heavy but necessary penance.

"Okay."

We got into dance position and Derrick began shuffling his feet in a random way that I couldn't follow. Finally I forced him to move into an area of the floor out of the way of the other couples, and got him to sway slowly from side to side. It might not have resembled dancing, but it gave us a chance to talk.

"Have you lived in Ravensford long?" I asked.

"I grew up here."

"But you worked in Boston. When did you come back to Ravensford?"

"A little over a year ago."

"But you've only worked for the *Chronicle* for a few weeks."

"Right. I worked on a local television station when I first moved out here. Then, like I told you, I decided that the print medium was better for me."

"Have you gone out much since you've been back in town?"

He gave me a stubborn look as if he was going to refuse to answer. But then he did.

"Not much. I've been too busy."

"It's just that I was surprised that a handsome guy like yourself didn't have a date for the dance."

It was true that he was quite good-looking. The problem was with his personality.

"I don't always make friends easily," he said, blushing slightly.

"You just have to relax more and let them see what you're really like."

That was standard Auntie Mabel advice, but in Derrick's case I wasn't sure it was going to help.

"Look," Derrick said, stopping his swaying, "maybe we should go now. I want to go back to the office tonight to write up the piece about this dance because I've got lots of other things to do tomorrow morning."

About an hour later, after Derrick had driven me home and given me a cool pat on the shoulder that was almost a shove out of the car, there was a gentle knock on my front door. I cautiously opened it, leaving the chain on, and saw Keeler standing on the doorstep. "Why didn't you come around back?"

"I figured if there was someone here with you it would be less suspicious than knocking on the back door. This way I could say I was a neighbor who needed a cup of sugar."

"Wearing a suit, surely a trained detective could come up with a better excuse than that," I said, letting him inside.

"So your date didn't come in for coffee?" he said, rather stating the obvious.

"My date couldn't wait to escape. He had to get back to work, although I suspect that was only an excuse. I guess I'm not his type."

Keeler shook his head. "The guy must be a fool," he said.

I smiled and was surprised to discover that I suddenly had tears in my eyes. I faced away so Keeler wouldn't see, but too late.

"Are you okay?" he asked, touching me gently on the arm.

I blinked my eyes and nodded. "Just a little tired. It's been a long night."

"It has. Let's go to bed."

I smiled at that, and he blushed.

"Separately, of course."

"Of course."

I turned to head into my bedroom.

"Have a good night's sleep," he called.

I told him the same. But once in bed I lay awake for a long time seeing Farantello's wife standing across the room from me. She was smiling complacently, her arm linked with his, as if she knew the answer to a question that I couldn't begin to fathom. I wanted to run across the room, pull them apart, and shout at Farantello that I could give him something that this beautiful but cold woman never could. But then her glance would meet mine, and I would turn to stone, unable to move and feeling helpless. The frustration never left me until, exhausted, I drifted off to sleep.

CHAPTER 20

Keeler and I didn't talk much over breakfast the next morning. I'm never the most cheerful of persons upon awakening, and my head was still a muddle from thinking about Farantello's wife. My answers to Keeler's attempts at conversation were generally monosyllabic. I did manage to ask him what his new assignment was for the day, and he said that Chief Moore had him looking into a burglary up on the Heights two nights ago. He was helping the detective assigned to the case.

I got the artist's sketch of Marion's boyfriend from my bedroom and put it in front of me while I ate my cereal, struggling to remember whom it reminded me of. But the more I pushed, the more the face I was trying to recall receded into the depths of my memory.

As Keeler and I stood in the hall together ready to go to our respective jobs, it seemed so domestic that I had to restrain myself from giving him a kiss. I think even he paused on the back doorstep for a moment as if realizing that something was missing.

When I got to work, Grissy was virtually bouncing up and down wanting to talk about the dance. She even came out from behind her desk to show me a new rhumba step that Chris had taught her. Mixed in with dance talk, there were also a lot of oblique comments about how attractive and nice Chris was. When I asked her if they had gone anywhere after the dance, her answer was so uncharacteristically demure that I wondered if she had broken her own rule about sex on the first date.

I was happy for Grissy, I really was. But all of her cheerful talk left me more than a little envious and down in the dumps. Since I wasn't quite close enough to Grissy to tell her my troubles and I also didn't want to burst her bubble, I decided to call Corinne. As my best friend in town she would have to listen to me.

"Hello," Corinne answered, sounding so subdued that I barely recognized her voice.

"Hi, it's Laura. What's wrong?"

"Nothing."

"Is that why you sound like you've lost your last friend?"

"I don't want to talk about it."

"How about I bring you some lunch, and if you don't want to talk about it that's fine, but if you do, I'll listen."

There was a long silence over the phone.

"Okay, fine. I'll see you around noon."

"Fine."

I hung up the phone, a bit concerned. In the relatively short time I'd known Corinne she'd impressed me as being very stable, not given to ups and downs. She was the one who usually encouraged me to see the big picture. I wondered if her mood had something to do with Jeff Ralston.

Figuring I would know soon enough what it was all about so there was no point speculating, I turned to my bag of letters and became Auntie Mabel for a while. Toward the end of the morning one of the printers brought up a couple of copies of the *Chronicle* for us to read. Before I got a chance to look at it, Derrick walked in the front door and came over to my desk.

"Have you read my piece on the dance?" he asked.

"Not yet."

He picked up a copy of the paper and pointed to the bottom of page one.

"Tell me what you think."

He stood over me as I read the article through. I was on the spot. His story consisted largely of a list of the public officials who were there and their comments about various pending issues. In passing he mentioned the name of the band and where the money was going. There was nothing about the atmosphere of the library or whether people were having fun. The one photograph was of the mayor talking to the head of the city council. There were no pictures of people dancing and having a good time.

"So what did you think?" Derrick urged.

"It's a little dry."

"Dry?"

"Yes. You don't say whether people enjoyed themselves, and there's no picture of anyone dancing. You make it sound like a political event."

"All social events are political events."

"In a sense, maybe, but a dance is different from a city council meeting. That doesn't come across here."

Derrick stood very erect and his face got red.

"Okay, if that's the way you see it," he said.

He turned and marched off to his office and shut the door. I figured he wouldn't be asking me out on any more dates. I decided that suited me just fine.

At eleven-thirty I told Grissy I was going out for lunch. She wanted to know when I'd be back, and I told her at around one.

"That's good," she said. "Will you be in the office for the next hour after that?"

"Sure. Are you going somewhere?"

"Out to lunch with Chris."

"He works fast."

"No, you misunderstand. I am the one asking him out to lunch."

"Oh, I see. You must really like him."

"He is very graceful and a perfect gentleman. Such men are not to be taken lightly."

She gave me a glance suggesting that's what I had done in the case of Chris. I didn't tell her that I hadn't taken him lightly. I'd taken him to be a serial killer. I'd been wrong, but the harm was done.

I walked into the center of town and went to the local deli. I got two of their pastrami on rye sandwiches, which were a favorite of Corinne's, then I swung by the cupcake shop to pick up one of their special chocolate crème cupcakes for Corinne and a coconut for me. I'd have to live on sesame seeds and water for the next week to lose the weight, but you have to be willing to make sacrifices for your friends.

When I went into Corinne's shop she had just finished setting up a table in the front of the room for us to use. She gave me a faint smile that got a bit stronger when she saw the sandwiches. Soon we were happily slathering mustard on them and taking that first, big juicy bite. For a couple of moments we just ate in satisfied silence. Finally I turned to Corinne.

"So what is the problem?"

She sighed, and for a moment I thought she was going to refuse to talk about it

"It's about Jeff," she finally admitted.

"What about him?"

"You know Myra who works at the Knife and Fork."

I nodded. Myra was a waitress at one of the better luncheon places in town. A busybody with ears like a rabbit that could pick up a conversation across a crowded room, she was always passing along tidbits of information. Telling people things that they *just had to know* about their friends and associates, Myra had single-handedly ended more relationships in Ravensford than beautiful secretaries and alcohol combined.

"What did Myra say?"

"She saw Jeff in the Knife and Fork for lunch yesterday, and he was with a beautiful young woman. She said they were having a very intense conversation."

I smiled. "Is that all you're worried about? I'm sure lawyers have to meet with all kinds of people because of their work. Maybe she was a client or an opposing attorney. It could all be perfectly innocent."

"Myra said Jeff reached over and touched her hand," Corinne said, a stubborn look on her face, as if she wasn't going to let go of this so easily.

"Haven't you ever innocently touched a man's arm or hand?"

She grinned sheepishly. "Of course, I touch men all the time and don't think anything of it."

"So maybe it's the same thing with Jeffrey."

Corinne picked up her sandwich and bit into it thoughtfully.

"I know you're right, and this could mean nothing at all. But I need to be sure."

"Feeling insecure?"

She frowned. "Maybe you were right in what you said last time about going out with a younger man. It does create special problems. It gives the imagination free rein to create all sorts of scenarios. Unless I know the truth, this will be a constant worry, threatening to undermine our relationship."

"Well, I'm no expert on relationships, but I think you should be forthright with Jeff and tell him what's bothering you."

"But then I'll sound like a silly, jealous, old woman."

"Better than suspecting him of something that might not be true."

Corinne sighed. "I guess you're right. Maybe if I just mention that someone saw him at the Knife and Fork yesterday, he'll tell me all about it without my asking."

"Probably so, if he's got nothing to hide."

That was a big "if." Jeff's behavior sounded suspiciously like Dickens: seduce the older woman, then move on. He was certainly suave enough to carry off the seduction part. As a successful lawyer, he didn't need the money, but again, what Dickens did was all about power, not money. Giving him money was just tangible proof that you were under his control.

"Has Jeff ever asked you for money?"

"We talked about this once before, and I told you that I never give my boyfriends money. Why do you ask?"

"Just because someone I know was telling me the other day that her younger boyfriend kept hitting her up for cash."

"Well, I'd kiss any relationship goodbye where that happened."

We finished our sandwiches, and although I was already full, I couldn't resist the coconut cupcake.

As I was unwrapping it, Corinne asked, "So what's with you and the guy you were at the dance with last night?"

"Nothing. It was just a date of convenience. I don't even like him much, and now I don't think he likes me." I explained to her about my criticism of his article on the dance.

"Did you see that Farantello was there last night?" she asked cautiously.

"He was with his wife and daughter. I'd never seen them before."

"The wife is certainly striking," Corinne said.

"Let's not pussyfoot around it, Corinne. His wife is absolutely stunning."

Corinne sniffed. "She looked like a cold fish to me."

"But a beautiful cold fish. And we may be confusing elegance with coldness."

Corinne bit into her cupcake and rolled her eyes. "These

cupcakes are wonderful."

I nodded, licking the coconut icing from my lips.

"But you have to remember, Laura, he did divorce her. She isn't really his wife anymore."

"They live in the same house and sleep in the same bed. That says 'wife' to me."

"That's only because his daughter guilt-trips him into it."

"I've been telling myself that for months, but now I'm starting to doubt it. Farantello is no fool, and he's a very disciplined guy. He wouldn't let his daughter get away with this if deep down he didn't want her to."

Corinne shrugged. "Maybe you're right. If you are, then you should move on."

"Move on to where?"

"Who was that other guy I saw you talking to?"

I asked Corinne to describe him and from what she said I recognized that she meant Keeler.

"Officer Keeler is just someone I know."

"Another policeman! What is it about you and cops?"

"They just happen to be the people I meet."

"Because you keep getting caught up in crimes."

"Not my fault," I said, stuffing the rest of the cupcake in my mouth.

Corinne waited for me to finish. "Well, anyway, this Keeler looked pretty good to me. Is he married?"

I shook my head.

"Does he have an ex-wife?"

"Not that I know of."

"Well, that gives him a big edge over Farantello. Why don't you ask him out? You wait for the guy to do it, and it can take forever."

"I'm just not sure."

"Sure about what?"

"That I'm over Farantello. How can I go out with someone new when I keep thinking about him?"

"Do you want a little advice from someone who's been around the block a few more times than you?"

I nodded.

"You're never going to be completely over Farantello."

"Don't tell me that."

"It's true. You'll always have a soft spot for him, so if you wait to get over that before dating new people, you'll never date anyone again."

"So what should I do? Go out with a new guy while I'm still thinking about the old one?"

"Exactly. And over time the new guy will pretty much take the place of the old one in your mind. Never completely, but enough so that you can move on."

I stared across the room thinking about Corinne's advice. It suddenly struck me that it was unreasonable to expect to get over Farantello before going out with someone else. And that I was just using this as an excuse to keep things the way they were, with me pining for Farantello and going back to him whenever he decided to leave his ex-wife for a few months. That was no way to live.

It's time to make a fresh start, Auntie Mabel said.

I recognized that this was exactly the advice I'd give to someone who wrote me a letter describing a situation such as my own.

I turned to Corinne, "You're absolutely right," I said. "I don't know why I didn't figure that out for myself."

Corinne smiled. "Because we never see our own problems as clearly as others do."

Fifteen minutes later I walked back to the office with a newly found spring in my step and a renewed determination to turn my life around. The first thing I did when I was behind my desk was to call Keeler's cell phone number.

When he answered I said, "How about we have dinner together tonight?"

There was a long pause. "You mean at your condo?"

"Actually I was thinking that I might take you out."

"You remember what I said about the other day about you and Farantello. He's my friend, and I don't want to come between the two of you."

"I've given what you said a lot of thought, and I think it's time that I moved on."

"Are you sure?"

"I'm as certain as you can be about something like that."

"So where are we going to eat? And by the way I'm not sure I like the idea of you taking me out. I should be the one doing the asking."

"Get with the times, John. Anyway, I owe you for all the trailing around after me that you did. I was thinking we'd kill two birds with one stone and go to eat at the Collins Inn."

"You're single-handedly keeping that place in business. Why do you want to go there?"

"I figured we could show the artist's sketch of our perp around to see if anyone can ID him."

"I guess it's worth a shot. Are you sure you aren't asking me along just to lend some police presence?"

"Nope. Your coming along is completely for pleasure."

"I like the sound of that."

"What time do you get off-duty?"

"The chief's been riding us pretty hard about this burglary. I don't think I'll be out of here before six."

"Okay. Meet me at the condo, and we'll go from there."

Grissy walked into the office about an hour later. She had a smile on her face that made her look positively girlish.

"Did you have a good lunch?" I asked.

She almost skipped across the room to stand by my desk.

"It was divine. Then we went back to Chris's studio, and he showed me some samba steps. He's wonderful to dance with."

"I'm sure he is."

"But he doesn't just know about dancing. He can talk about music and art. We had a wonderful conversation about Mozart."

My knowledge of classical music was so limited that even if I hadn't embarrassed Chris on our first date, we probably would have run out of conversation by the second. Grissy went on for several more minutes about the virtues of her new boyfriend. I nodded, happy for her and hoping that the relationship would continue to enjoy smooth sailing.

When she finally returned to her desk, humming what I imagined must be Mozart, I sat there trying to decide what to do for the afternoon. I was all caught up on Auntie Mabel, and I was trying to think of something I could do to help catch Dickens. I had the artist's sketch out on my desk. Staring at it again hadn't seemed to help, so I thought why not show it to some people who might have seen the guy. Two places, aside from the Collins Inn, we knew he had been in were Holly Preston's and Marion Jensen's neighborhoods. The only problem was Farantello didn't want to publicize the fact that we were treating Marion's death as a homicide, so I decided to make a vague reference to a burglary that was being investigated. I would identify myself as a reporter for the *Chronicle* so as not to be impersonating a police officer. I'd just have to see if folks would be willing to talk to me.

I started by driving through a quiet suburban neighborhood with little traffic, so I could make sure I wasn't being followed. Once I was pretty sure of that I drove over to Holly's neighborhood and went door to door to every house on her block. Aside from one woman who said she didn't want any and slammed the door before I could make my pitch, people were polite;

however, no one brought me any closer to identifying my suspect. I got in the car and traveled across town to Marion's street. Mrs. Hannity tried to invite me in for tea again, but this time I resisted. She said the picture looked a lot like the man she had seen from a distance and from the back. Other neighbors were even less helpful. It wasn't until I was interviewing a neighbor directly across from Marion that I got lucky.

The person who came to the door was a man, a man who was almost completely bald. He stared at the picture for a couple of moments.

"Yeah, I saw him go to Marion's house a few times."

"Do you know his name?"

He shook his head.

"Is there anything you can add to the picture?"

The man thought some more. "One day during the summer when it was hot, I saw him take off that baseball cap to wipe his brow. He had a full head of dark hair, probably brown. You can see how I might remember that," he said with a smile, running a hand over his naked pate. "I'll admit that I was kind of jealous."

My bald friend couldn't add anything more to the picture, but I figured every little bit helped. I'd see that Keeler got the information to a police artist who might want to talk with the man to tease out more details with regard to how the hair was styled.

Satisfied that the afternoon hadn't been a complete waste, I debated with myself about whether to go back to the *Chronicle* or not. Finally I decided there wasn't anything urgent for me to do at work, so I'd go home to get rested up for my date. When I got back to my condo and was securely locked inside, I found my poor night's sleep due to thinking about Farantello's wife catching up with me. Sitting on the sofa with a magazine in hand, I fell sound asleep.

CHAPTER 21

I woke up with a stiff neck and a feeling like something furry had died in my mouth. I looked at my watch and saw I had been asleep for over an hour. I just had enough time to shower and get ready before Keeler would be here. For the next forty-five minutes I rushed around getting ready, and I had just put my earrings in and brushed my hair for the fourth time when I heard a knock at the back door. I peeked out through the window and Keeler gave me a grin.

"How was your day?" I asked, feeling very domestic as I opened the door at the end of the day to a man.

"Aside from Chief Moore having it in for me, it was nothing to talk about. How was yours?"

"I'll tell you over dinner. I made a reservation at the Inn for six-thirty. So you have time to get changed if you want."

"I think I'll get into something more casual if you don't think Millicent Collins will toss me out for being in violation of their dress code."

"The way things are today, if you've got the money I'll bet you can get in with no clothes."

While Keeler was in his room getting dressed, I checked the doors and windows. Dickens might know where I lived, but I wasn't going to make it easy for him to spring a surprise. And if he was following me, being in the company of a strapping lad like Keeler might give him second thoughts about making an attack.

"All set?" Keeler asked, coming out of his room.

He was wearing a burgundy sweater that went well with his dark hair and dark gray trousers. I had never seen him wearing anything but a suit. He looked younger and more approachable in his casual attire.

"I'm ready."

We went out the front door and walked down to Keeler's car. Although I felt safe being with him, I'll admit that I did glance around to see if I could spot anyone suspicious hanging around. Keeler noticed.

"Keeping an eye out for Dickens?"

"Always," I replied.

"That's good, but I doubt he'll bother you when you're around others. It's during the day when you're alone that you have to be careful."

Once we were in the car Keeler asked me how I ended up working as Auntie Mabel. I gave him my usual speech about happening to move out to Ravensford, and my grandmother getting me the job.

"You must find the pace of life a little slow here compared to Boston," he said.

"Sure, but that has its advantages, too. Were you born here in Ravensford?"

He shook his head. "I'm originally from Vermont, up near Burlington."

"How did you end up here?"

"About five years ago a friend of mine in the department here called me and said they were planning to expand the force. I'd always wanted to be a cop. I even studied criminal justice in college. I moved down here right away and took up residence. I worked for a while in a copy shop until they announced the new positions. I applied and the rest is history."

"And now you're going to be a detective."

"If I can stay on the good side of Chief Moore."

"Sorry if I'm making that tough for you."

"If it wasn't you, it probably would be something else. It's virtually impossible to keep Moore happy."

"I gather that a lot of the folks in town would like to see him gone. My grandmother is one of them."

"Yeah, after that citizens group tried to get him ousted a few years back, the chief developed kind of a bunker mentality. He thinks everyone is out to get him. He's always telling us not to arrest anyone unless we've got an airtight case because he thinks most of the people in town are just waiting to sue him and the department for false arrest."

"He sounds paranoid."

"Oh, he has real enemies all right, but not nearly as many as he imagines."

I looked out the window for a moment as we circled the town green.

"I can't understand how Dickens found out my identity. There's no one working at the paper that fits the profile."

"People talk. Even in the department you can tell people to keep something secret, but there's always someone who blabs to a spouse or a friend. That person tells someone else, and before long the story is all over town. I bet a lot more people know you're Auntie Mabel than you might think."

We had reached the Collins Inn and Keeler pulled into the parking lot. I told him to park by the front door because the restaurant was off the main lobby. As we walked into the building, a sign that said "Collins Inn Restaurant" pointed through a door to our left. We entered a darkened hallway at the end of which stood a young woman at a hostess station. She pulled two menus out of a slot as we approached her.

"Two for dinner?" she asked.

Keeler nodded.

"Do you have reservations?"

I looked over her shoulder at the nearly empty dining room.

"Are they necessary?" I asked.

"Not during the week," she said, grinning. "But we get pretty crowded sometimes on the weekends."

I had my doubts about that.

We followed her around several tables until she reached a spot in the back of the room by a window. We assured her that it would be fine, and she told us our waitress would be with us shortly. We spent a couple of minutes looking around the room. The walls were covered with paintings so muddied either in their original execution or by the ravages of time that they were impossible to decipher. I guessed that they might have a Revolutionary War theme.

A tall thin woman came over to our table, brought us glasses of water, and told us her name was Kim and she'd be our waitress for this evening. She asked us if we wanted something to drink from the bar. I went with a white wine, while Keeler selected an imported beer.

"Do you know what you're going to have?" I asked, after spending a few more minutes perusing the menu.

"The roast chicken," he announced.

"I had you figured for a beef and potatoes kind of guy."

He shook his head. "I like chicken, and I know how I like it roasted. It's always what I order when I come to a new place. It gives me a good idea of its general quality."

"That's very methodical."

"One of my strengths," he said, smiling. "What are you going to have?"

"The flounder."

"A healthy choice, or are you on a diet?"

"Do you think I need to be?"

"Not at all. I think you look fine just the way you are."

"Good answer. But I stay looking this way because I'm always careful about what I eat."

"And I bet you get lots of exercise."

"I try to."

"That means that you're pretty disciplined as well. Something we have in common."

"Would it be okay if I changed the topic of conversation back to the case?"

He frowned. "If you must."

"Well, I wanted to tell you what I did today. I went out to the neighborhoods where Holly Preston and Marion Jensen lived and showed our artist's sketch around to see if anyone recognized the man."

I had expected Keeler to show some enthusiasm for my initiative. Instead he looked annoyed.

"What's wrong?" I asked.

"You should have run it by Farantello first. This is a police investigation."

"Are you saying that it wasn't a good idea?"

"No, the idea is fine. In fact, Farantello asked me to do it tomorrow morning. Of course, that's assuming Chief Moore doesn't insist that I stay on this burglary detail."

"Sorry, I didn't mean to step on anyone's toes."

"Doesn't matter. I'll go out there tomorrow anyway and tell them it's a follow-up. Having talked to you may have jogged their memories. So what did you find out?"

I told him about the bald man who had seen Dickens without his hat and his eyes lit up with enthusiasm.

"That's good. I'll bring the police artist along with his laptop and facial recognition software. We can sit with this guy in his own home and work on it. Did you get his name?"

I realized with a start that I had not asked the man his name.

"No. But I know his address."

"What is it?" Keeler took out his notebook and wrote it down. "I can use a reverse directory and get his phone number. I'll give him a call to make sure he'll be home."

"I'm afraid that nobody else I talked to could add to our description of this guy," I said.

"Piece by piece we're putting it together. It's only a matter of time."

"Speaking of that. Shouldn't we be out there in the lobby seeing if anyone recognizes our suspect?" I said, pulling a copy of his picture out of my bag.

Keeler reached over and took the picture from me.

"I think this is something I should do. After all, people might be willing to tell a police officer something they wouldn't want a newspaper reporter to get ahold of."

"Are you saying that I can't be trusted?" I snapped.

"No. Only that the average citizen might see it that way." Keeler stood up. "I'll be back shortly."

The young woman came over with my wine and his beer. She gave me a quizzical glance.

"He'll be back shortly," I told her. I sipped my wine. Let his beer go flat, I thought, it serves him right. He could have taken me along. He didn't have to tell anyone that I worked for a newspaper.

I don't think that would have been proper police procedure, Auntie Mabel said.

I knew she was right, but I still didn't like it. A few minutes later Keeler returned and gave the picture back to me.

"No luck. No one at the front desk or the hostess in the restaurant recognized him. I guess he must have confined himself to the bar."

"How are we ever going to find him?"

"I think eventually Farantello is going to be forced to go public with the story that Marion was murdered. Then we can run the picture in the *Chronicle* and in the Springfield paper. That should bring us some useful tips."

The waitress brought our salads, and we began to eat. I started telling Keeler about some of my experiences while working in Boston, and he told me stories about the things he'd experienced on the police force. We went on that way through the whole meal as if we'd tacitly agreed not to talk any more about the Dickens case. I found I was more relaxed than I had been in days. We were just debating whether to order coffee or have it back at my condo when Keeler's cell phone rang. I could tell by the expression on his face that the information was disturbing.

"What's the matter?" I asked when he was done.

"Farantello has had a heart attack. He's in the emergency room at DHM."

Ditmore Howarth Memorial Hospital was right in town.

"We have to see him," I said, starting to stand.

"They'll probably only let family in to the emergency room."

"That doesn't matter. If Farantello is dying I want to be there."

Keeler nodded, then rushed over to our waitress to pay our bill. I stood by the exit to the restaurant, pacing impatiently. Keeler soon joined me and we rushed out to the parking lot.

"Farantello is only forty, that's young to have a heart attack, but it also must increase his chances of surviving. Right?" I said. I knew I was only trying to convince myself, but Keeler played along by agreeing with me.

"Sure. He'll be fine."

Keeler drove above the limit to the hospital. We parked by the Emergency Room entrance and hurried inside. A woman sitting at a computer terminal asked us why we were there. After hearing that we wanted to see Detective Farantello, she shook her head. My heart sank. We were too late.

"He's not in the Emergency Room. He's been transferred to a regular room."

My heart sang, that had to be good.

She typed something into her computer, and then said, "He's in room 314. It's easiest to reach by walking outside and going in the main entrance."

We dutifully trotted out into the cool night air, and walked around the building. We went in the front door and took the elevator up to the third floor. Once there, we followed the numbers until we came to Farantello's room. We were about to go through the open door when two people came out. It was Farantello's wife and daughter. Surprised, I fell back on politeness.

"Hello, I'm Laura Magee."

"I know who you are," the woman replied, turning on her heel and walking away from me with her daughter in tow.

I took a big gulp. I didn't relish the role of the other woman.

"That was a little frosty," I mumbled.

"I guess you can't really blame her," Keeler said.

His balanced opinion may have been correct, but it wasn't what I wanted to hear.

"She divorced him. She doesn't have the right to be uppity."

Not waiting for another of his fair-minded replies, I pushed forward into the room. Farantello was sitting propped up in bed. His eyes were closed, but they opened when I loudly cleared my throat.

"Hi, Laura," he said. He nodded to Keeler.

"So what's the word here?" I said, sounding brusque in my effort to be upbeat.

"The good news is that I didn't have a heart attack."

I fell relief surge through my body.

"What was it then?"

"They think it was a panic attack brought on by anxiety. I've been under a lot of pressure lately."

"What kind of pressure?"

Farantello glanced at Keeler. "John, could you leave us alone for a few minutes?"

When there were just the two of us in the room, he said, "It's been a couple of things. Moore has been giving me more problems than usual now that he's worried about a citizens' petition to have him removed."

"But he's always been a pain, right? That's nothing new."

"There's something more." He paused as if reluctant to get into it.

"What?"

"My wife wants us to get remarried. She thinks it's wrong of us to be living together as a family without the normal legal protections."

"Wasn't she the one who wanted the divorce in the first place because she didn't like your job?"

He nodded. "She's still not happy about the job, but I don't think she's liked being a divorced woman."

"Let her marry someone else, then," I snapped.

"I'm the father of her daughter, and she thinks we owe it to her to get back together."

"What do you think?"

"I've been going back and forth on it for weeks. Between my wife and Moore I think something snapped." He smiled weakly. "I feel pretty sheepish at having thought I was having a heart attack when I was only a little stressed."

"It takes a lot more than a little stress to have a full-scale panic attack."

"I suppose. But every cloud has a silver lining because thinking I was going to die, the way I did tonight, has helped to clarify my thinking. I want us to live together."

I started to speak, not knowing exactly what I was going to

say, when he held up his hand.

"A couple of hours ago, I had a chance to take a long hard look at my life, and I decided that I didn't want to spend it pretending to be a married man. I can still be a good father to my daughter without living with her mother. There were good reasons why we split up, and most of them haven't changed. For the last year I've just avoided making a decision. Well, now I've decided." He gave me a long look. "What do you think?"

I paused, unsure what to say. Only a few days ago I would have jumped at the opportunity, but now that I had decided to move on this seemed like a long step backwards. And yet the chance to live together with Farantello had an almost over-whelming appeal. Just by delaying, however, I had given an answer. I saw a mixture of disappointment and regret pass over his face.

"I know this is coming at you rather suddenly," he said, try-ing to cushion the impact.

"It is," I said with an abrupt laugh. "I don't know quite what to say."

"I guess I expected you to see it as a pretty good idea. But, of course, what woman would want to tie herself to an emotional wreck?"

"Don't go feeling sorry for yourself," I said. "You're no kind of a wreck. But wouldn't you like to live alone for a while to adjust to being away from the family?"

"I lived alone for five years after we first got divorced. I know what living alone is like and I didn't care for it."

"But they weren't five years when you were worried about your daughter. And I have a feeling that she doesn't care for me."

"She doesn't know you. She's just mimicking her mother."

I shrugged.

"But maybe since we've been apart you've found that you

would like to go out with other people. I can understand that. Somebody like Keeler is a lot younger and doesn't come with as much baggage."

"Everybody is carrying baggage. It's just harder to see with some people."

I walked a step closer to his bed and leaned over him.

"Can you honestly tell me that in a couple of months you won't be going back to your wife and daughter again?"

There was a pause.

"I didn't think so," I said. "It's not your fault, but I have to move on."

I turned and walked away, but he called my name before I reached the door.

"Thanks for coming, Laura," he said.

I turned back to him. "I'm glad it was only anxiety."

Keeler was waiting in the hall outside the door. Without speaking we walked through the hospital and out to the car. We were on our way back to the condo before he spoke.

"So did he ask you to get back together with him?"

"How did you know?"

"When a man goes through something life threatening or that he thinks is life threatening, he's likely to decide to make some major changes in his life. I figured he was either going to come back to you or marry his ex."

"You're pretty smart."

"So what did you say?"

"I told him no."

"Was that a definite 'no' or an I'll think about it 'no'?"

I turned in the seat, so I could watch his face in the glow of the dashboard lights.

"Look, I can't guarantee that I'll never go back to him. A lot depends on what else comes my way, but right now I don't think he's in any condition to be making any major decisions about his life. And I'm not about to get involved in another temporary situation. I want to be in control of my own life, not changing course to fit every move that Farantello makes."

Keeler was silent for a moment.

"So you told him 'no'?"

"I did."

By the light of the dashboard I saw him smile.

CHAPTER 22

Keeler and I were both rather subdued the next morning over breakfast. We agreed that we had enjoyed our dinner together, but there was none of the giddy happiness that sometimes comes when a first date goes really well. I think it was just sinking in with both of us that Farantello, whom we had considered to be invincible, was only human, subject to the same stresses and failings that afflict everyone else. I was also second-guessing myself as to whether I had been needlessly cruel in rejecting his offer when he was lying in a hospital bed. But when I ran it through in my mind as to how I would feel if I had taken his offer, I came to the conclusion that I would have felt even worse.

"Don't let this Farantello thing prey on you," Keeler said like a mind reader, as we were about to go out our respective doors. "You have to remain alert to your environment. Dickens is still out there somewhere, and we don't know what he's planning."

I felt the familiar knot in the middle of my stomach.

"I'll be careful," I promised.

Keeler followed me all the way to the newspaper, then peeled off to go to the police station. As I walked in the door Grissy greeted me with an exuberant good morning. She was positively blushing with happiness and showed me a full smile with her strong white teeth.

"Did you have another date with Chris last night?" I asked.

"Oh, yes. We are now officially what people call 'an item.' "

I wasn't sure people still used that expression.

"I'm very happy for you," I said, sounding a bit formal even to myself.

Grissy decided that politeness required that she ask how I'd spent my evening, and I told her about my date with Keeler. I also went on to tell her about Farantello being in the hospital.

"What a shame. He seemed like such a nice man the one time I met him when he came here to see you. But how was your date going up until then?"

"Good. We're just starting to get to know each other."

"I understand what you mean. Sometimes there must be that period of getting acquainted; other times it seems as though you've known each other forever."

From the glow on her face I could guess which category she and Chris fell into. I'd had that same feeling with guys myself once or twice in my life, but it had always faded with time. I hoped Grissy would be more fortunate.

I settled in behind my desk and pulled the first bag in line closer to my chair. It was time to put on my Auntie Mabel hat. I pulled the first letter out of the bag and began to work. It was an hour and a half later when I looked up from my computer screen. I stood up, stretched out my back, and spotted, on the corner of my desk, the piece I had written on The Red Barn. I had promised to run it by Stephanie before it went to press, and Roger was anxious to have it completed. Since Stephanie had said she was in the store every day from ten to five except Monday, I figured she was there now. I thought about giving her a call, but then decided that I really wanted to get out of the office anyway, so I'd just drive up there.

I took my usual precaution of looking around the parking lot and nearby street for any suspicious-looking characters, then I got in my car and took the road north out of town. It was a bright, sunny morning and, aside from a slight frisson when I went past the spot where I had almost been pushed off the road, I enjoyed the trip.

When I entered The Red Barn I saw her boyfriend standing by the headboard he and Stephanie had been moving the last time I was there. His back was to me, and when I said hello he spun around, startled.

"Sorry, I didn't mean to surprise you."

"Not your fault," he said, smiling and taking a deep breath. "I was concentrating on where we should display this thing. It's huge, but we want to keep it up toward the front of the store where people will see it when they come in."

He was only a couple of inches taller than me and very slight.

"You aren't going to try to move it yourself, are you?"

He grinned. "No, my days of heavy lifting are in the past."

"But Stephanie said that the two of you hauled it back here."

He gave me a puzzled look. "No, Stephanie and her boyfriend picked up the mantel at an estate sale in Northampton."

"But aren't you—"

"Her boyfriend?" He gave a short laugh. "My goodness, no. I'm her assistant. She keeps me around because I know antiques, not for my more personal qualities. Her boyfriend is quite a bit younger and stronger than I am."

"I'm sorry. I guess I misunderstood. I'm the reporter from the *Chronicle* who was here the other day. I wanted to give Stephanie a chance to read this before it went to press," I said, waving the sheet of paper like a flag in front of me.

"I'm afraid Stephanie won't be in this morning."

"Isn't she usually?"

"Yes, but she called in and told me she wasn't feeling well and wouldn't be in until this afternoon."

I handed him the paper. "Well, when she comes in would you ask her to take a look at this? If there are any changes she wants made, she'll have to call me by noon tomorrow."

The man promised to show it to her as soon as she came in.

"You wouldn't be in the market for a fireplace mantel, would you?" he asked with a smile.

"I don't think that would even fit through the door to my living room."

"Yes, it would take a fairly large, one might even say, ostentatious house to do justice to this piece. Fortunately, there are lots of such places within a short drive of here. We've even got quite a reputation among folks in New York City, so when they come up to the Berkshires during the summer, they drive over here and pay us a visit. They'll pay a lot for something that's old and country. I grew up on a farm, and it makes me sick to think about the stuff my family threw away that I could sell today for thousands."

We talked for a while longer about the antique business, then I went back to my car. There was only one other vehicle in the parking lot other than mine, and I figured that belonged to the assistant. I took a leisurely pace heading to the paper, and aside from that one traumatic spot along the road, I got back feeling refreshed. I was about to dive back into the Auntie Mabel letters when my cell phone rang. It was Corinne, sounding very subdued.

"What's wrong?" I asked.

"Everything," she replied.

"Could you be more specific?"

"Jeff came over last night, and I mentioned to him, very casually like I said I was going to, that he had been seen having lunch with an attractive woman at the Knife and Fork."

"What did he say?"

"He went ballistic. He accused me of spying on him, and said that I should try to control my jealousy. Then he stormed out of here saying that he expected an apology before he would see me again."

"What did you say?"

"Not very much. He was so furious I was afraid to say much to him at all."

"Was he physically violent? Did he do anything to you?"

"No. But he shouted a lot. It frightened me. I felt that he was only an inch or two away from being violent."

"I take it that you have no plans to apologize."

"I'm glad he did storm off because there's no way I'd want to see him again. He's far too volatile for me. I'm not into a relationship based on fierce fighting followed by passionate reconciliations. I had enough of that with my husband."

"Plus you don't need a guy who's going to be unfaithful," I added.

"I spoke to Myra again after you left yesterday. And she told me the woman he was with is Deidre Fay."

"The real estate agent."

"And home wrecker. Remember she broke up the Hunter's marriage. She was showing them new houses and one thing led to another, and before long Dan Hunter had left his wife for her."

"I heard something about that."

"That's not the only time. Deidre collects men like some women collect costume jewelry."

"Would you happen to have a picture of Jeff that I could borrow?"

"I have one with both of us in it. I could just cut myself out of it. Nicely symbolic don't you think? But what do you want it for?"

"I can't tell you right now, but it's for something I'm working on."

"It won't lead to any bad publicity for the store or me personally, will it?"

"Not at all. No one will even know you gave it to me. I'll be by to pick it up in half an hour. Is that okay?"

"Sure. I'll be here. Now I've got nothing to do but work," she said sadly.

"It's not that bad. Better to pull out the bad tooth than have it there festering."

"That's quite an image, but I know you're right. I have to remember there are lots of men just waiting to meet me."

"That's the spirit."

"But you might have been on to something about the age difference. Maybe you do have two strikes against you when you go out with someone much younger. Eventually the younger person wants someone their own age."

I thought about Farantello and myself, wondering whether he was thinking the same thing right now.

"I'm sure that's not always true. But it sounds like Jeff would be no prize even for someone his own age."

"I guess. See you in a little while."

I sat at my desk and wondered whether Jeffrey Ralston could be Dickens. He was certainly charming enough, and he clearly had a liking for older women. But I didn't know enough about him to be sure. Just then Derrick came out of his office.

"Hey, Derrick," I called.

He came over to my desk looking a bit puzzled at having been summoned.

"Do you know anything about a new lawyer in town named Jeffrey Ralston?"

"I don't know anything about him as a lawyer, but I run into him all over town. He's heavily involved in civic events and stuff." A slow grin spread over Derrick's face that made him even less appealing. "I've also heard that he cuts quite a wide swath through the ladies if you know what I mean. He's only been in town about a year, and he's already been seen around with seven or eight different women. All of them real lookers."

"Any stories about him being violent?"

Derrick looked surprised and excited. "Do you know anything I don't know?"

Probably a lot, I thought.

"No, I'm just curious."

"Not that I've heard about. But if you find out anything let me know."

I thanked Derrick, and he left the newsroom. I got on the phone and called Keeler.

"Are you at the office?" I asked.

"Yeah."

"I was wondering if you could give me some information."

"Depends on what you want to know."

"I need the phone number of that bartender who gave you the description of Dickens."

"Give me a minute."

About five minutes passed, then Keeler came back on the line and gave me the number.

"What do you want it for?"

"I have another photo I'd like him to look at."

"Not another guy you're dating, is it?"

"Right now the only guy I'm seeing is you."

"Good."

"But that isn't to say that we're in an exclusive relationship. We haven't reached that point."

"That's fine," he said, but I thought I heard some disappointment in his voice. "So who is this guy?"

"I'll tell you all about it tonight. But there's nothing to worry about."

Keeler warned me several times to be alert before finally hanging up. I put a call through to Alan Westervelt, which turned out to be the name of the bartender. When he answered I presented my request. He said he'd be happy to look at the photo, and that he was currently at work and would be there through lunchtime.

I grabbed my bag, told Grissy that I was taking an early lunch, and headed out the door to go see Corinne.

She was puttering around with a feather duster when I got there.

"Have to keep the merchandise looking its best," she said with what sounded like a desperate stab at cheerfulness.

I gave her a long look. She had obviously taken less time with her makeup than usual, and her face looked pale and wan. For the first time since I'd met her she looked every one of her forty odd years.

"This has hit you pretty hard, hasn't it?"

"I don't like fighting. I put up with too much of it when I was married. Plus it came as such a surprise to me when Jeff lashed out like that. It was like suddenly being bitten by your own dog."

I smiled to myself thinking Jeff probably wouldn't care much for that comparison.

"You're well off without him. I've been asking around a little and apparently he's known to be quite a womanizer."

"Why didn't anyone tell me?"

"It's the usual story. Your friends didn't want to be the bearers of bad news and the others just didn't care. Fortunately, Myra is no one's friend, plus she loves to gossip, so she was happy to tell you."

"Whoever thought I'd ever be thankful to Myra for anything," she said wryly.

"Were you able to find a picture for me?" I asked.

Corinne walked up to the desk in the front of the shop. She took a picture off the blotter and handed it to me.

"That was taken when we went out to Cape Cod for a few days last week."

Ralston was in casual clothes, looking fit and tanned. He was leaning toward the center of the photo where Corinne had once been before being cut out.

"This will be fine," I said.

"You can't tell me what all of this is about?"

"Not right now. But I hope to be able to tell you soon."

Corinne nodded. "You know what I hope."

"What's that?"

"I hope that someday soon Jeff will be wanting to talk about something to someone with half a brain and realize what he's lost by not having me around. A woman you can talk to is even more important than one to sleep with."

"I'm not sure Jeff is capable of that much self-reflection," I said.

Leaving Corinne's, I turned right and headed out to the Collins Inn. I kept looking behind me to see if I had a tail, but there was too much traffic to be sure. No one followed me when I pulled into the Inn's parking lot, so I figured I was safe. There were only a handful of cars parked near the entrance to the bar. When I got inside the only patrons were three men with drinks in front of them watching the large-screen television. They were studying the news as if it were high entertainment. Alan, the bartender, looked to be alone, and he immediately walked down to me.

"Would you let me have a club soda with lime, Alan?"

I figured that I should at least order something since he was doing me a favor.

He nodded. When he returned with my drink, I handed him the photo. He put on his reading glasses and stared at it for a long time.

"I know this guy. He's some kind of a lawyer, isn't he?"

I nodded.

"He comes here all the time, sometimes with other guys and sometimes with women. He's a pretty smooth operator himself, but he isn't the guy you want."

"Are you sure? Imagine him with a baseball hat on."

Alan shook his head. "Not the guy."

I sighed. "Well, thanks anyway," I said, taking a long swallow of my drink.

"You know you might try Jeremy's. A lot of the younger people who come here go there as well."

Jeremy's was a place just off the center of town. I'd never been, but I'd heard a lot of folks my age frequented the place. It had a younger vibe than the Collins Inn, and it could be that Dickens sometimes liked a change of pace. Leaving Alan a healthy tip, I headed to Jeremy's.

There were only two cars in the parking lot. The front door was propped open with a broom to air the place out from the night before. I went inside and waited a moment for my eyes to adjust from the brightness of the fall day to the interior darkness. A man wearing an apron was sweeping in the far corner of the room near a row of slot machines. At the bar sat a man in a suit with a pile of papers in front of him poking at a calculator.

"We don't open until five, sweetheart," he said, hardly bothering to glance at me.

"That's okay, honey bunch, I just need a little information."

He paused and gave me a harder look.

"What do you want to know?"

I walked over to him and put the artist's rendering of Dickens on the bar in front of him.

"Do you recognize this man?"

He glanced at the picture, then looked back at me.

"We usually give our patrons a certain amount of privacy. Who are you and why do you want to know?"

"I'm a reporter for the *Chronicle*, so you don't have to tell me anything. But I can guarantee that if you don't answer my question, I can have the police here within the hour to ask you the same thing."

I wasn't quite sure that was true, but I liked the way it sounded.

"I've seen someone who looks like him in here a few times," the man said.

"Do you know his name?"

He shook his head.

"He's not the kind of guy you want as a patron, so it would help if you could identify him."

"I told you, I don't know his name." The man paused and slowly rubbed his chin. "But the last time he came in here, I recognized the woman he was with. It was Stephanie Fleming, who owns that antique store right outside of town. Talk to her, she must know his name."

"Thanks."

The man didn't say anything, but returned to his calculator.

CHAPTER 23

When I got back to the paper, the first thing I did was call The Red Barn. I could finally see the light at the end of the tunnel, and I was practically panting into the phone when her assistant answered.

"Hi, this is Laura Magee again."

"Stephanie still hasn't come in. She called and said she'd be out all day today."

"Would you have a number where I can reach her? Her cell phone, maybe?"

"I promise I'll show her your article as soon as she comes in tomorrow morning."

"I really need to speak to her today."

There was a long sigh on the other end of the line.

"She didn't sound at all well. I really don't want to disturb her."

"This is something that's time sensitive and is a really good opportunity for her. I'm sure if she knew about this, she'd want to be disturbed."

"I'm taking your word for this," he said finally, then he recited her cell phone number. "I hope I don't get in trouble for what I'm doing."

"Don't worry. In the long run Stephanie will thank you." I didn't tell him that in the short run she would probably be furious.

I punched in her cell phone number, but the call went directly to voice mail. I put my arms on the desk and wondered exactly what I should do. I might skip the phone altogether and go see her at home. I pulled out the phone book and saw that her name and address were listed in the white pages. I could call Keeler and bring him up to speed on what I'd discovered and see what he thought I should do. But I wanted to wait until I knew more before getting him involved. Once I had the man's name, there would be plenty of time to call the police.

I heard a harrumph and looked up to see Roger standing over my desk.

"Contemplating a difficult Auntie Mabel response?" he asked.

"Something like that."

He handed me a piece of paper. On it was a name and the word "cakes."

"What's this?" I asked.

"The next in our series on local businesses. This woman teaches people how to make elegant cakes. She works out of her home, but she's also a high school home economics teacher. She said she'd be available today from two until two forty-five in Teachers' Room A. Interview her, and if need be arrange a time to photograph her kitchen."

"I'll take care of it."

"How are things going with the story on The Red Barn?"

"The piece is finished. I'm just waiting for the owner to take a look at it to make sure all the facts are correct. I had to put in quite a few details about antiques."

Roger nodded. "Try to have it in by the end of the day tomorrow."

"I'll do my best."

He paused as if mentally changing the subject.

"I haven't received any responses to my letters to the colleges."

"It hasn't even been two days."

212

"Your grandmother thinks I should make follow-up calls, so they know I'm serious."

"I'd give it at least a week before I did that. It takes awhile for a letter to get to the right person in a large bureaucracy."

"That's what I think, too. But you know your grandmother, when she isn't counseling oriental patience she's hell on wheels."

I smiled. "Tell her you want to wait a few more days."

Giving me a nod, he went back to his office. I checked the clock on the wall and saw that it was almost one forty-five. If I hurried I could get to the high school a little after two. I grabbed a notebook and told Grissy where I was going.

"I didn't think you covered education news," she said.

"I don't. That David Oliver guy does that. But this is about a local business."

Waving, I went out to my car, as usual casting a wary eye around the parking lot. Seeing nothing suspicious, I got in and headed northwest. It was just going on two when I pulled into the visitor parking for the school. I went in to the principal's office and told them why I was there. They looked me over carefully as if I might be a dangerous person, then issued me a temporary visitor's pass and gave me directions to the Teacher's Room. Classes must have changed at two because there were still some stragglers rushing down the hall: some walking with expressions of grim determination, others strolling along as if they didn't care whether they ever arrived in class. A man came out of a room to close the door.

"Hi, Laura," he said, peering at me through his thick glasses.

"Hi, Brian." I hadn't seen Brian Nash since that day at the gym when I'd given him my phone number just before York had come along.

"I've been meaning to call you. I did write down your number. I've just been going flat out with all the papers to grade."

"Not a problem. Call me when you get a chance."

He nodded and disappeared back into the classroom. I wondered if I would ever hear from him. I wondered even more if I should want to. Now that I was definitely moving on from Farantello was I going to go out with Keeler exclusively? It seemed a bit soon to decide that. Having Keeler right in the house with me made playing the field a bit difficult, but surely that wasn't going to go on much longer. I found myself reluctant to go from one serious relationship right into another. I wanted a chance to breathe and to see what's out there. Grissy was right when she said that I didn't take advantage of every opportunity.

I went into Teacher's Room A and said hello to Barbara Tucker, who proved to be a sizeable woman who looked like she might enjoy sampling her own productions a bit too much. But she had a large notebook with pictures of the cakes she'd made, and before long I could see how the temptation to indulge would be considerable. She was very enthusiastic about her subject, and before long we were deep into flour, frosting, and fondant. I took copious notes. I tried photographing some of her pictures, and I set up an appointment to meet her at her house tomorrow after school. I was hoping that she might have some samples available.

When I was done, I sat in my car feeling somewhat happier with the world. It occurred to me that the high school was almost three quarters of the way to Stephanie's house, so why not keep going and see if she was home. Surely she wouldn't close the door in my face if I was as tactful as possible. I decided it was worth a shot. So I headed even further away from the center of town up into the hills. As the road climbed, the trees became more colorful since fall was earlier at the higher elevations. The snow came sooner as well. Stephanie would have a challenging ride to The Red Barn on a stormy winter's day.

I made a right turn onto a narrow country lane, and, about a mile further, I came to Stephanie's house, which was quite close to the road. I pulled into her driveway. She had a garage so I couldn't be sure whether anyone was home. I decided there was nothing to be lost by trying, so I got out of the car, walked up to front door, and rang the bell. There was no answer. I was about to ring the bell again, when the door opened. Through the glass in the storm door I saw Stephanie. Gone was the well-put-together businesswoman of yesterday. She had on a baggy knit sweater and worn jeans, and her hair hung limply down to her shoulders. Her eyes had a bruised look as if she had been recently crying.

She pushed open the storm door.

"What do you want?" she asked.

"I need to ask you a few more questions for the story. I left a copy of it at The Red Barn, but tomorrow is my deadline. Since you aren't going in today, I thought maybe I could ask you my questions in person."

"I'm really not feeling very well today, but let's get it done."

She stood back out of the doorway and motioned for me to come inside. She directed me to the living room, which was off a short hallway to the left. I went in and sat on a chrome and leather sofa. Most of the furniture in the room was contemporary with only a couple of antique pieces on display.

"I thought you'd have a room full of antiques."

"My taste is eclectic, I like to mix different periods," she said wearily. "Now how can I help you?"

I got out my notebook and tried to remember the questions I'd had about the article. They were all written down on the copy of the story I'd given to her assistant, but slowly I was able to recall them. She answered my questions briefly in a dull monotone, pausing frequently as if it took a great effort to respond. She pulled up the right sleeve on her sweater and I

215

noticed a dark discoloration on her forearm.

"That looks painful," I said, nodding at her arm.

"Yes, I bumped it on a chest back at the shop."

It looked to me like finger marks, the bruises left by someone holding her arm too tightly.

I asked her my remaining questions for the story, then tried to make a gentle segue to a different topic.

"When I was in the shop yesterday, I was talking to your assistant. You know, I had thought he was your boyfriend, but he told me it was someone else."

"Yes."

"Who is he? Maybe I know him."

"I don't want his name included in the article."

"It wouldn't be. This is just for my information."

She frowned and looked at the floor. "He's a very private person. We don't want our relationship made public."

I smiled. "Surely you don't need to be that secretive about it."

Stephanie stood up. "I think that's all for now, Laura," she said, shooing me toward the door.

I took a reluctant step in that direction.

"Your assistant mentioned that your boyfriend was quite a bit younger than you. You know there have been a couple of women in town who had a younger boyfriend who tried to get money from them. The man even got violent when he didn't get what he wanted."

"Well, my boyfriend may be younger, but he's different," she said, continuing to herd me out.

"Are you sure? Those bruises on your arm didn't come from bumping up against furniture."

"Go *now*, Laura."

"Okay. But if you ever need someone to confide in, I'll be happy to listen."

I opened the storm door. It had a strong spring, and when I let go of it, the door sprang back, hitting Stephanie hard on her right arm. She winced.

"Sorry," I said.

She made a waving motion with her left hand indicating that I should make myself scarce. She watched me as I got in my car and backed out of the driveway and was still watching as I drove down the street away from her house.

Her boyfriend was the best candidate so far to be Dickens. But how was I going to find out his name? Stephanie was obviously deep into denial that he could be a dangerous person, and there was nothing I could do to force her to talk to me. I wondered if it was time to confide in the police.

CHAPTER 24

I drove back to the office, debating with myself over whether I should inform the police. Talking to them before I had Dickens's name seemed a bit like giving up. I would have done all the legwork, and the police would be the ones who grabbed the prize. But the sooner Dickens was off the street, the sooner I'd be safe. Once I was behind my desk at the paper, I called Keeler on his cell.

"Hey, Laura," he said, sounding rushed.

Using as few words as possible, I filled him in on what I had learned about Dickens's identity.

"You've made a lot of progress, and I'd like to help you. But the chief has me on this burglary detail, and it's really heating up. Technically Dickens isn't my case anymore, and with Farantello still out on medical leave, there's no one to reassign me except for the chief, and he thinks this is all some fantasy of yours."

"So there's no chance of your going out there today."

"None at all, I'm afraid. Plus I won't be able to see your witness who lived across the street from Marion Jensen. That will all have to wait. And don't be looking for me at suppertime tonight. I'm scheduled to work until ten or so."

"When will you have a chance to follow up with Stephanie?"

"Depends on this burglary thing. Maybe I can find some time tomorrow afternoon if nothing new breaks."

"Will you be able to make her talk?" I asked. Stephanie had

impressed me as a pretty stubborn woman.

Keeler shouted something to someone in the office, then came back on the line.

"Did you ask if she'll talk?"

"Yeah."

"Well, we can certainly say that her boyfriend is a person of interest in a murder case, and if she won't give us his name, she'll be interfering with an investigation, which is a crime."

That sounded like it might make even Stephanie cooperate.

"I'll see you tonight. I'll save some supper for you."

"I'll get something here."

"You might still want a second meal by ten."

After I hung up, I picked up the phone again and called Farantello's cell. I felt guilty about how we had left things last night, and I wanted to see how he was doing.

When he answered I asked him just that.

"Good. All the anxiety symptoms have gone away. They've got me on a pill that's supposed to relax me, but it makes me too relaxed. I want to get off it as soon as possible. I'd like to be back to work in a couple of days."

I told him how happy I was that he was feeling better.

"Yeah. And I'm sorry about putting you on a spot last night. That was the anxiety talking."

"It's okay. I'm sorry if I was a bit abrupt."

"You were just being honest. I can respect that. But I have made a decision. I'm going to move out on my own. Living with my family like we've never divorced is crazy. My wife is right, if I'm going to live there, we should remarry. I don't want that, so I have to be a big boy and realize I can't have it both ways. I can't be divorced and still live like it never happened."

"So now you're looking for a place to stay?"

"Starting tomorrow I'm going to begin hunting seriously for

an apartment. How have you been making out on this Dickens thing?"

I filled him in on all that had happened.

"That's great work, Laura. If Keeler can't find time to go out to see Stephanie Fleming tomorrow, let me know, I'll go, medical leave or no medical leave. We have to wind this thing up as soon as possible for your safety and Stephanie's."

"Thanks, Michael," I said.

There was silence on the other end of the line for a moment.

"Do you think now that I'm moving out that we could ever get together again?"

"Maybe, but not exclusively."

"I never asked you for that."

"I know, but it was kind of understood, wasn't it?"

He paused. "I guess it was. And I can appreciate that you want to be able to look around. All I can say, if it means anything to you, is that I won't be going back home to play the father and husband. I can support my daughter just fine while living on my own."

"That means a lot. Thanks for telling me."

We said goodbye and I sat for a moment staring across the newsroom. I wasn't sure that Farantello and I would ever get back together. I felt the other night in his hospital room as if I had made a permanent break with the past. And I wasn't sure if I started seeing Farantello again that I would feel comfortable dating other men at the same time.

"Goodnight," Grissy called from her desk. She was standing with her bag on her shoulder. I looked at the clock and was surprised to see that it read five. The time can really get away from you when you're daydreaming about your future.

"See you tomorrow," I called out.

I got my things together and prepared to leave. Even though Sam Aaronson was probably still in his office bent over the computer screen, I didn't want to sit all alone in the newsroom. I was out the door minutes after Grissy. I checked the near empty parking lot and didn't see any suspicious vehicles, but I didn't relax until I was locked in my car and moving out onto the road.

When I got home, I hauled out some spaghetti and meatballs I'd made a few days ago and microwaved some of it for my dinner. There was plenty more for Keeler when he got home. I put together a tossed salad, and sat down to eat. Even though Keeler had only been here a couple of nights, I was feeling a bit lonely sitting by myself eating supper. I didn't know if it was Keeler particularly, but it was nice to have someone else around the place. I could always get a roommate to help with the rent when I started paying it next year, but that might cramp my social life. I laughed to myself. That would depend on whether I had any social life. It was true that in the last week I'd had more dates than in the previous six months, but who knew whether that trend would continue.

Bored and listless after supper, I decided to do what I often do when feeling at loose ends: I clean. I started in the kitchen, worked my way through the living room, did the hall bathroom, and went on to my own bedroom. Since Keeler wasn't there, I thought it would be a good time to clean the guest room. I use that room as a combination guest room and office. So I have several shelves of my old college textbooks arranged along one wall. I was brushing the dust off the top shelf when I noticed that I had two novels by Dickens next to each other: *David Copperfield* and *Oliver Twist*. I had read *Oliver Twist* through from beginning to end, but a piece of paper interleaved in *David Copperfield* showed that I stopped somewhere around the middle. If I wanted to finish it, I'd have to start from the beginning again because I no longer remembered what I had read.

I held the two books up in front of me, and suddenly the

coin dropped: *David Oliver.* Could it be? That was the name of our education reporter on the paper. What if that wasn't his real name? I remembered Roger telling me that our education correspondent at one time had been a teacher who used a pseudonym in order to protect his identity and not jeopardize getting tenure. Reporting on school board meetings could be controversial and might get you crossways of the administration. So who was David Oliver?

I picked up the phone and called Roger.

"Hi, Laura," Roger said. "I'm glad you called. One of the colleges in Florida that I applied to called me back this afternoon. They're very interested in having me teach a course called Introduction to Journalism."

"That's great. But the reason why I called—"

"The only problem now is that I haven't the foggiest notion how to begin structuring such a course."

"Don't you know someone at Ravensford College who teaches journalism?"

"Greg Watkins in the English Department teaches a couple of courses in journalism. He's brought his classes down to tour the paper. I always try to emphasize to the students how important it is to stay on top of all the details when running a paper."

"Right. Well, why don't you contact Greg? He could probably recommend a textbook or something that you could use."

"That's a great idea, Laura. I'll pick his brain to get ideas on how to teach this course."

I had a feeling Greg Watkins was going to thoroughly regret knowing Roger before all this was over.

"Roger, I wanted to ask you about David Oliver."

"Who?"

Mr. I'm-on-top-of-the-details was obviously having a senior moment.

"The guy you've got writing the education stories."

"Yes. I vaguely remember hearing the name."

"Is it a pseudonym?"

"I really have no idea, Laura. Sam handled the whole thing. I believe he met the man and hired him."

"So you don't know his real name?"

"No clue. I would suggest that you call Sam. I think I have Watkins's home number here somewhere. I'll give him a call tonight and get the ball rolling."

"Right, you do that Roger. I'll see you in the morning."

I searched through my stored phone numbers until I found the one for Sam's cell. I punched in the number, but it went right to voice mail. I went into the kitchen and dug the phone book out of a drawer. Sam's home number was listed.

"Hello," a woman's voice said.

"Hi, this is Laura Magee. I work on the *Chronicle* with Sam. I was wondering if he's available."

"No, Sam's not here right now. This is his poker night. He spends it with a group of friends. They have dinner together, then play poker."

"Do you know where he would be right now?"

"I'm sorry. I don't think he told me whose house it was going to be at this evening. I suppose you could call the homes of everyone in the group until you got the right one," she suggested doubtfully.

"Sam isn't answering his cell. Is that normal as well?"

"Oh, yes. They have a strict rule about not taking phone calls while playing poker."

I debated the idea of calling the homes of every member of the group, but decided it would be too intrusive. After all, there was no real emergency. I told her I just wanted to find out David Oliver's true identity. Then I thanked her for her time and hung up.

I went back to my cleaning, but when I found myself dusting

the same vase three times in a row, I knew it was hopeless. I had to know who David Oliver was, and I had to know tonight. The only option open to me was to try to worm it out of Stephanie Fleming. Now that I could tell her I had a definite way of discovering his name and would do so tomorrow morning, she might see there was no point in holding out on me. I grabbed my bag and headed out to the car. As I pulled out of the parking lot, I glanced behind me. No one was following. It would be a relief after tomorrow not to have to worry about looking behind me anymore.

CHAPTER 25

The drive to Stephanie's became progressively darker. Once outside the limits of town there were few streetlights, and the houses along the road were widely spaced and set back in the woods. I had to keep my eyes peeled to find Stephanie's place because the numbers on the rural mailboxes were invisible in the darkness. After pulling to the side of the road several times for false alarms, I finally came to the right house. A light was on in the living room window. I pulled over to the side of the road just beyond the house. I didn't park in the driveway because I saw no need to announce my arrival and have Stephanie not answer the door. Better to be facing her on the front porch where she had to listen to me.

She had a one-car garage and the driveway was empty so it seemed she was alone, but I decided to play it safe. Even though the moon was shrouded in clouds, I walked up on the dark side of the driveway, then slid over behind the bushes in front of the house. That enabled me to peek in through the front picture window into the living room. A light was on in the living room and in the dining room in the back of the house. I didn't see anyone in either room. Could it be just security lights left on? I didn't think anyone would leave so many lights on simply to deter burglars. I checked my watch. It was nine-thirty. A little late to go knocking on a near stranger's door, but I needed an answer tonight. I started to reverse out of the bushes when suddenly I felt a hand on my back.

I spun around. Brian Nash was staring down at me through his thick glasses. He smiled.

"Hi, Laura."

"What are you doing here, Brian?" I asked. "I didn't know you knew Stephanie."

"Oh, yes, I know her very well." He smiled again. Then he raised his right hand and I saw it held a gun. "Why don't we go in the house?"

My stomach clenched in fear. I staggered awkwardly out of the bushes, and Brian motioned for me to precede him into the house.

"I would never have spotted you, Laura, but I was taking the garbage out to the cans in the back when you pulled up," Brian said as we went up the steps. "It was smart of you to pull past the house. I did the same thing. I'm just a little further up the road than you."

"Why were you taking the garbage out?" I asked, just to have something to say.

"When Stephanie doesn't show up for work tomorrow, I want the house to be nice and clean, just as if she had decided to take a spontaneous little trip. That should slow down the police investigation by a few days."

We walked in the front door. Brian told me to go left into the living room.

"Where's Stephanie?" I asked.

"She's in the trunk of my car."

I licked my lips, which had suddenly become very dry.

"She's dead?"

"Not yet, but soon to be. I spent much of this evening digging a deep hole a little further out into the hills. Although I didn't expect company, fortunately I dug it deep enough for two."

"It doesn't have to end this way," I said, hearing a tremble in my voice.

Brian took off his glasses and stood up straight. The stoop disappeared and suddenly he looked like a different man, stronger and more determined.

"Window glass," he said, "just part of the costume. I double majored in college in English literature and drama. I was quite good at using props and posture to get into a role. No one pays much attention to nerdy Brian Nash. But when the glasses come off and the back straightens, then the women get interested."

"But didn't the women wonder why you had two different personalities?"

"They never knew. On dates, I took off the glasses and put on the baseball cap and became a swaggering he-man. Stephanie is the only one who saw me in both roles. She ran into me at a party once in my nerdy persona, so I had to tell her. She found it a real turn-on to know there was a secret me."

"Is that why you have to kill her?"

"No, that's because of you, my dear. When I tried hitting her up for some serious money, she resisted."

"So you twisted her arm?"

"She tried to walk away from me when I was explaining my dreams to her. I was trying to tell her that I need money so I could stop teaching and devote myself to writing my book. She would have come around eventually. But then you had to barge in telling her about other women whom a younger boyfriend had defrauded. When I called her on the phone this afternoon she was furious, threatening to go to the police. I knew what I had to do."

"The same thing you did to Marion Jensen."

"Another woman whose death is on your hands."

"How's that?"

"She called me on my cell phone a few weeks after we split

up. Marion said she'd written to you, and I knew you would answer with a similar response to the one Holly Preston had given my previous girlfriend. Marion was angry enough with me to go to the police if you told her to. So I killed her and made it look like an accident. Poor Marion, she knew I liked literature, so she started reading the classics to impress me."

"Why did you threaten me?"

"Because I wasn't going to leave town this time. A little over a year ago when I was here substitute teaching, there was another woman, and Holly told her to go to the police. She never did, but I was worried enough that I left town. Of course, I had to after I'd used my car to hit Holly. I had to go far away to get it fixed."

"But you came back."

"I like it here, and now I have a tenure track job. I need that until I put together enough money to just write." He walked into the dining room and turned off the light. "I should have killed you right away and skipped the threats. I would have if I'd known you were going to keep gnawing at this like a dog with a bone. I know your type, the kind who doesn't want women to be obedient to men."

"And you knew I was Auntie Mabel because you're David Oliver and work on the paper."

He smiled smugly. "I'd worked on the paper when I was first in town as well. That's how I knew Holly Preston was Auntie Mabel. I had a key to the office to use if I wanted to work nights, so it didn't take me long to find out her identity or yours."

"You think you can kill Stephanie and me and stay in town? The police will be all over this. They already know that you're David Oliver," I lied.

Brian frowned for the first time and looked worried. He motioned with his gun toward the door.

"I'll take my chances. Time to get this show on the road. You are going to drive my car out to the burial spot."

"Why should I?"

"Because I'll shoot you right here if you don't. Wouldn't you rather live another ten minutes?"

I nodded and walked to the door. Brian stopped along the way to turn off the last of the lights. I went through the door, holding the storm door open until Brian was right in the doorway. Then I let it snap shut. He gave a yelp of surprise when the door hit him hard in the right arm, but by then I had jumped from the porch and was heading around the side of the house. I kept expecting to hear the sound of gunshots at any minute. I darted across the back yard and into the trees. Although it was only early fall, there were enough dead leaves on the ground that by running into the woods I was making enough noise to give away my location. I immediately stopped and ducked down.

I could see Brian standing in the middle of the back yard staring into the woods.

"You may as well come out now. I'm going to get you eventually. If you make me wait, I'll kill you right here, and I'll make it slow."

I waited to see if a flashlight clicked on. When nothing happened, I figured he didn't have one with him. That was good for me. He stood there staring into the trees. There were times when I could have sworn he was looking directly at me. But the clouds stayed over the moon, keeping me shrouded in darkness. One time he came to the very edge of the trees, and I thought he was going to charge in and try to find me. But I guess he felt that gave me too much of a chance to get behind him, because eventually he walked back around the house in the direction of the road.

I stayed in my spot and waited. My watch told me that it was almost ten-thirty when I heard a car start up out on the road. I watched and a car that could have been red slowly went past the house. I didn't know if he was heading back toward town for some reason or going to kill and bury Stephanie. It could also have been a ploy to get me to come out of the woods. I stayed where I was and waited. Another half-hour passed, and I heard nothing.

Even though I was cold, I was starting to get sleepy. I didn't want to take the chance of dozing off and being caught. Finally I decided it was time to make my move. Trying to walk as quietly as possible I made my way out of the trees and into the back yard. I quickly went up to the back of the house and crouched in the deep shadows. I crept to the corner of the house and peeked around it. I saw nothing but empty lawn. Feeling very exposed, I quickly walked around the side of the house and up to the driveway. From there I made my way into the shadows of the trees by the side of the driveway, and slowly walked up to the road. Staying in the shadows, alert for a trap, I made my way to the car. I spent a while staring at it, looking for any signs of life. It sat there peacefully, offering me an opportunity to escape and get far away.

I approached the car. I stared in the rear window, but couldn't see anything because of the darkness. Finally I slowly opened the front door. I had slid into the seat and sat up straight when it occurred to me that something was wrong. The interior light hadn't come on.

"Gotcha!" Brian shouted, putting an arm around my neck.

If he hadn't shouted, it probably would have been all over for me. But his shout gave me a second to tuck my chin in, so his arm was around my mouth instead of my neck. I opened my mouth and bit him as hard as I could on the arm. Fortunately he wasn't wearing a jacket, so I easily punctured the skin. I bit until I tasted blood. He squawked and swore but released me. I dove out of the car. My hands and knees hit the road. Brian was right behind me. We were both on the ground. He grabbed my left foot and slowly began to pull me toward him. I bent my right leg and kicked back hard with it and had the satisfaction of feeling my sole make contact with his nose. But he wouldn't let go. He kept pulling me backwards. I cocked my knee again, ready to kick him in the face one more time.

"Do that and I'll shoot," he said angrily.

I paused. I'd run out of options. Suddenly the scene was bathed in light as a car's headlights stopped a few yards away. Brian stood up with the gun in his hand.

"He's got a gun," I shouted.

The headlights blinded both of us, and Brian couldn't tell where to shoot.

"Drop the gun, Nash," a voice I recognized as Keeler's said. "This is the police."

Brian hesitated for just a second, then the gun left his hand. It fell in the road, and I rushed over to pick it up. Slowly Keeler came forward out of the shadows.

"Are you okay?" he asked me.

"Much better now," I replied.

"Out on another date?"

I didn't dignify that with an answer.

CHAPTER 26

The next morning when I woke up I lay in bed recalling all the events of yesterday. After Brian Nash was arrested, I had been taken to the police station and interviewed. Keeler had wanted me to go to the hospital first to be checked over, but I turned it down. I wasn't hurt. And I took some grim satisfaction in seeing Nash's bloody face from where my shoe had broken his nose. An officer drove my car back, with me as passenger. I think they were afraid I might be too upset to drive. At the station Keeler and Farantello interviewed me together. I gave them a step-by-step account of my investigation, including all the events of the night. I asked how Stephanie Fleming was, and they said that aside from minor injuries from being tied up and dumped in the trunk, she would be fine. When the questioning was over, the two men stared hard at me as if trying to discern how well I really was. They wanted to have someone drive me home, but I insisted I was fine. Reluctantly, they agreed.

As Keeler walked me out to my car, I asked him how he had happened to show up at Stephanie's when he did. He explained that when he arrived at the condo and found me gone, he'd gotten worried. Sam Aaronson had then returned my call with the true identity of David Oliver. Realizing how determined I must be to find out the truth, Keeler took a chance that I had gone back to Stephanie's to grill her again. Fortunately he arrived in the nick of time.

Back home, I fell asleep as soon as my head touched the pillow. Keeler must have come in later, but I didn't hear him. By the time I got up and dressed, he was already standing in the kitchen with a cup of coffee in his hand. He poured a cup for me and asked how I had slept.

"Very soundly," I said.

He cleared his throat as if about to embark on an unpleasant subject.

"It's not unusual for people who have been through a traumatic event like the one you've experienced to feel depressed and have trouble sleeping."

"I'll be fine."

"In case you're not." He took out a card and placed it on the table. "This is the name of a psychologist the department uses. You can always go to see her."

I nodded and took a long sip of coffee. I held the mug up in front of me.

"Thanks, John, but I think this is all I need."

I saw that Keeler's packed suitcase already stood by the front door. He followed my eyes.

"I didn't see any reason to stay now that Nash is in custody."

He looked at me as if hoping I would say something different. I just nodded. I didn't want to slide into another commitment so quickly. Time to myself was in order. I saw Keeler off to work with a thank you and a gentle kiss on the lips. Being alone might be hard for the next couple of nights, but it was better to get right back into it.

I went in to work the next morning. No one there seemed to have heard about last night's adventure. Grissy was talking about her latest date with Chris. Apparently she had agreed to become his dancing partner and work in the studio.

"Does that mean you're leaving the newspaper?" I asked, alarmed.

"No. This is only a part-time evening job. That's when Chris does most of his business. I will continue to work here during the day."

I breathed a sigh of relief.

A few minutes later, Roger stopped by to tell me what a great conversation he'd had with the journalism teacher up at Ravensford College, and finally Sam Aaronson came out of his office and walked down into the newsroom, a rare event, worthy of comment. He strolled over to my desk.

"I hear you called my wife last night. Something about David Oliver."

"I wanted to get his real name."

"Brian Nash."

"I know that now. He was arrested last night. I was at the scene of his apprehension. Can I cover the story?"

Sam raised an eyebrow. "Get right on it," he said.

Fifteen minutes later Derrick walked in, bursting with enthusiasm.

"There was a big arrest last night. Some guy that they think killed a couple of women."

"I know. I was there when he got caught."

Derrick's jaw dropped.

"So you've—"

"Got the story."

Shoulders slumped, he retreated into his office.

I sat in front of my blank computer screen, which was challenging me to write something worth reading. I thought about all the women I'd met in the last week—some sad and lonely, some not—who had been in bad relationships. I thought about how much damage a sociopath like Brian Nash could do. I thought about men like Jeffrey Ralston, not sociopaths but incredibly selfish. Then there were men like Michael Farantello, neither sociopathic nor selfish, but a man who couldn't decide what he wanted.

"What's a woman to do?" I asked my computer screen.

The best work she can, Auntie Mabel answered.

Deciding that as usual Auntie Mabel was right, I started to type.

ABOUT THE AUTHOR

Glen Ebisch has had over fifteen mysteries published for both young adults and adults. This is his fifth book for Five Star. *To Grandmother's House, Breaking the Rules,* and *The Blank Canvas* also feature Laura Magee as the sleuth. He lives with his wife in western Massachusetts, and his interests include philosophy, eastern religions, and yoga.